The Changing Chemistry
of the Oceans

Nobel Symposium 20

The Changing Chemistry of the Oceans

Proceedings of the Twentieth Nobel Symposium
held 16–20th August, 1971 at Aspenäsgården, Lerum and
Chalmers University of Technology, Göteborg, Sweden

Edited by

DAVID DYRSSEN and DANIEL JAGNER

Professor of Analytical Chemistry,   Assistant Professor of Analytical
University of Göteborg, Sweden   Chemistry, University of Göteborg,
Sweden

WILEY INTERSCIENCE DIVISION

John Wiley & Sons, Inc. *New York, London, Sydney*

ALMQVIST & WIKSELL *Stockholm*

Library of Congress Catalog Card Number 75-39644

Wiley ISBN 0-471-22935-0

Almqvist & Wiksell ISBN 91-20-05043-7

Printed in Sweden by
Almqvist & Wiksells Boktryckeri AB, Uppsala 1972

Preface

The Twentieth Nobel Symposium was held 16th–20th August, 1971 at Aspenäsgården, Lerum, 25 km north-east of Göteborg. It dealt with physical, chemical and biological processes in the oceans including air-sea and sea-bottom interactions, with special reference to the question: "How large is man's impact on these processes?" The main body of the 40 participating oceanographers were chemists or geochemists, but the physical, meteorological and biological aspects of the theme: "The Changing Chemistry of the Oceans" were also well covered. Owing to the interdisciplinary nature of the symposium, it was necessary to provide an effective form of introduction of the participants to one another. This was achieved by an offset-printed manual presenting each participant with a photo and a curriculum vitae. This presentation proved to be well worth the effort of compilation. The organizers believe that participants found the lectures, discussions and informal talks very stimulating and with direct impact on their research programmes. We hope, moreover, that some of the enjoyable atmosphere that was created by good weather and excellent catering at Aspenäsgården is preserved in the symposium book. We wish at this point to thank the participants for filling in the "Discussion Forms" so willingly and for the help given in this connection by the session secretaries.

An important task was delegated to the seven chairmen. Not only were they to conduct the discussions in each session of the symposium, but they were also to build working groups in order to try to summarize the impact of man on different marine processes. After each working group had made a statement in their particular field, the chairmen of these groups made a condensed version of the most important aspects of the human impact on the marine environment. The final resolution, which is reproduced in the symposium book, was unanimously accepted by the participants and has been forwarded by the Nobel Foundation to Mr Maurice Strong, Secretary General to the UN Conference on the Human Environment to be held in Stockholm, 8–16th June 1972. The organizers would especially like to express their gratitude to Robert Stewart and Alasdair McIntyre for their skilful work in formulating the final resolution.

The idea of holding a Nobel Symposium on oceanography in connection with the celebration of the 350th anniversary of the founding of Göteborg was first conceived by Nils Gralén, Rector of Chalmers University of Technology. His idea was strongly supported by Arne Tiselius and the Symposium Committee of the Nobel Foundation. The preliminary plans for this symposium were made in March 1970 by a group consisting of Bert Bolin, David Dyrssen, Lars

Gunnar Sillén and Pierre Welander. Pierre Welander left Göteborg to carry out research at MIT, Department of Earth and Planetary Sciences and Lars Gunnar Sillén died on the 23rd July 1970 after a year's illness. His death was a tragedy not only for his family and friends, but also for Swedish Chemistry and Oceanography. His department, which was run in a remarkably informal way, had become a Mecca for those interested in complex equilibria. Two books will appear to commemorate him, one of which "Contributions to Co-ordination Chemistry" is to be edited by four of his former collaborators, while the other will be Volume 5 of "The Sea", dedicated to Lars Gunnar Sillén's ideas on the ocean as a chemical system and edited by Edward Goldberg.

The symposium was planned in greater detail at a meeting between Bert Bolin, David Dyrssen, Edward Goldberg and Daniel Jagner in Stockholm in September 1970. The rest of the organizing work was then left to the Department of Analytical Chemistry with David Dyrssen acting as chairman and Daniel Jagner as secretary. At this point we wish to express our gratitude to Ulla Holmberg for secretarial work and to Kenneth Berndtson for skilful work in preparing photographs and other material for duplication and offset-printing. Susan Jagner has throughout the organisation of the meeting and the production of this book suggested improvements in the English texts. At the symposium the lecturers were assisted by Ingemar Hansson and Göran Östling. The tourist program was organized by Margareta Dyrssen, Susan Jagner and Kerstin Árén. We wish to thank all these co-workers for their cheerful willingness to support the organizers in trying to make the symposium a success.

The symposium was sponsored by the Nobel Foundation through grants from the Tri-Centennial Fund of the Bank of Sweden, the Nobel Institute of the Royal Swedish Academy of Sciences and the Science Fund of Wilhelm and Martina Lundgren. The City of Göteborg showed its generosity by inviting the participants to a most enjoyable banquet, a cordial welcome being extended by the Lord Mayor, Captain Hans Hansson.

David Dyrssen   *Daniel Jagner*

Contents

The editors regret that circumstances did not permit the contributions by Wolfgang Seiler "Influence of the oceans on the global budget of carbon monoxide and hydrogen" and by Bert Bolin "Carbon dioxide" to be included in this volume.

Sponsors

The Nobel Foundation
The Royal Swedish Academy of Sciences
The Tri-Centennial Fund of the Bank of Sweden
The Science Fund of Wilhelm and Martina Lundgren

Nobel Foundation Symposium Committee

Ståhle, Nils K., Chairman, Executive Director of the Nobel Foundation
Hulthén, Lamek, Professor, Member of the Nobel Committee for Physics
Tiselius, Arne, Professor, Chairman of the Nobel Committee for Chemistry
Gustafsson, Bengt, Professor, Secretary of the Nobel Committee for Medicine
Gierow, Karl Ragnar, Dr. Ph., Permanent Secretary of the Swedish Academy
and Chairman of the Nobel Committee for Literature
Schou, August, Director of the Norwegian Nobel Institute (Peace)

Organizers of the Symposium

David Dyrssen (chairman)
Daniel Jagner (secretary)
Bert Bolin

List of Participants

ROBERT A. BERNER, Department of Geology and Geophysics, Box 2161, Yale Station, Yale University, New Haven, Connecticut 06 520, USA

BERT BOLIN, Meteorologiska institutionen, Stockholms Universitet, Tulegatan 41, S-104 32 Stockholm 19, Sweden

VAUGHAN I. BOWEN, Woods Hole Oceanographic Institution, Woods Hole, Massachusetts 02 543, USA

ROGER CHESSELET, Centre des Faibles Radioactivités, 91 Gif-sur-Yvette, France

ROY CHESTER, Department of Oceanography, The University of Liverpool, Bedford Street North, P.O. Box 147, Liverpool L 69 3 BX, England

EGBERT K. DUURSMA, IAEA, Musée Océanographique, Monaco

DAVID DYRSSEN, Göteborgs Universitet, Institutionen för analytisk kemi, Fack, S-402 20 Göteborg 5, Sweden

STIG H. FONSELIUS, Fiskeristyrelsen, Hydrografiska Avd., Box 4031, S-400 40 Göteborg 4, Sweden

ERNST FØYN, Universitetet i Oslo, Institutt for Marin Biologi, Avd. A, Fredriksgate 3, Oslo 1, Norway

WILLIAM D. GARRETT, CODE 8330, Ocean Sciences Division, Naval Research Laboratory, Washington, D.C. 20 390, USA

EDWARD D. GOLDBERG, Scripps Institution of Oceanography, P.O. Box 109, La Jolla, California 92 037, USA

NILS GRALÉN, Rector, Chalmers Tekniska Högskola, Fack, S-402 20 Göteborg 5, Sweden

KLAUS GRASSHOFF, Abt. Meereschemie, Institut für Meereskunde an der Universität Kiel, Niemansweg 11, 23 Kiel, West Germany

ROLF HALLBERG, Geologiska Institutionen, Stockholms Universitet, Box 6801, S-113 86 Stockholm 6, Sweden

JÜRGEN HAHN, Max–Planck-Institut für Chemie, Saarstrasse 23, Postfach 3060, 65 Mainz, West Germany

GOTTHILF HEMPEL, Abt. Fischereibiologie, Institut für Meereskunde an der, Universität Kiel, Niemansweg 11, 23 Kiel, West Germany

IVAR HESSLAND, Geologiska Institutionen, Stockholms Universitet, Box 6801, S-113 86 Stockholm 6, Sweden

DANIEL JAGNER, Göteborgs Universitet, Institutionen för analytisk kemi, Fack, S-402 20 Göteborg 5, Sweden

BENGT-OWE JANSSON, Zoologiska Institutionen, Stockholms Universitet, Box 6801, S-113 86 Stockholm 6, Sweden

ARNE JERNELÖV, W.H.O., 8 Scheofigsvej, Copenhagen, Denmark

J. DONALD JOHNSON, University of North Carolina, School of Public Health, Department of Environmental Sciences & Eng., Chapel Hill, North Carolina 27 514, USA

FOLKE KOROLEFF, Havsforskningsinstitutet, Box 141 66, Helsinki 14, Finland

DEVENDRA LAL, Tata Institute of Fundamental Research, Homi Bhabha Road, Bombay 5, India

LESTER MACHTA, Director, Air Resources Laboratories, NOAA, 8060 13th Street, Silver Spring, Maryland 20 910, USA

ALASDAIR D. McINTYRE, Department of Agriculture and Fisheries for Scotland, Marine Laboratory, P.O. Box 101, Aberdeen AB9 8DB, Scotland

JEROME NAMIAS, Chief, Extended Forecast Division, National Weather Service, NOAA, Silver Spring, Maryland 20 910, USA

HOWARD T. ODUM, Department of Environmental Engineering, University of Florida, Gainesville, Florida 32 601, USA

ERIC OLAUSSON, Maringeologiska laboratoriet, Medicinaregatan 14, S-413 46 Göteborg, Sweden

CLAIR C. PATTERSON, California Institute of Technology, Division of Geological and Planetary Sciences, Pasadena, California 91 109, USA

RICARDO N. PYTKOWICZ, Department of Oceanography, Oregon State University, Corvallis, Oregon, USA

LENNART RAHM, Department of Hydraulics, Chalmers Tekniska Högskola, Fack, S-402 20 Göteborg 5, Sweden

DAVID RICKARD, Geologiska Institutionen, Stockholms Universitet, Box 6801, S-113 86 Stockholm 6, Sweden

JOHN P. RILEY, Department of Oceanography, University of Liverpool, P.O. Box 147, Liverpool L69 3BX, England

WOLFGANG SEILER, Max-Planck-Institut für Chemie, Saarstrasse 23, Postfach 3060, 6500 Mainz, West Germany

YURI SOROKIN, Institute of Fresh Water Biology, Borok, Jaroslavl, USSR

JOHN H. STEELE, Department of Agriculture and Fisheries for Scotland, Marine Laboratory, P.O. Box 101, Aberdeen AB9 8DB, Scotland

ROBERT W. STEWART, Marine Sciences Branch, Pacific Region, 1230 Government Street, Victoria, B.C., Canada.

WERNER STUMM, Eidg. Anstalt für Wasserversorgung, Abwasserreinigung und Gewässerschutz, Annexanstalt der Eidg., Technischen Hochschulen, Überlandstrasse 133, CH-8600 Dübendorf-Zürich, Switzerland

ARNE TISELIUS, Vetenskapsakademins Nobelinstitut, Box 531, S-751 21 Uppsala 1, Sweden

JUN UI, Sanitary Engineering Laboratory, Department of Urban Engineering, The Faculty of Engineering, University of Tokyo, Bunkyoku, Tokyo, Japan

GEORGE VERONIS, Department of Geology and Geophysics, Box 2161, Yale Station, Yale University, New Haven, Connecticut 06 520, USA

MICHAEL WALDICHUK, Fisheries Research Board of Canada, Pacific Environment Institute, 4160 Marine Drive, West Vancouver, B.C., Canada

GÖSTA WALIN, Meteorologiska Institutionen, Stockholms Universitet, Thulegatan 41, S-104 32 Stockholm 19, Sweden

Working Groups and Discussion Chairmen and Secretaries

Working group 1: Currents and dilution (mixing, transport) processes
Chairman: Robert Stewart
Secretary: Gösta Walin
Jerome Namias
George Veronis

Working group 2: Gases (except carbon dioxide)
Chairman: John Riley
Secretary: Stig Fonselius
Jürgen Hahn
Wolfgang Seiler

Working group 3: Surface films and aerosol formation
Chairman: William Garrett
Secretary: David Dyrssen
Roger Chesselet
Jan Christer Eriksson (spec. invited)

Working group 4: Carbon dioxide
Chairman: Bert Bolin
Secretary: Daniel Jagner
Lester Machta
Ricardo Pytkowicz

Working group 5: Marine pollutants in general
Chairman: Michael Waldichuk
Secretary: Klaus Grasshoff
Vaughan Bowen
Egbert Duursma
Ernst Føyn
Arne Jernelöv
Donald Johnson
Folke Koroleff
Clair Patterson
Werner Stumm
Jun Ui

Working group 6: Biological effects and fates of pollutants
Chairman: Alasdair McIntyre
Secretary: Bengt-Owe Jansson
Gotthilf Hempel
Ann-Marie Jansson (spec. invited)
Howard T. Odum
Yuri Sorokin
John Steele

Working group 7: Sediments and airborn dust. Hydrogen sulfide

Chairman: Edward D. Goldberg
Secretary: Eric Olausson
          Robert Berner
          Roy Chester
          Rolf Hallberg
          Ivar Hessland
          Devendra Lal
          David Rickard

Introductory Address

By Arne Tiselius

Mr Chairman, Ladies and Gentlemen,

As a representative of the Nobel Foundation and its committee for the symposia I wish to extend a warm welcome to the participants of this symposium on "The Changing Chemistry of the Oceans". You have come from many countries and some of you have travelled a long way. I sincerely hope that you will find the coming days of discussion and personal contacts worth while. I have the impression that your hosts have done everything in their power to prepare this meeting to make it fruitful and agreeable and I am convinced that they will make their utmost to assist you in every way possible.

Among the advance material you have received there is also some information about the Nobel Symposia, their purpose and their background. I shall only add a few brief remarks. The motivation for starting this new activity of the Nobel Foundation was two-fold. During its 70 years of existence the Nobel Foundation in its main activity—awarding the Nobel prizes—has gained an almost unique position in the international scientific and cultural community. It has seemed natural—and also in accordance with Alfred Nobel's ideals—to make use of this good will to promote international activities in these fields also in other ways than by awarding prizes. It seemed to us, that international symposia on problems of great actual interest in the "Nobel fields", aiming above all at close personal contacts between a selected elite of personalities from many different countries would be worth trying. So far we have the impression that the Nobel Symposia have been a success. But we are aware of the fact that they still have not yet found their final form—each new symposium gives some new experiences from which we gain inspiration for the future.

Another motivation was perhaps a more egoistic one. If Sweden (and Norway) are to carry on in serving as a kind of international jury, we must keep in touch with what is going on in the world of science and culture. And we are all aware that reading and writing is not enough, that personal contacts with leading authorities often may deepen and widen the perspectives.

A special reason why the Foundation believed that a symposium on the changes taking place in the Oceans was particularly timely just now has of course been the large U.N. Conference on the Human Environment which is to take place in Stockholm in June 1972. The work of this conference, which will involve not only specialists but also decision-makers, will be greatly facilitated if authorative groups like that assembled here are able to contribute valuable material by presenting reports or resolutions.

For this particular Nobel symposium there is an additional, rather special motivation. The City of Göteborg, which this year celebrates its 350 years anniversary, has desired to mark this event by a number of cultural manifestations of which the present Nobel Symposium is one. I shall leave to the following speakers to refer to this particular motivation. This was, however, an additional reason why the Nobel Foundation was happy to support the initiative. It remains for me only to wish you all a successful and fruitful meeting. I hope you will have a very good time here at Aspenäsgården and in Göteborg.

In Memoriam

Arne Tiselius 1902–1971

Professor Arne Tiselius, born in Stockholm in 1902, took his fil. mag. at the University of Uppsala in 1924, became fil. lic. in Chemistry in 1928 and docent in 1930. He was Professor of Biochemistry at the University of Uppsala from 1938 to 1968.

Professor Tiselius commenced his postgraduate studies in 1925 as a pupil of The Svedberg who the following year received the Nobel Prize for Chemistry for the development of the ultracentrifuge. In 1948, Professor Tiselius was also awarded the Nobel Chemistry Prize for his research on electrophoresis and adsorption analysis and especially for his discoveries concerning the complex nature of the serum proteins. Under his leadership, the Department of Biochemistry at the University of Uppsala became internationally recognized as a centre for the development of methods for biochemical analysis.

Many famous universities awarded him honorary doctorates—Paris in 1948, Cambridge in 1949, Bologna in 1955, Glasgow in 1956, Madrid in 1957, Oxford in 1958, Oslo in 1961, Lyon in 1962, Berkeley in 1964, Ann Arbor in 1967 and Prague in 1969. He also received several medals including the gold medal of the Franklin Institute and the Messel medal.

Professor Tiselius became a member of the Swedish Royal Academy of Sciences in 1939 and was its President in 1956. He had been a member of the Nobel Committee for Chemistry of the Royal Academy of Sciences since 1946 and Chairman of this Committee since 1965. He served as Deputy Chairman of the Board of Directors of the Nobel Foundation from 1947–1960 and as Chairman from 1960–1964. Professor Tiselius was largely responsible for the initiation of the Nobel Symposia, the first of which was held in 1966, and he took a special interest in those concerned with chemical problems. The organizers of Nobel Symposium 20 feel sure that all those who had the pleasure of meeting him at Aspenäsgården will be particularly sorry to learn of his death on 29 October, 1971.

Physical Models of Large Scale Ocean Circulation

By George Veronis

Introduction

Large scale ocean circulation is generated by wind stresses and by heat fluxes and salt fluxes (associated with evaporation and precipitation) at the surface. These driving mechanisms each give rise to motions which are affected by the motions generated by each of the other mechanisms. However, for theoretical purposes it is much simpler to treat wind-driven ocean circulation separately and, once it has been so analyzed, to consider its effects on the circulation derived by leaving out wind effects. Although there is no obvious *a priori* justification for such a treatment, the simplicity that is introduced thereby makes the problem tractable and the results are consistent with the crude, overall picture available to us from observations.

This approach will be adopted here in order to bring out those aspects of the circulation which can be associated with specific mechanisms and to introduce some of the problems and ambiguities of our present theoretical picture of ocean circulation. The results are dynamically consistent with known physical processes in the oceans. However, some assumptions must be made to enable us to obtain a result without extensive, brute force numerical computations. These assumptions are not obviously valid and may lead to questionable results. However, a clear picture of the present status of physical models should help to promote a fruitful exchange of information between geochemists and physical oceanographers.

Wind-Driven Ocean Circulation

The rotation of the earth and the relatively strong stratification of the upper kilometer of the oceans leads to a rather simple theoretical picture of mean ocean circulation. The fact that the large scale motions in the ocean are relatively slow implies that the planetary vorticity (i.e., the vorticity associated with the earth's rotation) is important and the stratification of the oceans restricts the importance to the vertical component of the planetary vorticity. In the absence of strong viscous dissipation the planetary vorticity of an element of fluid is conserved except for external input by the wind. Hence, a balance exists between the rate of change of the vertical component of planetary vorticity of a column of fluid and the rate of input of vertical vorticity by the wind. This balance is expressed by

$$\int_{D}^{0} \frac{d}{dt}(2\Omega \sin\varphi)\,dz = \frac{k\cdot\nabla\cdot\tau}{\varrho} \tag{1}$$

Here, $2\Omega\sin\varphi$ (φ is the latitude) is the vertical component of the planetary vorticity, k is the unit vector in the vertical direction, $\nabla\cdot\tau$ is the curl of the wind stress at the surface, the vertical integral is taken over the depth of the column of fluid, ϱ is the average fluid density over the column and $\frac{d}{dt}$ corresponds to a total derivative. Hence, equation (1) leads to

$$\beta V \equiv \frac{2\Omega\cos\varphi}{a} V = \frac{k\cdot\nabla\cdot\tau}{\varrho} \tag{2}$$

where V is the vertically integrated velocity in the north south direction.

If the curl of the wind stress is negative (positive) there must be a net equatorward (poleward) transport at that location. It is obvious that the assumptions leading to equation (2) must break down somewhere because if the wind-stress curl were of one sign across an entire ocean basin, a steady-state unidirectional flow would be required by (2). It can be shown that equation (2) is not valid in the vicinity of western boundaries and that the correct equations there lead to a return flow.

A simple argument can be put forth to show that the correction must be at the western boundary. If the wind-stress curl were negative (clockwise) over an entire region, a clockwise circulation must result and that can occur only if the required northward boundary current is on the western side.

An additional consequence of the present theory can be obtained by making use of the geostrophic relation to determine that the thermocline is deep under anti-cyclonic gyres and shallow under cyclonic gyres. The reasoning is similar to that used in reading weather maps where surface wind velocities are related to pressure patterns on a surface pressure chart.

The simple, foregoing argument serves to provide a zero-order picture of the circulation. Higher-order corrections give rise to important results concerning heat and momentum flux between oceanic gyres. It is possible that the gross circulation picture given by the simple theory could be altered by higher-order effects but as yet this has not turned out to be the case.

Thermally Induced Flow

Flow below the wind-driven circulation is normally attributed to differences generated by differential solar insolation between equator and pole. However, at the present time the most completely worked-out theory (Stommel and Arons, 1960) makes use of an indirect argument to derive the deep circulation. The reasoning goes as follows:

In the upper kilometer of the mid-latitude oceans relatively sharp thermal gradients are observed with temperature increasing upward. Hence in a steady state the turbulent heat flux into the ocean must be removed by some process and it is assumed that an upward flux of cold water serves to keep the temperature constant. The required upward velocity is of the order of 4 m/year.

Since the deep water is nearly homogeneous, it suffices to consider the effects of an upward flux of fluid through a fixed surface when the entire system is rotating with angular velocity $\Omega \sin \varphi$. The flow has an analogy to a laboratory experiment in which the depth of a column of rotating fluid is changed. When the depth of the column is increased, conservation of mass of the column necessitates a horizontal convergence. Conservation of angular momentum then requires that the angular velocity of the particles increase. As a result the relative vorticity associated with the angular velocity is increased. Hence, the net effect of a vertical velocity is to change the vorticity of the column of fluid. If the total vorticity of the column of fluid is to remain unaltered, as it does in the absence of viscous dissipation, a change in the vorticity of the column is accompanied by a flow to a different latitude so that the rate of change of vorticity of the column is compensated by the rate of change of the planetary vorticity. The mechanism that operates is similar to that described above for wind-driven circulation except that in the present situation the vertical flow replaces the curl of the wind stress. The analogy between wind stress curl and vertical flow can, in fact, be made exact.

Because the mean vertical velocity in the thermocline is much too small to be measured, the usual assumption is that the forced upward flow in the thermocline is positive (because the temperature increases upward) and constant. The result is a poleward flow of fluid everywhere in the deep ocean. As in wind-driven circulation, it is necessary to include boundary layer flow to compensate for the unidirectional interior flow. This boundary current is again on the western side of each basin. From observational evidence the sources of deep water appear to be in the Weddell and Greenland Seas. Hence, a complete model of the deep circulation can be constructed.

Distribution of Tracers

The pattern of abyssal circulation shown in Fig. 1 was derived by Kuo and Veronis (1970) using the foregoing model. In order to include the circulation for the Pacific and Indian Oceans, which appear not to have substantial sources of deep water of their own, a Circumpolar Current of given intensity around

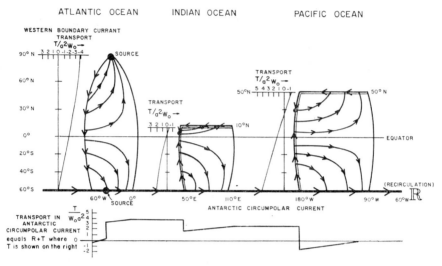

Fig. 1. The model for the abyssal circulation of the world ocean and the transports (T/a^2W_0) in the boundary currents. Equal sources are chosen in the Atlantic at 90° N and at 60° W, 60° S to balance the uniform upward flux of water, W_0, into the upper layers. R is the recirculation in the Antarctic Circumpolar Current, and a is the earth's radius.

Antarctica was added as a connecting link between the South Atlantic, South Indian and South Pacific Oceans. The sources of deep water for the Pacific and Indian Oceans are contained in the western boundary currents. Fluid flows from the Circumpolar Current into the western boundary layer; then it makes its way into the interior and eventually upward through the thermocline.

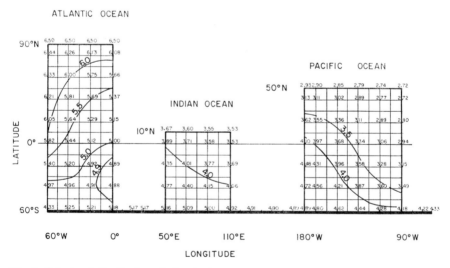

Fig. 2. Calculated distribution of dissolved oxygen (ml/l) in the deep oceans of the world. ($W_0 = 1.25 \times 10^{-5}$ cm/sec, horizontal mixing coefficient $K_H = 10^7$ cm²/sec, recirculation $R = 10^7$ m³/sec).

Kuo and I then assumed that concentrations of dissolved oxygen of observed intensity were given in the two source regions and a consumption rate of dissolved oxygen of 2 ml/l (Riley, 1951) was taken for all of the oceans. Using an advective diffusion equation, we then calculated the resulting distribution of dissolved oxygen consistent with the flow pattern of Fig. 1, a uniform upward flow of 4.5 m/year and a horizontal diffusion coefficient of 10^7 cm²/sec. This distribution, shown in Fig. 2, shows some of the gross features of the observed dissolved oxygen distribution. The relative minima in the eastern North Indian Ocean and the eastern North Pacific Ocean as well as the minimum in the eastern Atlantic off the coast of Africa are observed. So is the decrease of oxygen from the Weddell Sea eastward. The calculated ages of the waters in the different ocean basins agree with estimates using other methods of age determination.

The principal result of our calculation is that the concentration is the result of both advective and diffusive processes. Estimates made on the basis of advection alone would yield incorrect information.

Refinement of Circulation Models

The abyssal circulation model outlined in the previous sections is only a first attempt to construct a dynamically consistent circulation. It does not include the effects of bottom topography, the stratification of the deep water or sources of water at intermediate levels. Even more basic is the mechanism for generating the deep circulation itself.

According to the reasoning of Arons and Stommel (1960), the deep circulation is forced by the thermal structure of the thermocline region. Their assumption of a forced upward flow through the thermocline is not the only possibility for removing the downward flux of heat. It is equally possible that the incoming heat is removed from the subsurface layers by horizontal advection into the boundary currents which transport it poleward. If the latter were the case, the upper circulation would be separated from the abyssal circulation and each could be self-contained. A possible driving mechanism for the deep circulation would have to have a *local* overturning in the polar regions which would mix the waters vertically and produce horizontal density differences in both the deep and the upper circulation. M. E. Stern (private communication) has suggested this as a possibility because of the observed generation of deep water by local overturning in the northern Mediterranean. The details of such a circulation have yet to be worked out but it appears likely that the principal flow would occur in boundary layers (both east and west) in the major ocean basins and the interior would be affected only through horizontal mixing. In such a case tracers would indicate that the oldest abyssal water is in the interior of the ocean basins with younger water along all of the boundaries.

Bottom topographic effects cannot really be considered separately from effects due to stratification because of the very different behavior between a stratified and a non-stratified rotating fluid. However, bottom topography must exercise some control on the movement of deep waters and this effect should be clearly discernible in the distribution of tracers. Experimental and theoretical studies to determine the influence of bottom topography on abyssal circulation are currently underway at Yale. Our initial results show that seamounts of large horizontal scale can serve as fluid traps with nearly self-contained circulations (closed streamlines). Such regions, if they do indeed exist in the ocean, would contain older water than their environs, other conditions being held constant.

Water of intermediate density can be generated at or near the surface and sink to intermediate levels. Examples of such intermediate flows in the Atlantic are Mediterranean Water, eighteen-degree water and Antarctic Intermediate Water. The flow patterns of these waters are not known at the present time. The highly simplified circulations described in texts are simply direct flows from points of origin to points of observation. The dynamics of these flows certainly merit study. On a smaller scale, there is increasing evidence of layers of constant salinity and temperature separated by thin layers with sharp gradients. How these layers enter into the circulation picture is not understood.

As we form a more complete picture of these layered structures, we may find that the ocean is not, after all, a single fluid with continuous stratification but that it is like an onion with layers of varying thicknesses, each of which is nearly homogeneous but which differs from its neighbors above and below both in its identifying properties and its flow pattern.

It should be observed that western boundary currents play a fundamental role in all of the circulation patterns discussed here. The physical mechanism leading to western boundary currents is the nearly geostrophic character of the interior flow and the derived planetary vorticity equation which requires that interior meridional flow be of one sign if the driving mechanism is of one sign. Hence, western boundary currents are needed to provide mass continuity. When the driving mechanism along a latitude circle can change sign it is possible to have both northward and southward flow so that only the residual flow need be balanced by a western boundary layer. The latter will occur in all situations where the net meridional interior flow does not vanish. Other boundary currents may occur because of topographic features. When they do, they may serve to alter the balance described above.

For the oceanographic observer the ubiquity of boundary currents suggests that western oceanic boundary regions (both abyssal and coastal) as well as regions of substantial topographic relief be selected as sites for dense samp-ling. These regions are in contact with the deep water sources for most of the world's oceans and should provide the geochemist with the freshest con-centrations of various tracers for each ocean. Observed concentrations in the interior basins can then be more easily understood and interpreted.

I am grateful to the National Science Foundation for support through Grant GA-25723.

References

Kuo, H.-H. & Veronis, G., Distribution of tracers in the deep oceans of the world. Deep-Sea Res. *17*, 29–46 (1970).

Riley, G. A., Oxygen, phosphate and nitrate in the Atlantic Ocean. Bull. Bingham Oceanogr. Coll. *13*, 1–126 (1951).

Stommel, H. & Arons, A. B., On the abyssal circulation of the world ocean-II. An idealized model of circulation pattern and amplitude in oceanic basins. Deep-Sea Res., *6*, 217–233 (1960).

Large-Scale and Long-Term Fluctuations in Some Atmospheric and Oceanic Variables

By Jerome Namias

Introduction

It has long been known that great variability characterizes the atmosphere—variability on time scales ranging from hours to millenia and even to periods as long as the Ice Ages. Therefore one cannot assume that mean values computed for any period will be the same for other periods. This variability underscores the subject of "climatic fluctuations," which I shall define as deviations of any average from a still longer period base. Thus, there are climatic fluctuations of weekly, monthly, or annual averages from 30-year averages, as well as decadal, centurial, millenial fluctuations and upward from still longer averages. There is reason to believe that climatic fluctuations in the atmosphere of a month, season, or year are produced by circulation phenomena which, if persistent enough, can produce decadal, millenial and longer climatic aberrations. In other words, recent short-period climatic fluctuations differ only in degree and not in kind from great fluctuations of the past—a conclusion reached many years ago by H. C. Willett.

More recently, ocean variability of a similar sort has come into sharp focus. No longer is the ocean believed to be static in any of its properties; in fact, data collected over the last few years by oceanographic cruises, buoys, and satellites indicate just the opposite. Therefore, oceanographic atlases portraying climatic conditions, like their meteorological counterparts, should be used only to afford first guesses for values which have a large spread about the mean.

While the above concept underlies much new research, and opens up exciting vistas for scientists, the concept is by no means new. Meteorological phenomena with time scales of a month or more and space scales as large as half an ocean were identified and studied by Teisserenc de Bort (1883) in the last half of the 19th century, and by many followers since his time [e.g., see references in Namias (1968)]. Oceanic variations of somewhat similar scale were studied by Helland-Hansen and Nansen (1920) around the turn of the century and occasionally by subsequent oceanographers and meteorologists. The new accent on these longer-period problems arises because:

1. Observations in both atmosphere and ocean are now taken routinely on

at least a hemispheric scale and modern data processing facilities are able to cope with millions of data with relatively easy storage and retrieval.

2. Anyone who works with time-averaged meteorological and sea surface temperature data—and there are now many—soon recognizes that large-scale coupling mechanisms exist.

3. New knowledge of the general circulation of the atmosphere and of the sea gained over the past 20 years makes air-sea problems more tractable than in earlier times.

4. A new urgency has arisen because of the fact that man influences his environment, and it is necessary to understand natural fluctuations before attributing to him the aberrations from "normality" frequently observed. Not only "base lines" are required, but also an understanding of what causes short and long period deviations from these base lines.

The Nature of the Climatic Fluctuations at the Sea Surface and in the Overlying Atmosphere

During the past two decades a tremendous amount of work has illuminated the role of the atmosphere and the ocean in transporting, depositing, and altering chemical constituents—both natural and man-made. My mentor, the late Carl-Gustav Rossby, a pioneer in this geochemical field, would have been delighted to see that this subject has expanded to form the basis for this Nobel symposium here in his native land.

While many variations in atmospheric and oceanic constituents can be attributed to transport by air and sea currents in the horizontal and vertical, it is not so easy to ascribe the atmospheric or oceanic behavior to variations in constituents. In other words, it appears that short and long period regional variations in such things as ozone, CO_2, particulate matter, atomic debris, etc. are related to atmospheric and oceanic circulation and interaction, but conclusive evidence that climatic fluctuations are *caused* by variations of the trace substances has yet not been presented (Singer 1970). This is in spite of the fact that some of these substances, if they varied substantially and worldwide, could very well produce such fluctuations. The complexity of this problem is perhaps highlighted by the paradox of the fairly steady secular rise in CO_2 since the turn of the century at the same time when earth temperatures suggest either a global rise of about 0.5°C up to 1940 and cooling trend thereafter (Mitchell, 1963) or virtual stationarity (Dronia, 1967)—depending upon whose global statistics one has faith in. Landsberg (1970) expresses the opinion, borne out by Dronia (1967), that only urban areas have warmed slightly since the turn of the century and that the worldwide temperature exhibited no long-term trend over the past century. Nevertheless, opinions on causes of "global" climatic change are indeed varied (Shapley, 1953; Mitchell, 1968), and involve the whole gamut of possible causes ranging from extraterrestrial solar variations to volcanic activity and even to man-created pollution. The state of our ignorance is indicated by prophecies of an imminent ice age on the one hand and a worldwide warming and glacier melt on the other. The solar-terrestrial hypothesists cannot be comforted by recent studies (Shedlovsky et al., 1970) of radionuclides and rare gases from moonrocks which show no substantial difference in the character of solar activity for at least 10^6 years. The effect of volcanoes (Lamb, 1970) or pollution (Singer, 1970) on worldwide or regional temperatures is certainly not clear because of the great difficulty of separating these effects from many others.

In view of this confused state of affairs I hesitate to invoke still another "cause" of climatic fluctuations. This "cause" is large-scale air-sea interaction, where the time scales of phenomena in the two media, air and sea, differ about an order of magnitude. It seems that studies of short period (from months to decades) air-sea interactions during the period of historical record provide clues which until recently have been neglected in the quest.

The Time and Space Scales

When meteorological data are averaged over a week, month, or season, suppressing higher frequency and smaller scale systems such as cyclones and anticyclones, there emerge macroscopic patterns such as shown in Fig. 1 by the 700 mb contours for winter of 1962–63.* By subtracting long term (about 20 year) averages from these, we obtain isopleths of anomaly (the broken lines) which give the geostrophic anomalous wind components. Figure 1 shows that the long waves in the westerlies in the winter of 1962–63 were appreciably amplified relative to normal, with both troughs and ridges stronger than normal. This anomalous flow led to large areas (Fig. 2) of highly anomalous temperatures in the lower troposphere. Such anomalous quasi-stationary mean systems usually result from persistently recurrent synoptic systems—and the weather maps at surface or aloft in any one long period regime often undergo strikingly repetitive sequences (Namias, 1966). This persistent recurrence results in standard deviations of monthly, seasonal, or annual means which are larger than expected from daily values. One gets the distinct impression that the atmospheric circulation is being forced by some external agent.

When the underlying sea-surface temperatures (SST) are studied in conjunction with these patterns, it becomes clear that the two media, air and sea, are

* The author regrets that the available data made it necessary or at least highly convenient to employ Fahrenheit and foot rather than Celsius and meter scales.

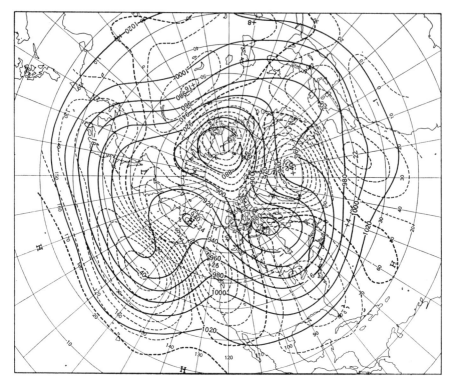

Fig. 1. Mean 700 mb contours (solid) and isopleths of anomaly (broken) (both in tens of feet) for winter (December, January, February) 1962–63.

coupled. The coupling takes place largely through heat exchange between sea and air and through water advection and mixing.

Fig. 3 illustrates three cases which show the macroscale coupling process between surface winds (the anomalous components) and sea-surface temperatures. Note that the isopleths of sea level pressure (SLP) anomaly refer to the three month period ending with the indicated month. This was done to incorporate both contemporary and lag responses of the sea to the air circulation. Anomalously warm water is found where the winds have had a more than normal southerly component and cold water is associated with northerly components. This relationship is perhaps not surprising in view of the increased latent and sensible heat loss expected with northerly components (vice versa with southerly) and the implied advection of cold or warm water in the Ekman layer. However, it should not be concluded from Fig. 3 that the sea is merely "a slave" to the atmosphere, because the anomalous gradients in water temperatures (cold west of warm) tend to be transferred to the overlying atmosphere and lead to a boost in cyclonic activity in the zone of contrast (the barocline zone) as pointed out by Bjerknes (1962) and the author (Namias, 1959).

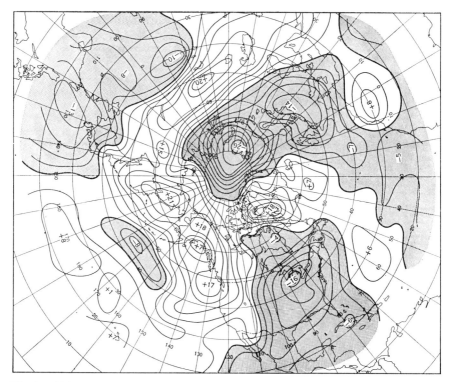

Fig. 2. Thickness departure from normal (1 000 to 700 mb, in tens of feet) for 1962–63 Winter. (Thickness departures are nearly proportional to layer temperature departures.)

The space scales of time-averaged meteorological and oceanic systems are further illustrated by Fig. 4. This figure shows the high spatial coherence in both air and sea patterns (upper and middle) and the similarity of the correlation fields. The characteristic dimensions of both air and sea anomalies are roughly the order of 1/3 to 1/2 of the North Pacific. The lower chart in Fig. 4 implies an anomalous geostrophic wind (parallel to the isopleths of correlation) which accompanies anomalous warm or cold water at the diamond area —in agreement with the concepts discussed previously.

A striking indication of the differing time scales in ocean and atmosphere is afforded by Fig. 5. The *patterns* of SST, SLP, and 700 mb height were autocorrelated at discrete lags of 1 to 12 months by using standardized anomalies computed for each 5° square for each month of each of the twenty years, 1947–66. The resulting correlations give a measure of the degree of similarity of the anomaly patterns for one month to any other month. Obviously the sea retains its anomalous temperature pattern for a much longer time than the atmosphere retains its pressure pattern, and thus can provide a heat storage memory to influence the overlying atmosphere at a later date. To a large extent this strong pattern autocorrelation in the sea is a result of the high specific

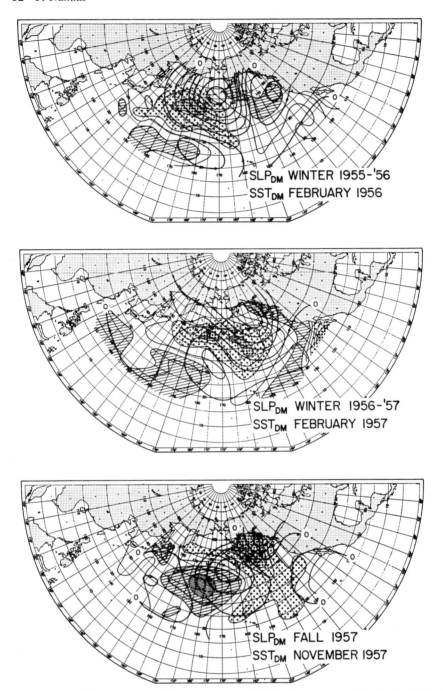

Fig. 3. Monthly mean sea surface temperature (SST) departures overlain by isopleths of seasonal mean sea level pressure (SLP) departures from 1947–66 mean. Contour intervals are 1°F and 2 mb respectively. Stippled areas are above normal by more than 1°F, and hatched areas below by more than 1°F. Arrows indicate geostrophic anomalous component of wind.

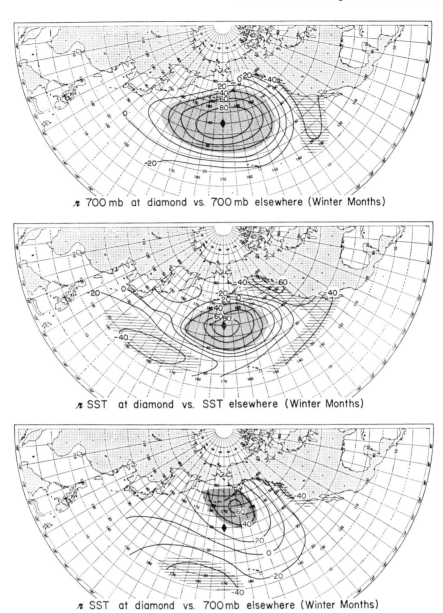

r 700 mb at diamond vs. 700 mb elsewhere (Winter Months)

r SST at diamond vs. SST elsewhere (Winter Months)

r SST at diamond vs. 700 mb elsewhere (Winter Months)

Fig. 4. Contemporaneous correlations between 40° N–170° W (diamond) and elsewhere for 700 mb heights (upper), sea-surface temperatures (SST) (middle), and SST vs. 700 mb (lower). Shaded areas represent correlations exceeding 1 % level of significance—positive correlations stippled, negative hatched.

heat of water, the substantial depth of anomalies (often below 100 m) and the slow current movements. Another contributory process involves a frequently observed feedback condition wherein the thermal state of the sea encourages the formation of atmospheric patterns which sustain its characteristic SST

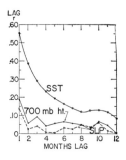

LAG
r

Fig. 5. Overall autocorrelations of standardized values of monthly mean sea-surface temperature (SST), 700-mb height, and sea-level pressure (SLP), determined from a 5° grid of points covering the North Pacific (north of 20° N) during the twenty-year period 1947–66.

signature (Namias, 1963). For example, anomalous warm water temperatures in the cold months seem to encourage cyclone growth, while the cyclones frequently lessen evaporative heat losses by dampening the lower air with rain and by reducing back radiation through the formation of clouds.

When the autocorrelations of SST pattern are stratified by initial month (Fig. 6) it becomes clear that resurgence of SST patterns occurs from cold season to cold season with lessened coherence in the intervening warm season. This appears to be a manifestation of the ability of the sea to store warm or cold water masses generated in a deep mixed layer during cold months, to cover them over with a shallow layer of unrepresentative water during warm months, and to resurrect them by renewed stirring during the ensuing stormy cold season (Namias and Born, 1970).

The above paragraphs refer principally to the temperate latitudes of the North Pacific. However, similar large-scale phenomena in the North Atlantic have been described by Rodewald (1963), Neumann et al. (1958), Lee (1967) and Murray and Ratcliffe (1969).

While temperate latitudes of the Southern Hemisphere also have corresponding large-scale atmospheric and sea-surface temperature anomalies

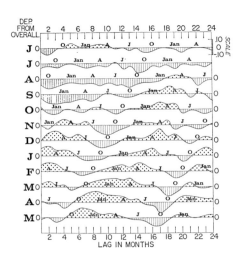

Fig. 6. Deviations of individual months' autocorrelations (according to initial month) from the overall autocorrelation, beginning with June. Some subsequent months are labelled on the curves for convenience of the reader.

(Priestley, 1966), the dearth of data has up to now limited their study and description. But what about the tropics—the area formerly thought to be climatically invariant? Some of the most dramatic changes of sea temperatures and meteorological elements, especially rainfall and wind, have come to light in the last decade, largely through the work of J. Bjerknes (1966). These sea-surface temperature anomalies in the equatorial Pacific may vary as much as 3°C from one January to another and extend over an area perhaps 10 000 km long in a zone about 1 000 km wide. The variations appear to be due largely to the intensity of equatorial upwelling which is dependent on the strength of the flanking southeast and northeast tradewinds which cause horizontally diverging water in the Ekman layer. These tradewind systems often span an area almost as broad as the North Pacific. The temperate latitude anomalies are characteristically smaller since they are primarily responsive to the atmosphere's sea level centers of action and associated upper level long waves (∼4 000 km wave length). While equatorial variability of pressure is small, the impact of sea-surface temperature variations on other meteorological elements, particularly rainfall, is large, as Bjerknes (1969) has shown. These rainfall variations are attributed to enhancement or inhibition of convective rains through variations in static stability of the overlying air caused by differences in sea-surface temperatures. More recently Bjerknes has introduced the concept of the "Walker" circulation, a large zonal cell on the equator where air sensitive to oceanic heating rises in the Western Pacific and sinks over eastern portions where the waters are cool—a vast circulation system with a driving mechanism like the small-scale sea breeze. According to Bjerknes, the lateral dimension of this large equatorial cell and its intensity depend upon sea temperature differences between east and west. In addition, variable sea temperatures also produce a variably intense "Hadley" cell, the meridional circulation in which rising air near the equator moves poleward, conserves its angular momentum, and thereby results in the upper level westerlies over the subtropics (the subtropical jetstream). Some of this westerly momentum is transferred downward to maintain the prevailing westerlies of temperate latitudes. Employing the concepts of the variable Hadley and Walker cells, Bjerknes attributes many atmospheric circulation abnormalities of temperate latitudes to equatorial sea-surface temperature variation.

Undoubtedly there is a complex interplay between extratropical and tropical systems, so that events in each area affect the other. However, the question of cause and effect has not yet been completely resolved, so reliable long range prediction of behavior in either medium from equatorial variables is still to be achieved.

Perhaps the largest scale air-sea interaction phenomenon is the "southern oscillation," first described by Walker (1924) and later studied by Berlage

(1966), Troup (1965), and others. Essentially the southern oscillation is a standing fluctuation of opposite pressure anomalies in both eastern and western hemispheres. Its cause, while still not clear, appears to lie in large-scale air-sea coupling which originates in the Pacific and is transferred to other parts of the world by atmospheric "teleconnections." Research on the southern oscillation, although a fertile field, is hampered by the paucity of Southern Hemisphere data.

Let me now return to the North Pacific anomalies where there exists a good supply of historical atmospheric and oceanic data which I have studied for over a decade.

Although the characteristic scale of temperate latitude SST anomalies is about 1/3 of the size of the North Pacific, it must not be assumed that anomalies cancel one another, leaving the mean SST anomaly over the entire North Pacific invariant. The mean variability of this large area is, for example, illustrated by a plot of seasonal values for the past couple of decades (Fig. 7). Here we see that, even for the entire North Pacific north of 20° N, there may be differences of as much as 1°F between two different years. This value implies a difference in heat of evaporation of 47.8×10^{20} calories, corresponding to the precipitation of 8.14×18 grams or 23.4 cm of water over the entire North Pacific. Sometimes SST differences between seasons result from the domination of extreme anomalies (positive or negative) at the expense of small ones of different sign, but most of the time there is proportionality between the mean North Pacific SST anomaly and the area covered by anomalies of one sign. Thus, the biggest mean anomalies often consist of vast areas in which only temperature anomalies of one sign are observed and very small areas of the opposite sign. For example, in the fall of 1964 only 14% of 5 degree squares had positive anomalies, and in the summer of 1967 only 27% had negative anomalies. Indeed the correlation between the entire Pacific mean SST anomaly and percentage of 5° squares with positive anomaly is 0.84.

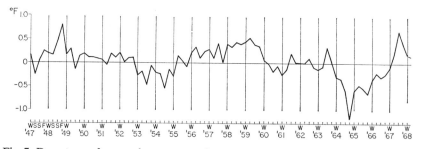

Fig. 7. Departures of seasonal mean sea-surface temperature (SST°F) from the 1947–66 averages over the entire North Pacific, north of 20° N. The winter season so taken to begin in December.

How do relatively oceanwide SST anomalies arise when the coupled atmospheric centers of action and their anomalies are usually appreciably smaller? The answer to this question lies in the differential persistence between ocean and atmosphere. When an abrupt season to season change takes place in the atmosphere's general circulation, the response time of the ocean to this change varies from area to area because of differing thermocline depth, variations of heat exchange, etc. Highly anomalous SST areas that penetrate deepest, often to more than 150 m, remain relatively unmodified, while other areas, often with shallow thermocline, respond rapidly to air circulation and related air mass changes. Thus, while one area retains its thermal anomaly, another may change rapidly, so that the mean for the entire ocean may show a substantial deviation from normal for an entire season. This sequence of events happened during the extreme cases of summer 1954, fall 1964, and summer 1967 (Fig. 7). Such extremes are bound to be transitory since the sea is constantly forced to adapt to the modal smaller scale atmospheric systems and must yield to these after a sufficient time lag.

Examples of Air-Sea Interactions Producing Climatic Fluctuations over Seasons and Years

While the time scales associated with large-scale air-sea interactions can range from days to millenia and beyond, our historical record permits detailed studies of only the shorter period fluctuations. In the following we shall describe evolutions ranging from seasons to decades, making the tacit assumption that similar phenomena can account for much longer period fluctuations of atmosphere and sea.

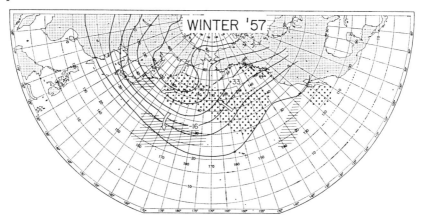

Fig. 8. Sea-surface temperature (SST) anomalies (base period 1947–66) and 700 mb contours for winter, 1956–57. Stippled areas are more than 1°F above 20-year mean and hatched areas more than 1°F below. Numbers (expressed in tens of feet) are placed at centers of 700 mb anomalies. Arrows fly in direction of principal anomalous geostrophic flow (i.e., parallel to isopleths of height anomaly which are not reproduced).

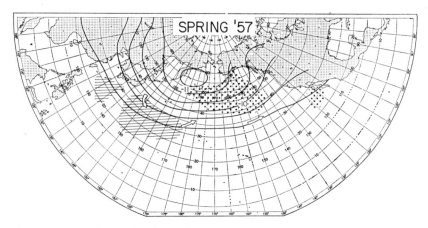

Fig. 9. Same as Figure 8 but for Spring, 1957.

The series of maps reproduced in Figs. 8 to 13 show coupled air and sea systems for seasons beginning with winter 1957 and ending with spring 1958. In these charts the mean 700 mb contours have been superimposed on the SST departures from 20-year means (1947–66). Numbers on these charts give the intensities of the 700 mb anomaly centers and open arrows show the broad scale anomalous components of flow (taken from isopleths of anomaly which are on the original analyses but which are not reproduced).

The maps in Figs. 8 to 13 are shown because they bring to light several remarkable phenomena:

1. The SST patterns underwent a complete cycle from winter of 1957 to spring of 1958, anomalously cold water replaced originally warm, and warm replaced originally cold water. The beginning and end charts of the cycle are quite opposite as far as thermal pattern is concerned. (Some individual months' SST anomalies during this evolution were shown in Fig. 3.)

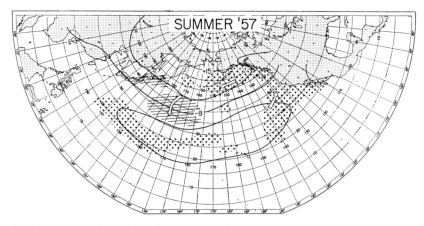

Fig. 10. Same as Figure 8 but for Summer, 1957.

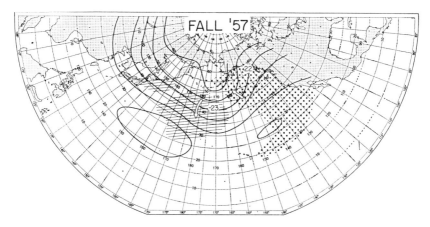

Fig. 11. Same as Figure 8 but for Fall, 1957.

2. Despite the span of 18 months (6 seasons) one can trace eastward continuity of the long atmospheric wave and to a lesser extent the anomalous SST pools. The long wave trough which appeared east of Japan in spring 1957 may be followed in its steady eastward migration to the west coast of the United States in the spring of 1968, moving about 155° of longitude at 40° N. Sea-surface temperature anomalies relative to the long wave system are found in the expected places as described earlier—anomalously cold water to the rear of the trough and warm water in advance, with the anomalous air flow components directed as described earlier.

3. The long wave reaches its greatest amplitude and the trough its greatest negative anomaly in the fall of 1957—in the very area where the horizontal gradient of SST is a maximum (actually 5.3 degrees F per 40 degrees of longitude as determined from the original isopleths of SST).

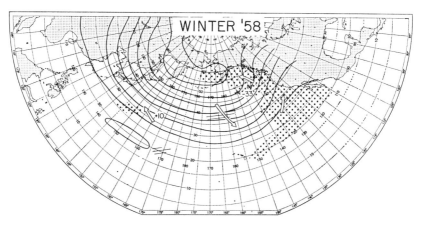

Fig. 12. Same as Figure 8 but for Winter, 1957–58.

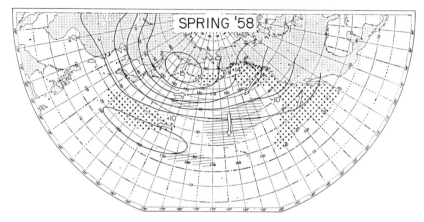

Fig. 13. Same as Figure 8 but for Spring, 1958.

4. This period of great upheaval in the atmospheric circulation and SST pattern over the North Pacific, as we shall see, ushered in a new stable climatic wintertime regime which has dominated not only the North Pacific but North America and possibly Europe. As of 1971 this new regime was still operative.

5. It so happens that the 1958 period was so abnormally warm in the eastern Pacific that a special interdisciplinary conference was held by the Scripps Institution of Oceanography. This conference is a milestone in the history of air-sea interaction and served to stimulate related work on these time scales in such apparently diverse fields as marine biology, fisheries, meteorology, and oceanography. A most enlightening report emerged from that meeting (Marine Research Committee, 1960). However, no participant surmised at that time that the 1957–58 change signalled a recurrent weather and climate aberration.

The progressive eastward motion of the mean trough from spring 1957 through the following spring appears to be associated with an increase in stationary wave length as measured from the climatologically anchored Asiatic coastal trough as the westerlies over the Pacific strengthened, particularly after the summer of 1957. Both factors, anchoring of the Asiatic coastal trough in the cold seasons and increasing strength of the westerlies from summer through the subsequent winter, are climatologically dependable events. A central physical question, however, involves the amazing longevity of the slow migratory trough, which was naturally associated with many cyclones. This longevity can reasonably be ascribed to the contrasts in SST which the trough helped to develop and maintain—that is, anomalously warm water to the east of cold water. The abnormal heat exchanges to the overlying air masses then provided the additional baroclinicity upon which individual cyclones could feed, further maintaining a deeper-than-normal mean trough through the action of enhanced cyclogenesis. Some weight is lent to this theory by the observed increase in strength of the eastward migratory anomaly, for it is during the colder months and in areas of largest SST contrast that abnormal heat exchanges would have their maximum effect.

The transition period just discussed lay between two roughly decadal climatic regimes. Relative to the 1947–66 averages, the first decade (1948–57) was characterized by anomalously warm water during nonsummer months in

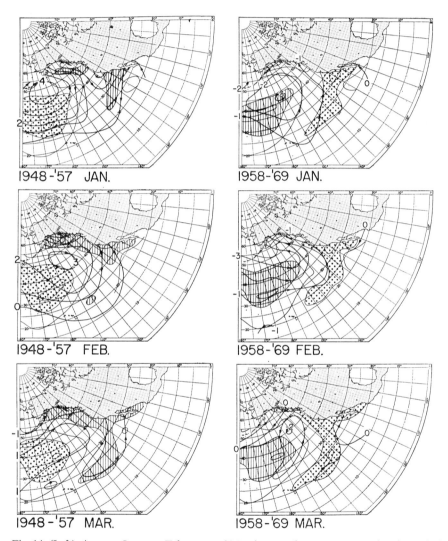

Fig. 14. (Left). Average January, February and March sea-surface temperatures for the period 1948–57, shown as departures from the 1947–66 base period. Stippled areas are above normal by more than 0.5°F; hatched areas, below normal by the same amount. Corresponding isopleths of average sea level pressure, at 1 mb intervals, carry arrows showing the anomalous component of geostrophic flow.
Fig. 15. (Right). Same as Figure 14 but for the period 1958–69.

the central Pacific and cold water off the west coast of the United States, while the subsequent regime (1958–69) had the opposite SST patterns. As a representative illustration, the means of the Januaries of each decade are reproduced in Figs. 14 and 15. The superimposed departures of sea level pressure from the 20-year mean indicate the close coupling of air and sea described earlier. Differences of both sea level pressure and SST between decades are significantly large. Note the general similarity of the SST decadal pattern for 1948–57 to that for winter 1957, (the end of the first regime), and the similarity of the 1958–69 pattern to that of winter 1958, (the initiation of the second regime).

An objective way of demonstrating the coherence between SST regimes and the abrupt transition between them in 1957–58 is illustrated by Fig. 16. This graph gives the one year lag pattern correlations between the same seasons of different year pairs. The correlation was performed with standardized (normalized) SST anomalies computed for each 5° square over the North Pacific for each season for the years 1948 through 1970. The use of standardized values avoids biasing the correlation coefficients by the climatological differences in variability. Each point was weighted by the area of a 5° square at that point. In all, Fig. 16 represents the end product of about 9×10^6 ship observations.

Fig. 16 shows that except for the occasional negative spikes a moderately strong coherence existed between the same seasons of adjacent years. The period 1957–58 is especially interesting, for it was during this period that the year-to-year coherence disappeared, after which the new pattern became stable. This period is by far the most persistent of the negative spikes, representing five seasons over which a different SST pattern was emerging. Apparently a sustained period of change was required to break up a regime which had been entrenched for years. Other negative spikes can be looked upon as abortive attempts to break the regime—abortive because the changes were not sustained over a long enough period and probably represented shallow rather than deep water mass changes.

Referring once more to Figs. 8–13 we see that the 1957–58 changes were produced by air-sea coupling of a type wherein strong anomalous northerly flow over the central Pacific existed for the four seasons from summer 1957

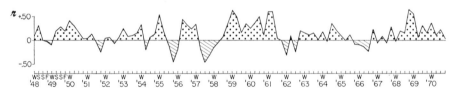

Fig. 16. Correlations of seasonal standardized sea-surface temperature (SST) anomaly *patterns* over the North Pacific from the previous year to the corresponding season of the listed year. (See text for further details.)

through spring of 1958. It is unlikely that any large-scale warm water pool such as observed in the earlier decade could survive with the implied extraction of sensible and latent heat, advection of colder water masses and suggested upwelling under intense cyclonic centers. Likewise, the sustained anomalous southerly air flow off the west coast of United States would force warm waters more northward than normal and extract less heat from the water, resulting in a net warming of the sea relative to the early decade.

The two decadal regimes show up in other meteorological data, often thousands of miles distant from the Pacific. These responses are due to well-documented "teleconnections" through which the atmosphere transmits influences to distant areas. Many of these were given physical meaning and indeed were brought to light by Rossby et al. (1939) and now are routinely used in long range weather prediction along with statistical adjuncts (O'Connor, 1969). For example, during the winters of the 1960's the Aleutian Low was appreciably south of normal (see Fig. 15) and the associated upper level trough deeper than normal (see Fig. 17). The downstream response (teleconnection) over North America, seen from the contours and isopleths of 700 mb height and anomalies in Fig. 17 was an amplified long wave—with a stronger than normal ridge or crest in the long wave over western North America and a stronger than normal trough over the east. This pattern conforms with known physical and statistical teleconnections from North Pacific atmospheric circulations. As a result of the increased frequency of Arctic outbreaks implied by the anomalous wind components (an inference supported by objective translations of upper air wind patterns into surface weather patterns) areas east of the Continental Divide have been abnormally cold—in fact colder than normal in every winter of this decade. This temperature fluctuation, as well as the 1957–58 abrupt transition, is strikingly illustrated by a plot of the mean winter temperatures at Atlanta, Georgia (Fig. 18), a representative station well removed from maritime influences. Also in Fig. 18 are plotted the annual snowfall amounts recorded at Atlanta. These also display a decadal difference in spite of the fact that Atlanta is far south and normally gets little snow. I shall resist the temptation to speculate on the climatic significance of the implied (and observed) greater frequency of snows at higher latitudes and its possible bearing on the Pleistocene glacial epochs.

The spell of cold winters in Europe during the 1960's is also implied by the Icelandic upper level ridge shown in Fig. 17 and the anomalous *northerly* wind components associated with the deep European trough. It is entirely possible that this long wave amplification and its geographical positioning was at least in part responsive to the upstream events over North America and the North Pacific.

We can also find evidence of the regimes and the abrupt transition in the

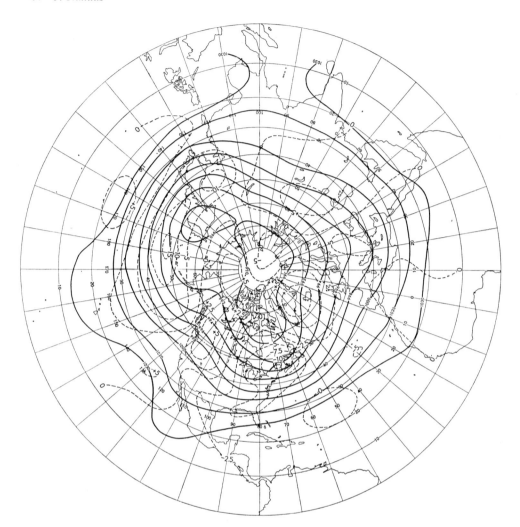

Fig. 17. Mean 700 mb height contours (solid lines) and isopleths of departure from normal (broken lines) for the winters of the decade from 1960–61 through 1969–70. Contours and isopleths of anomaly are labelled in tens of feet.

West Coast records of the mean height of sea level (Fig. 19). Here the changes in prevailing wind stress and sea temperature gradient seem to be the main causes—not the atmospheric pressure itself which accounts for little of the change in the indicated height of sea level.

Undoubtedly many other elements will be found to reflect this decadal climatic fluctuation—some of them chemical or biological. Already some evidence of this exists for atmospheric ozone (Komhyr, personal communication) and CO_2 (Bainbridge, 1971; Pueschel et al., 1971).

Let us now return to the stability of the decadal regimes, for this phenomenon and the abrupt transition between regimes, are most important problems

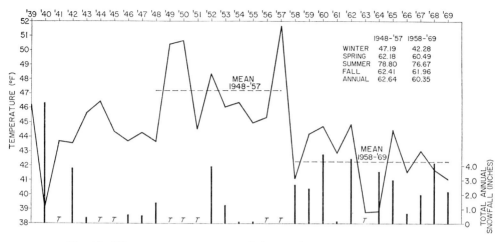

Fig. 18. Winter mean temperatures (°F) at Atlanta, Georgia. Vertical bars at base of figure give total annual snowfall (inches).

crying for solution. Meteorologists and oceanographers are far away from achieving quantitative physical interpretations of such anomalous regimes, although a promising start has been made in simulation of the oceans' and atmosphere's rough climatic patterns with a coupled ocean-atmosphere model (Manabe and Bryan, 1969). A thermodynamic model designed for predicting air and sea anomalies a month in advance is being explored (Adem, 1965). One important process not currently being considered by modelers is the revival of cold season SST patterns as discussed earlier and illustrated in Fig. 6.

Since atmosphere-ocean interactions occur chiefly at the air-sea boundary —especially the heat exchange—SST pattern recurrence would seem to play an important role in generating persistently recurrent atmospheric anomalies. For example, fronts and cyclones can be intensified in areas of strong ano-

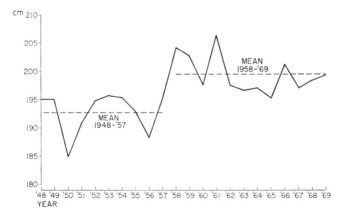

Fig. 19. Winter mean height of sea level at San Diego, California (in centimeters above an arbitraty reference level).

malous SST gradients (Bjerknes, 1962; Namias, 1959). Anticyclones are encouraged in certain anomalous areas where the stability in their frictional boundary layer is influenced by the temperature of the underlying surface waters (Namias, 1969). There seems to be no reason why these and other forms of atmospheric forcing by anomalous SST patterns cannot generate climatic regimes lasting for years. Abrupt breaks in such regimes, such as described in the 1957–58 period, could well be triggered as a threshold development wherein the atmospheric circulation and SST patterns are no longer compatible. The 1957 patterns were apparently of this unstable type. Of course, with deep ocean turnover, climatic fluctuations of the order of 500 to 1 000 years may be possible as envisioned by Rossby (Bolin, 1959). On an intermediate scale Bjerknes (1965) has offered an explanation of the European "Little Ice Age" from 1600 to at least 1850 AD based on air-sea coupling. As further ocean climate data come to light from the study of cores obtained by deep sea drilling, it may be found that even the Ice Ages are grand manifestations of air-sea interactions, eclipsing in importance extraterrestrial, astronomic, volcanic, and other proposed factors.

I wish to express appreciation and thanks for the help given me by Mr Robert Born (programming and editing), Mrs Madge Sullivan (computations), Mrs Lorayne D. Buck (typing), and Mr Fred Crowe and Miss Keiko Akutagawa (drafting). These assistants are all staff members of the Scripps Institution of Oceanography.

References

Adem, J., Long-range numerical weather prediction experiments. WMO Tech. Note 66, WMO-IUGG Symposium on Research and Development Aspects of Long-Range Forecasting, Boulder, Colorado, 1964, 138–140 (1965).

Bainbridge, A. E., Atmospheric carbon dioxide variation. Presented at the fifty-second annual meeting American Geophysical Union, Wash., D. C., April 12–18, 1971 (unpublished).

Berlage, H. P., The southern oscillation and world weather. Mededelingen en Verhandelinger, Meteorologisch Institut, Netherlands, No. 88, 152 p. (1966).

Bjerknes, J., Climatic change as an ocean-atmosphere problem. Arid Zone Research, Changes of Climate. Proceedings of the Rome Symposium Organized by UNESCO and WMO, 297–321 (1962).

Bjerknes, J., Atmosphere-ocean interaction during the "Little Ice Age" (seventeenth to nineteenth centuries, A.D.). WMO Tech. Note 66, WMO-IUGG Symposium Research and Development Aspects of Long-Range Forecasting, Boulder, Colorado, 1964, 77–88 (1965).

Bjerknes, J., A possible response of the atmospheric Hadley circulation to equatorial anomalies of ocean temperature. Tellus, *28*, 820–828 (1966).

Bjerknes, J., Atmospheric teleconnections from the equatorial Pacific. Monthly Weather Review, *97* (3), 163–172 (1969).

Bolin, B. (Ed.), The Atmosphere and the Sea in Motion. The Rossby Memorial Volume, The Rockefeller Institute Press, New York, 509 p. (1959).

Dronia, Horst, Der stadteinfluss auf den weltweiten temperaturtrend. Institut für Meteorologie und Geophysik der Freien Universitat Berlin. Band LXXIV Heft 4, 65 p. (1967).

Helland-Hansen, B. & Nansen, F., Temperature variations in the North Atlantic Ocean and in the atmosphere, introductory studies on the causes of climatological variations. Miscellaneous Collections, Smithsonian Institute Publication 2537, Wash., D. C., *70* (4), 408 p. (1920).

Komhyr, W. D., Barrett, E. W., Slocum, G., and Weickmann, H. K., Atmospheric total ozone increase during the 1960s. Nature, *232*, 390–391 (1971).

Lamb, H. H., Volcanic dust in the atmosphere; with a chronology and assessment of its meteorological significance. Philosophical Transactions of the Royal Society of London, Series A, *266*, 425–434 (1970).

Landsberg, Helmut E., Man-made climatic changes. Science, *170* (3964), 1265–1274 (1970).

Lee, A., Selected papers from a special meeting of the environmental subcommittee May, 1967, on fluctuations in sea and air temperature in the ICNAF area since 1950. Redbook 1967, Part 4, Issued from the headquarters of the Commission, Dartmouth, N. S., Canada, 105 p. (1967).

Manabe, S. & Bryan, K., Climate and the ocean circulation. Monthly Weather Review, *97*, 739–827 (1969).

Marine Research Committee. California Cooperative Oceanic Fisheries Investigations, Reports, *7*, 217 p. (1960).

Mitchell, J. M., On the world-wide pattern of secular temperature change. United Nations Educational, Scientific and Cultural Organization, Arid Zone Research, *20*, 161–181 (1963).

Mitchell, J. Murray. (Ed.), Seventh Congress of INQUA, August, 1965, Meteorological Monograph, American Meteorological Society, Boston, 159 p. (1968).

Murray, R. & Ratcliffe, R. A. S., The summer weather of 1968; related atmospheric circulation and sea temperature patterns. Met. Mag., *98*, 201–219 (1969).

Namias, J., Thirty-day forecasting—a review of a ten-year experiment. Meteorological Monograph, American Meteorological Society, Boston, Mass., *2* (6), 83 p. (1953).

Namias, J., Recent seasonal interactions between North Pacific waters and the overlying atmospheric circulation. Jour. Geophys. Res., *64* (6), 631–646 (1959).

Namias, J., Large-scale air-sea interactions over the North Pacific from summer 1962 through the subsequent winter. Jour. Geophys. Res., *68* (22), 6171–6186 (1963).

Namias, J., A weekly periodicity in eastern United States precipitation and its relation to hemispheric circulation. Tellus, *18* (4), 731–744 (1966).

Namias, J., Long-range weather forecasting—history, current status and outlook. Bull. Amer. Meteorological Soc., *49* (5), 438–470 (1968).

Namias, J., Autumnal variations in the North Pacific and North Atlantic anticyclones as manifestations of air-sea interaction. Deep-Sea Res., Supplement to vol. 16, 153–164 (1969).

Namias, J. & Born, R., Temporal coherence in North Pacific sea-surface temperature patterns. Jour. Geophys. Res., *75* (30), 5952–5955 (1970).

Neumann, G., Fisher, E., Pandolfo, J. & Pierson, W. J., Jr., Studies in the interaction between ocean and atmosphere with application to long-range weather forecasting. Final Report, AFCRCTR-58-236, (ASTIA-AD-152 555), AF 19 (604)–1284, New York University, Dept. Meteorology and Oceanography, 100 p. (1958).

O'Connor, J. F., Hemispheric teleconnections of mean circulation anomalies at 700 mb. ESSA Tech. Report WB 10, U. S. Dept. Commerce, 103 p. (1969).

Priestley, C. H. B., Droughts and wet periods and their association with sea-surface temperature. Aust. Jour. Sci., *29*, 56–57 (1966).

Pueschel, R. F., Ellis, H. T., Chin, J. F. S. & Mendonca, B. G., On a relationship between turbidity and CO_2 trends in the atmosphere. Presented at the fifty-second annual meeting Amer. Geophys. Union, Wash., D. C., April 12–18, 1971 (unpublished).

Rodewald, M., Sea-surface temperatures of the North Atlantic Ocean during the decade 1951–1960, their anomalies and development in relation to the atmospheric circulation. Arid Zone Research, XX, Changes of Climate, Proceedings of the Rome Symposium Organized by UNESCO and WMO, 97–107 (1963).

Rossby, C. G., Allen, R., Holmboe, J., Namias, J., Page, L. & Willett, H. C., Relation between variations in the intensity of the zonal circulation of the atmosphere and the displacement of the semi-permanent centers of action. Jour. Mar. Res., *2* (1), 38–55 (1939).

Shapley, Harlow. (Ed.), Climatic Change: Evidence, Causes, and Effects. Harvard University Press, Cambridge, 318 p. (1953).

Shedlovsky, Julian P., Honda, M., Reedy, Robert C., Evans, John C., Jr., Devendra Lal, Lindstrom, Richard M., Delany, Anthony C., Arnold, James R., Loosli Heinz-Hugo, Fruchter, Jonathan S. & Finkel, Robert C., Pattern of bombardment —produced radionuclides in rock 10017 and in lunar soil. Science, *167*, 574–576 (1970).

Singer, S. Fred. (Ed.), Global Effects of Environmental Pollution. Symposium, Dallas, 1968. Springer-Verlag New York, Inc., 218 p. (1970).

Teisserenc de Bort, L, Étude sur l'hiver de 1879–1880 et recheres sur la position des centres d'action de l'atmosphere dans les hivers anormaux. Bureau Central Météorologique de France. Annales, 1881, Pt. 4, 17–62 (1883).

Troup, A. J., The 'southern oscillation'. Quarterly Jour. Roy. Meteorological Soc., *91*, 490–506 (1965).

Walker, G. T., Correlation in seasonal variations of weather IX. A further study of world weather. Memoirs of the Indian Meteorological Dept., Calcutta, *24* (9), 275–332 (1924).

Discussion 1. Ocean Circulation. Atmospheric Variations

Pytkowicz

It may be better to use apparent oxygen utilizations instead of concentrations to eliminate source bias in the plots. Matter of fact, Redfield charted PO_4 in the oceans and, as phosphate variations almost correspond to oxygen utilizations, obtained a circulation which, if my memory serves me right, was not too far from that in your dynamic model.

Veronis

I will look into apparent oxygen utilizations.

Pytkowicz

Chemical oceanographers tend to use unrealistic one-dimensional models, based on vertical two-sources mixing models, to explain distributions of dissolved chemicals. This corresponds to seldomly found linear T-S diagrams. To what extent can physical oceanographers provide us with 3-dimensional models from which regional advective and eddy diffusion terms can be ascertained so that non-conservative terms can be calculated and chemical distributions explained?

Veronis

There are models explaining some aspects of three-dimensional circulation. These break down into thermocline models such as those by Welander and by Robinson and Stommel and numerical models such as those by Bryan. The latter are the only three-dimensional *transient* models available to us and non-conservative terms can be calculated. However, it should be noted that, at the present time, specific values of eddy diffusion coefficients are used in these models and the calculations are much too elaborate to allow for experimentation with these values.

Lal

The concentration of Si-32, a radioisotope (produced by cosmic radiation) of half-life about 500 years has been measured in the Pacific Ocean; three profiles were taken during NOVA-expedition and the results, which have not yet been published, show that Si-32 does serve as an ideal tracer for water circulation studies. This work, which has been carried out in a Tata-Scripps collaboration program, will be extended during Geosecs expedition.

Analogous to the case of C-14, the corrections for *in-situ* particulate contribution can be made easily in the case of Si-32 by measuring the concentration of silicon (total dissolved). The shorter half-life of Si-32 makes its application as a tracer more advantageous compared to C-14, however.

Waldichuk

The dramatic break-over in oceanographic conditions during 1957–58 seemed to occur first along the California coast in 1957, and then was followed by intrusions of warm water along the British Columbia coast in 1958. Is there any basis for this time lag from meteorological processes?

Namias

The slight lag in the warming off the British Columbia coast relative to California (of the order of one or two seasons) appears to be associated with the onset of anomalous southerly prevailing winds sooner off California, which in turn were related to the form and position of the long wave central Pacific trough.

Waldichuk

Is there evidence of a cyclic change of 10- or 11-year period in climatic conditions, or was it just a restoration of "normal conditions" in 1957–58?

Namias

The 1957–58 break in weather and sea surface temperature pattern was not a "return to normal" but a complete change in *anomalies*. It is unlikely that truly cyclic periods of 10 or 11 years occur in the air-sea coupled system, although occasionally a period of this kind may be found (e.g. the mean sea surface temperature of the North Pacific was high in 1948 and 1958).

Duursma

What is the minimum variation in a parameter (e.g. surface temperature) that is related to climatic processes (trains of depressions) that can cause abnormalities?

Namias

Observed atmospheric and sea surface temperature (SST) patterns suggest that temperature anomalies of 2°C or more extending at least over 10° square areas are apt to disturb the paths of cyclones and anticyclones. Usually compensations lead to anomalous *gradients* of sea surface temperature, which appear to influence storm tracks and development.

Føyn

Small variations in the temperature of the surface water may be correlated to the turbidity as the absorption of sun energy must be higher in such water than in clear water. This brings in the chemical composition of the water especially the content of plant nutrients which induces phytoplankton growth, and turbid water.

In areas with upwelling water, the concentration of plant nutrients may influence large bodies of surface water. Such variations therefore perhaps also influence the meteorological conditions. Even the pollution of the sea by man-made nutrients could be of importance.

Namias

While this is a possibility it appears that these effects would usually be rather small in comparison with other phenomena affecting sea surface temperatures. Perhaps experiments might be set up to check this.

Stewart (summarizing remarks)

Physical oceanographers (and meteorologists) have now a fairly satisfactory grasp of the mechanisms and nature of the average circulation of the ocean —both as a wind-driven system and as a thermo-haline system. Many details have yet to be incorperated into these concepts, however, and many important processes are still very crudely parameterized. Some ideas are also available about the time dependent motions—but there we are on far less secure ground and the relation between observations and theory is tenuous indeed. About the very important and very complex upper couple of meters of water we know far less than we need to know.

Nitrous Oxide in Air and Sea Water over the Atlantic Ocean

By Jürgen Hahn

Introduction

Several years ago, C. Junge and his co-workers started a program to study the atmospheric trace gases nitrous oxide, carbon monoxide, and more recently hydrogen. In 1970, I have joined this team to continue the N_2O measurements.

N_2O has been known to be a regular constituent of the atmosphere since the discovery of its absorption bands in the sun's spectrum by Adel (1939). But about one hundred years ago, it was found already, that denitrifying bacteria in soil can produce N_2O, so that this compound could be expected in the atmosphere. The official discovery of the N_2O by Adel and the subsequent measurements and discussions are summarized in several papers, so it will not be necessary to repeat them here (Bates and Witherspoon, 1952; Goody and Walshaw, 1953; Craig and Gordon, 1963; Bates and Hays, 1967).

Estimates and theoretical considerations, based primarily on laboratory studies and a few measurements in the atmosphere pointed to soil bacteria as the major source and to photochemical dissociation in the troposphere and stratosphere as the major sink for N_2O. In a recent paper (Schuetz et al., 1970) we discussed N_2O data obtained during a comprehensive field program. A compilation of all these data is shown in Fig. 1. The N_2O values are plotted as a function of altitude. The altitude is given in kilometers, the N_2O values in ppmv in terms of mixing ratios by volume in air. The number of measurements for each value in the diagram is given behind in parentheses. The values for the upper troposphere and for the stratosphere were normalized to a tropopause height of 10 km. The dotted lines give the standard deviations, about 10%, for the individual measurements for those series with sufficiently numerous values, as there are the measurements from Mainz in Western Germany, from the Black Forest mountain station Schauinsland in Western Germany, too, and from aircraft. The dashed lines a and b are calculated profiles by Bates and Hays (1967) for stratospheric eddy diffusion coefficients of 10^3 and 10^4 cm²/sec, respectively.

Our measurements in Mainz from November 1966 to December 1968 gave an average value of 0.279 ppmv N_2O in air. From the Schauinsland mountain station, which is located 230 km south of Mainz, at the long flat upper Rhine

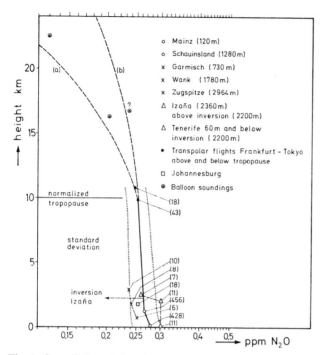

Fig. 1. Compilation of data from a comprehensive field program as a function of altitude. The dotted lines give the standard deviation of the tropospheric series of measurements with sufficiently numerous values. The dashed lines a and b are calculated profiles of Bates and Hays (1967) for stratospheric eddy diffusion coefficients of 10^3 and 10^4 cm^2/s, respectively. Number of measurements is given in parentheses.

Valley, to Mainz there is a difference in altitude of 1 150 meters. From June 1967 to November 1968 this station gave a N_2O average value of 0.266 ppmv. The size of the standard deviation of the average values gives for the Mainz N_2O average a range of 0.270–0.272 ppmv and for the Schauinsland N_2O average a range of 0.265–0.267 ppmv. That means that the difference between Mainz and Schauinsland values is significant, as well as the difference between Schauinsland and tropopause region values. N_2O data from the tropopause region we obtained on transpolar flights on the route Frankfurt–Tokyo. For the N_2O data below and above the tropopause, however, the difference is not significant. Besides our measurements in the tropopause region by aircraft, we succeeded in getting at least a few values from the stratosphere by means of balloons. We see, that all our N_2O data show a very systematic decrease with altitude. This is also true for the small data sets from Garmisch in the German Alps and from Izana on the Island of Tenerife. The concentration level of these data sets is somewhat different from that of the much longer series from Mainz and Schauinsland, but still within those limits, that can be expected on the basis of the standard deviations.

The value symbolized in the graph by a little quadrat is the average N_2O value for a series of 18 samples from Johannesburg in South Africa. This average of 0.252 ppmv is close to that from Schauinsland, what means that we can not await great differences between the N_2O levels of the hemispheres.

Our stratospheric data are close to the lines a and b, what seems to verify the theoretical calculations of the photochemical destruction rates given by Bates and Hays (1967). Assuming no other sinks than photochemical destruction, the calculations result in atmospheric life times of N_2O of about 70 years. However, the N_2O gradient Mainz-Schauinsland and variations of N_2O with time—the N_2O average from Mainz was 0.253 ppmv for the year 1967 and 0.292 ppmv for the year 1968—seem to point to higher production rates and to life times of 10 years or less. This means that within the troposphere there must be other sinks for N_2O besides photochemical destruction.

The first data from sea water were those measured by Craig and Gordon (1963) in sea water from the South Pacific Ocean. These very preliminary data seemed to indicate, that the sea water acts as a slight sink for N_2O. Reliable and more numerous data on this question were, therefore, of particular interest to us, and so we joined in three expeditions of the german research vessel "Meteor" in 1969, 1970 and in 1971. The cruise no. 16 (Atlantic Expedition 1969) offered excellent opportunities to obtain N_2O data from the surface air of large sections of the Atlantic Ocean. In addition, we started to measure the N_2O concentration in sea water. During the cruise no. 20, in June 1970, we got N_2O data from the air and the sea water over the Iceland–Faeroe–Ridge. In June 1971, we joined the cruise no. 23, which starting in Lisbon brought us to the North East Atlantic Ocean and then through the English Channel back to Hamburg.

Analytical Method

For the analysis of air samples the gas chromatographic method developed by Bock and Schuetz (1968) was used. Sampling was accomplished by sucking 10–20 liters of air through a train of three absorption tubes. The first tube is filled with sodium asbestos to remove CO_2, the second tube is filled with P_2O_5 to remove water vapor and the third one contains molecular sieve 5 Å which adsorbs quantitatively the N_2O. After collecting the sample the N_2O tube is carefully closed and can so be stored for a longer period of time prior to gas chromatographic analysis.

For gas chromatographic analysis the N_2O tube is heated in a little furnace to 300–350°C. The released gas is sucked off by a Toepler pump and transferred after compressing to a gas chromatograph. We are using a Hewlett & Packard model 5750 equipped with a heat conductivity detector and a 3-feet column of 35/70 mesh molecular sieve 5 Å, 1/4 inch in diameter. The gas chromatographic analysis is performed isothermally at 250°C with helium as carrier gas.

For a sample size of about 10 liters and a mixing ratio in air of 0.2 ppm by volume, the standard deviation of a single measurement was 10 %. In order to improve the accuracy and the reliability further, in all cases two parallel samples were taken.

Calibration was achieved by preparing N_2O—air mixtures of known contents by dilution in different ways to exclude systematic errors. During the expeditions the calibration was controlled in appropriate intervals. Further details of the method are given by Bock and Schuetz (1968).

The sea water samples were first transferred into 5-liter glass stoppered bottles, because it was not possible to process them as they came on board during deep sea sampling. The transfer of the samples to the 5-liter bottles was done as fast as possible to avoid any loss or exchange of N_2O. The 5-liter bottles were filled completely with sea water, so that no N_2O could escape from the water prior to analysis. The processing of the sea water samples started immediately after sampling and was performed in the following way: A 6-liter glass bulb is fitted with a stirrer, a gas inlet tube, and an efficient condenser. The condenser is connected to an absorption train similar to that used for air sampling. After evacuating the 6-liter bulb and the condenser 3–4 liters of a sea water sample are sucked from the 5-liter storage bottle into the bulb taking extreme care that no outside air entered with it. The size of the sea water sample to be processed in the bulb is determined by weighing the storage bottle before and after transferring the sea water into the bulb. Then clean nitrogen carrier gas is admitted through the gas inlet tube into the bulb to raise the pressure to one atmosphere. In order to exclude any N_2O from the bulb the nitrogen before entering the gas inlet tube passes a tube filled with molecular sieve 5 Å. After pressure equalization, the bulb is heated by means of a heating cap with the stirrer working, so that the water boils slowly. The nitrogen carrier gas passes through the sea water, enters the condenser to eliminate most of the water vapor, and subsequently passes through the absorption train to eliminate most of the CO_2, the rest of water vapor, and to adsorb the N_2O from the sample on molecular sieve. After one hour of operation all N_2O from the sea water sample has been transferred to the molecular sieve.

The molecular sieve tube loaded with N_2O is then treated for gas chromatographic analysis in the same manner as described for air samples.

The overall accuracy of the determination of N_2O in water samples was found to have a standard deviation of about 20 %.

In principle the molecular sieve tubes loaded with N_2O can be stored for later gas chromatographic analysis until after return to the laboratory. However, since we did not know, what to expect during the cruises, it was considered essential to have the analyses as soon as possible during the voyage. As a precaution a sufficient number of N_2O adsorption tubes was available during the cruises, in case analyses could not be performed due to bad weather or due to difficulties with the equipment. This turned out to be very useful after our gas chromatograph broke down during the third part of the 1969 Expedition.

The operation of a Toepler pump on board a ship is not without problems. After the 1969 Expedition, therefore, we modified the analytical method in the following manner: The molecular sieve tube loaded with N_2O is directly connected to the gas sampling valve of the gas chromatograph. The gas sampling valve together with the connected molecular sieve tube is then evacuated for about one minute by means of a vacuum pump. After switching the gas sampling valve and heating the molecular sieve tube to 300–350°C for 10 minutes, the gas adsorbed on the molecular sieve is transferred by the helium carrier gas to the gas chromatograph. On the column hold at 65°C adsorption takes place again. After 10 minutes the gas sampling valve is switched once more. Now the gas chromatographic analysis starts by raising the temperature of the column with 20°C/min to 250°C.

This technique eliminates the Toepler pump, separating the compounds adsorbed on the molecular sieve even better than before.

Before setting out on the 1970 Expedition the volume of the glass stoppered 5-liter bottles was determined and the processing of the sea water samples was modified in such way, that the contents of the 5-liter bottles when filled with a water sample is sucked into the 6-liter glass bulb down to a rest of a few milliliters. So, under shipboard conditions, the size of sea water samples can be determined more exactly than by weighing the 5-liter bottles before and after the transfer of the samples.

Another modification is the removal of the stirrer. We found, you know, that using a suited gas inlet tube the stirring of the sea water sample in the bulb by the nitrogen carrier gas is sufficiently good.

By these modifications we succeeded in getting an overall accuracy of 5 % for air samples and about 10 % for water samples, respectively.

Results

Fig. 2 shows the map of the cruises. During the 1969 Expedition, the route of which is marked in the map by a full line, air samples were taken in the first and in the third part of the cruise. That is from January through February 1969 during the voyage from Hamburg to Recife in Brazil and through April 1969 from 10° S to 60° N along 30° W. Sea water samples were taken exclusively in the third part.

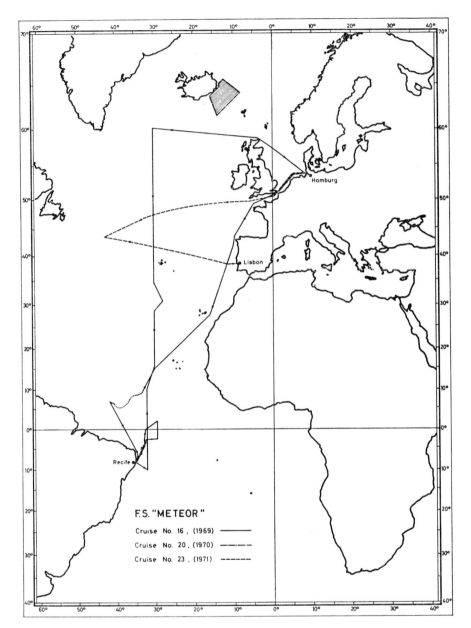

Fig. 2. Map of the "Meteor" cruises 1969, 1970, and 1971.

During the 1970 Expedition the N_2O measurements were restricted to the area of the Iceland–Faeroe-Ridge, which is hatched in the map. Through June 1970 air and sea water samples were taken and measured immediately on board the ship.

This year we joined in the North East Atlantic Expedition. The route is marked in the map by a dashed line. Starting from Lisbon we collected air and

Table 1. *Comparison of average N₂O mixing ratios obtained for different areas and altitudes from previous and present measurements*

Location	Altitude above sea level (m)	Average N$_2$O mixing ratio (ppmv)	Number of data
A) Mainz 1966–1969	120	0.271	573
Schauinsland Mountain Station Black Forest 1967–1968	1 280	0.266	456
Transpolar Flights Frankfurt–Tokyo 1967–68	below Tropopause	0.252	43
Johannesburg South Africa	1 800	0.253	18
Tenerife, Canary Isles March 1968	100	0.303	11
B) Part I.			
"Meteor" 1969, all samples	10	0.246	67
W. African Air January, February 1969	10	0.236	36
Part III.			
"Meteor" 1969, all samples	10	0.254	38
south of ITC	10	0.260	9
W. African Air	10	0.233	12
N. African Air April 1969	10	0.266	17
"Meteor" 1970, all samples Iceland–Faeroe-Ridge June 1970	10	0.252	60
"Meteor" 1971, all samples North East Atlantic June 1971	10	0.242	34

sea water samples through June 1971. The N$_2$O contents of the samples were measured immediately after sampling on board of the research vessel.

The Table 1 is a compilation of all our N$_2$O data from air. In part A of the table, we see N$_2$O average values from the older measurements just shown in Fig. 1. Part B of the table shows average values of the N$_2$O measurements during the three cruises. All air samples were collected on the uppermost deck of the "Meteor" about 10 meters above the sea's surface.

The N$_2$O measurements from the 1969 Expedition gave interesting results. The average N$_2$O mixing ratio from all air samples collected during the first part of the cruise was 0.246 ppm by volume. This is slightly less than the average values found in our previous studies, and comes from a number of very low N$_2$O values which dropped down to 0.170 ppmv. These N$_2$O mixing ratios in air were the lowest we ever found. They were obtained while we were passing through air masses of West African origin (C. Junge et al., 1971). For the time period of passing through West African air, the average N_2O mixing ratio in air dropped to 0.236 ppmv. These low N_2O values seem to suggest that the air from the Sahara region can have at least under certain conditions N_2O concentrations lower than elsewhere. This observation was confirmed by more conclusive data from the third part of the cruise. The third part of the cruise offered the unique opportunity to obtain a straight cross section from 10° S to 60° N along the 30. meridian. The air masses of the South East trade wind region south of the I.T.C. we passed through in the beginning of the third part of the cruise, could be regarded as of maritime origin. For this region a N_2O average of 0.260 ppmv was found. After passing through the I.T.C. the visibility record dropped from 80 to 15 kilometers. The air north of the I.T.C. was loaded with Sahara dust which was even found as a slight deposition on the ship's decks, and which was well represented by our measurements of the 5 micron particle concentration in air. This concentration rose by more than a factor hundred. The N_2O mixing ratio did not change as dramatically as the other parameters, but in the following days rather low values were encountered. The trajectories (determined with the help of geostrophic winds based on the surface maps and the streamline maps of 1 000 feet issued by the WMO regional center in Miami, USA) indicated fairly definitely West African air about three days old. For this time period we got an N_2O average of 0.233 ppmv. Leaving the dust loaded air masses the N_2O values rose again, and it is interesting to note that the N_2O increased to higher values before the dust contents started to drop very much. The air samples collected during the cruise northward, after leaving the West African air masses, gave an average N_2O mixing ratio of 0.266 ppmv. The N_2O average for the third part of the cruise, as a whole, was found to be 0.254 ppmv. That agrees quite well with the older data, and also with those from the first part of the cruise.

As we had expected, the N_2O values obtained during the 1970 Expedition from the surface air southeast of Iceland did not vary very much. N_2O mixing ratios in air from 0.244 ppmv to 0.260 ppmv were found, resulting in an average N_2O mixing ratio of 0.252 ppmv.

The N_2O measurements during the 1971 Expedition are still not fully evaluated. The average of all N_2O values obtained from the surface air is 0.242 ppmv. This is somewhat less than the previous N_2O averages from the northern Atlantic Ocean. At present, we can not say, yet, what are the reasons for this.

On the whole, the table I shows the rather uniform distribution of N_2O within the troposphere, and that is what we expected, after we had estimated the tropospheric residence time of N_2O at a few years, at least.

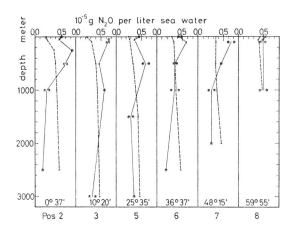

Fig. 3. Vertical profiles of N_2O in sea water at various positions during the third part of the 1969 Expedition. Crosses are plotted for those samples where some N_2O losses can not be excluded. The dashed lines are calculated concentrations in equilibrium with the N_2O concentration in air of 0.25 ppmv according to the water temperature.

During the third part of the 1969 Expedition sea water samples were taken from the surface and from different depths down to 3 000 meters. These sea water samples were processed on board of the research vessel. But the gas chromatographic analyses were not performed until after return to our laboratory. The results are plotted in Fig. 3 to give vertical profiles of N_2O in sea water at various positions. In some cases duplicate samples could be analysed. We plotted all the individual data to give an indication of the actual accuracy of the measurements. The scatter of data suggests that the profiles can be considered correct within only about 40 %. This may be due to the fact that the accuracy of the analytical method was determined in our laboratory. When one has been on board a ship like the "Meteor", he knows that there can be some differences between working in a laboratory on land and working in a ship's laboratory. Crosses are plotted in the figure for those samples where some N_2O losses can not be excluded. The correct values can be somewhat higher than indicated. Despite of these uncertainties we can say that there is a general tendency for high values in the upper 1 000 meters. At least, in 0° and in 25° N a maximum seems to exist between 300 and 600 meters. But the spacing and the accuracy of the values is not sufficiently good to give much details.

It is interesting to see how these values compare with equilibrium values of atmospheric N_2O. Such N_2O equilibrium values can be calculated from Henry's Law by:

$$C_{eq}^W = 10^3 \varrho \alpha(T) mp \qquad (1)$$

C_{eq}^W = N_2O equilibrium concentration in water in μg/liter water

ϱ = density of STP N_2O

$\alpha(T)$ = solubility of N_2O in water as a function of water temperature in cm³ STP N_2O/cm³ water × atmospheres

m = mixing ratio of N_2O in air in ppmv (for wet air)

p = air pressure in atmospheres.

If we consider the vertical stream patterns of the Atlantic Ocean assuming the sea water to be saturated with N_2O from the atmosphere in high northern latitudes, we can use in our calculations 0.25 ppmv as a reliable N_2O average value for the atmospheric mixing ratio, and 1 atmosphere as the average air pressure. In the literature there are no solubility data of N_2O in sea water available. So we used data given by Markham and Kobe (1941) for NaCl solutions of different molality and temperature thinking the sea water to be represented best by a solution of 35 g NaCl in one kilogram water. For more details reference is made to the paper of C. Junge et al. (1971). We think that the α-values used in our calculations are correct within about 10% for the temperature range of interest. In Fig. 3 the equilibrium concentrations calculated by Eqn. 1 are indicated by dashed lines. We see that in the upper layers there is a N_2O supersaturation with respect to air, whereas in the deeper water layers the sea water is undersaturated.

Fig. 4 shows the N_2O data obtained in June 1970 from the sea water in the

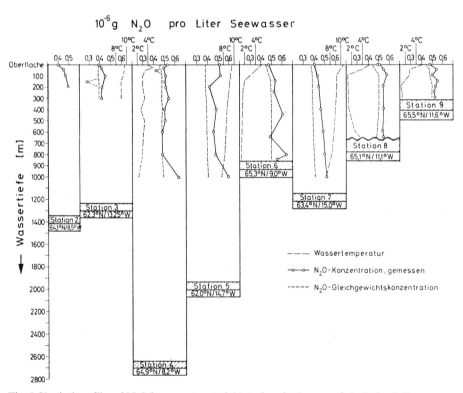

Fig. 4. Vertical profiles of N_2O in sea water at eight stations in the area of the Iceland–Faeroe-Ridge during the 1970 Expedition. The dashed lines are calculated concentrations in equilibrium with the N_2O concentration in air of 0.25 ppmv according to the water temperature.

area of the Iceland–Faeroe-Ridge. We see vertical N_2O profiles from three stations at the southwest slope (station 3, 5 and 7) and from five stations at the northeast slope of the ridge (station 2, 4, 6, 8 and 9). Besides the N_2O contents of the sea water which are given in μg/liter sea water, the water temperatures and the corresponding N_2O equilibrium concentrations are plotted. The dashed lines represent the N_2O equilibrium concentrations and the dashed-dotted lines represent the water temperatures. For technical reasons sampling was restricted to depths from the surface down to 1 000 meters. The depth of water at the various stations is indicated in the diagram by the lower limitation of the profile columns. We see that the N_2O supersaturations given by the distance between the full and the dashed lines are lower than those found during the 1969 Expedition. N_2O undersaturations do not seem to occur, except the two undersaturation values from the station 3 and the station 4 are true. After improving the analytical method, as described above, we got an accuracy of the measurements of 10 % and better; and this was the actual accuracy in 1970 on shipboard, too, as was tested by analyzing duplicate samples. So the variations in some of the profiles can be considered to be real, what is confirmed by other parameters such as salinity and oxygen contents.

In Fig. 5 this is shown for two stations at the northeast slope of the Iceland–

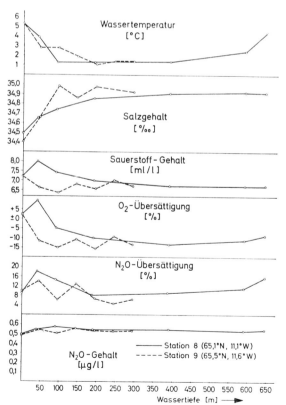

Fig. 5. Vertical Profiles of water temperature, salinity, oxygen contents, oxygen supersaturation, N_2O supersaturation, and N_2O contents at two stations northeast of the Iceland–Faeroe-Ridge during the 1970 Expedition.

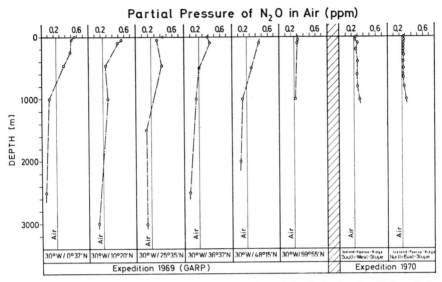

Fig. 6. N_2O concentrations in sea water as a function of depth during the 1969 and the 1970 Expedition in terms of equilibrium mixing ratios with respect to air to show saturation conditions. Average N_2O mixing ratio in air 0.25 ppmv.

Faeroe-Ridge. In this diagram the temperature, the salinity, the oxygen contents, the oxygen supersaturation, the N_2O supersaturation, and the N_2O contents of the sea water are plotted as a function of depth. We see that there are for each of the two stations comparable variations in the profiles.

In Fig. 6 we plotted our N_2O data from the 1969 Expedition and from the 1970 Expedition in terms of equilibrium mixing ratios with respect to air as a function of depth, in order to give an idea of the different saturation conditions of the sea water. These equilibrium mixing ratios were calculated by transforming the Eqn. 1 to:

$$m_{eq} = \frac{C^w}{10^3 \cdot \varrho \cdot \alpha(T) \cdot p} \tag{2a}$$

$$m_{eq} = \frac{C^w}{C^w_{eq}} \cdot m \tag{2b}$$

m_{eq} = equilibrium mixing ratio in air corresponding to the N_2O contents of the sea water in ppmv

C^w = N_2O contents of the sea water in $\mu g/l$ sea water.

The left part of the diagram shows the six N_2O profiles from the 1969 Expedition between the latitudes $0°$ and $60°$ N along $30°$ W. The vertical lines represent the average N_2O mixing ratio in air (0.25 ppmv). We see that in general the upper layers of the sea water show supersaturation with respect to air with maximum values of about twice the saturation concentration. Obviously the supersaturation decreases northward in a fairly systematic way. The deeper water layers show undersaturation with downward directed saturation gradients in intermediate waters. As we had expected, the N_2O supersaturations found in the upper layers of the sea water in the area of the Iceland–Faeroe-Ridge are small. In the right part of the diagram, we see two average profiles calculated from the N_2O data from three stations at the southwest slope of the ridge and from the N_2O data from four stations at the northeast slope, respectively. In general, there is only little variation of the N_2O supersaturations with depth. From a depth of about 500 meters to a depth of 1 000 meters the supersaturations increase with depth. Obviously the sea water from the southwest slope of the Iceland–Faeroe-Ridge is somewhat more supersaturated with N_2O than the water from the northeast slope of the ridge.

In June 1971, we got the opportunity to take sea water samples from a region of the northern Atlantic Ocean we passed through during the 1969 Expedition. So it was possible, to check some of our 1969 measurements by means of the improved analytical method. As said above, the 1971 measurements are still not fully evaluated. However, we are already able to show three vertical N_2O profiles obtained from the recent data. These three profiles are given in the left part of Fig. 7. Again, we plotted the N_2O data in terms of equilibrium mixing ratios with respect to air to show saturation conditions. As we found in 1969, the upper water layers are supersaturated with respect to air up to a factor of two. However, the 1971 profiles are somewhat different from those obtained from the 1969 measurements. The surface water is supersaturated to no more than 10 % of the equilibrium concentration as a maximum. While the 1969 profiles show no definite maxima, we see that here is in each of the three profiles a marked maximum of N_2O supersaturation between 400 and 800 meters, and a smaller one between 50 and 250 meters. From about 800 meters to 1 600 meters the N_2O values decrease to give just saturation in the water layers between about 1 600 and 2 000 meters. Below 2 000 meters the N_2O supersaturation seems to increase again. N_2O undersaturation values were not found. In the right part of Fig. 7, we plotted the average N_2O profiles obtained from the Iceland–Faeroe-Ridge data once more, to show the different saturation conditions. If we compare these average profiles with the 1971 profiles, we are under the impression that inspite of generally smaller supersaturation values in the upper water layers there are also small maxima indicated between 50 and 250 meters and 400 and 600 meters, respectively.

As we have seen, there are partly rather high N_2O supersaturations in the sea water. This may indicate N_2O production in the sea. However, it is known from studies of noble gases in sea water (Bieri et al., 1968; Craig and Weiss, 1971; Bieri, 1971) that supersaturation does not necessarily mean that there is

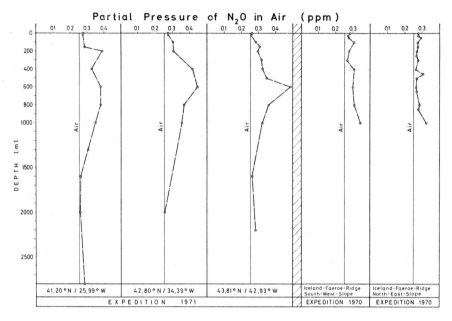

Fig. 7. N_2O concentrations in sea water as a function of depth during the 1970 and the 1971 Expedition in terms of equilibrium mixing ratios with respect to air to show saturation conditions. Average N_2O mixing ratio in air 0.25 ppmv.

a gas production in the sea. Physical processes such as bubble injection into surface waters and mixing processes of water masses of different temperatures can result in gas supersaturations in sea water (Kanwisher, 1963; Bieri et al., 1966). If we use the noble gas data, we can check to what extent our N_2O supersaturations can be due to physical processes. In Fig. 8 we plotted N_2O average supersaturations of sea water obtained from the 1969, 1970 and 1971 data as a function of depth in terms of percent of equilibrium concentration in sea water. Together with these average N_2O data average argon supersaturations calculated from Bieri's 1968 argon data are given. The argon data were obtained during the Woods Hole A—II—20 Expedition in the tropical North Atlantic Ocean (Bieri et al., 1968).

The bubble effect will depend on the solubility of the gas and should decrease with increasing solubility. The solubility of N_2O is about 20 times larger than that for argon. So the bubble effect should be negligible for N_2O, for, as shown in the diagram, the argon supersaturations found by Bieri are not higher than 10%. The mixing process of water masses should depend on the second derivative of the variation of solubility with temperature, which is in the temperature region of interest for N_2O about 1.5 times that for argon. So we should expect the N_2O supersaturations caused by physical processes to be comparable with the argon supersaturation percentages.

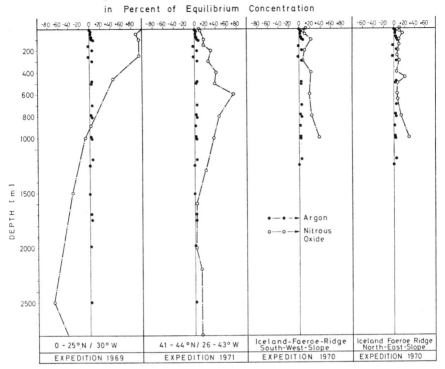

Fig. 8. Average N_2O supersaturations in sea water as a function of depth during the 1969, 1970, and 1971 Expedition and average argon supersaturations during the Woods Hole Expedition A-II-20 (Bieri, 1968) in terms of percent of equilibrium concentrations in sea water.

The vertical lines in Fig. 8 represent 100% gas saturation of the sea water. We see that the smaller N_2O supersaturations in the area of the Iceland–Faeroe-Ridge may partly be due to physical processes. The high N_2O super-saturations further south, however, must be interpreted as N_2O production in sea water. One can conclude, therefore, that most of the tropical and sub-tropical North Atlantic Ocean is a net source for atmospheric N_2O. This came as a surprise to us, because, as was said in the beginning, we were looking for a sink for atmospheric N_2O.

We know that over land N_2O is produced by nitrate reduction due to bac-terial activities (Verhoeven, 1952; Wijler and Delwiche, 1954; Matsubara and Mori, 1968). Since most of the soil bacteria are also found in waters, it is not unreasonable to assume a similar mechanism for the N_2O production in sea water. The work of Kriss et al. (1961) seems to support this suggestion. They determined the concentration of heterotrophic micro-organisms in Atlantic waters, just along the 30° meridian from 60° N to the equator, and found the highest concentrations of micro-organisms in equatorial waters with rapid decrease to low concentrations in middle latitudes.

It may be of interest to see how the N_2O concentrations in sea water compare with those of other nitrogen compounds, primarily nitrite and nitrate. We found average concentrations of N_2O in the upper 500 meters of about 0.5–0.6 μg N_2O/liter sea water or 0.3–0.4 μg N_2O–N/liter sea water. According to Vaccaro (1965) we can assume 1.5–3.0 μg NO_2^-–N/liter and 140–430 μg NO_3^-–N/liter for the same water layers. This shows that N_2O–N is a very small fraction of the nitrogen budget in sea water. Junge et al. (1971) estimated the N_2O escape from Atlantic surface waters to be about 10^{-5} g N_2O–N/cm^2 × year. Comparison of this value with the net upstake of nitrogen in sea water of 270×10^{-5} g N/cm^2 × year supports the conclusion that the N_2O cycle is rather small compared with the total nitrogen cycle in sea water.

In spite of this, parallel sea water samples for N_2O, argon, nitrite, nitrate and ammonia should be taken, so that in the future corresponding vertical profiles can be plotted. This together with studies of micro-organisms in sea water, particularly studies of the activities of nitrifying and denitrifying micro-organisms under changing conditions, should give interesting details in N_2O production in sea water.

It is known from the literature, that there are microorganisms which are able to produce and to consume N_2O as the conditions are changing. So we can imagine, that in sea water the N_2O cycle will be very complex, for both production and consumption of N_2O may occur. Therefore, it may be possible, that under certain conditions there are N_2O undersaturations in sea water which were caused by biological processes. So it remains an open question to what degree our results from the northern Atlantic Ocean hold also for the other oceans.

References

Adel, A., Note on the atmospheric oxides of nitrogen, Astrophys. J., *90*, 627 (1939).

Bates, D. R. & Witherspoon, A. E., The photochemistry of some minor constituents of the earth's atmosphere, Mon. Notices Roy. Astron. Soc., *112*, 101 (1952).

Bates, D. R. & Hays, P. B., Atmospheric nitrous oxide, Planet. Space Sci., *15*, 189 (1967).

Bieri, R. H., Koide, M. & Goldberg, E. D., The noble gas contents of Pacific sea waters, J. Geophys. Res., *71*, 5243 (1966).

Bieri, R H., Koide, M. & Goldberg, E. D., Noble gas contents of marine waters, Earth Planet. Sci. L., *4*, 329 (1968).

Bieri, R. H., Dissolved noble gases in marine waters, Earth Planet. Sci. L., *10*, 329 (1971).

Bock, R. & Schuetz, K., Gaschromatographische Bestimmung von Distickstoffoxid-Spuren der Luft, Anal. Chem., *237*, 321 (1968).

Craig, H. & Gordon, L. I., Nitrous oxide in the ocean and the marine atmosphere, Geochim. et Cosmochim. Acta, *27*, 949 (1963).

Craig, H. & Weiss, R. F., Dissolved gas saturation anomalies and excess helium in the ocean, Earth Planet. Sci. L., *10*, 289 (1971).

Goody, R. M. & Walshaw, C. D., The origin of atmospheric nitrous oxide, Quart. J. Roy. Meteorol. Soc., *79*, 496 (1953).

Junge, C., Bockholt, B., Schuetz, K. & Beck, R., N_2O measurements in air and in sea water over the Atlantic, "Meteor"-Forschungsergebnisse, Reihe B, in press (1971).

Kanwisher, J., On the exchange of gases between the atmosphere and the sea, Deep-Sea Res., *10*, 195 (1963).

Kriss, A. E., Mitzkevitch, I. N., Mishustina, I. E. & Abyzov, S. S., Micro-organisms as hydrological indicators in seas and oceans—IV, Deep-Sea Res., *7*, 225 (1961).

Markham, A. E. & Kobe, K. A., Solubility of carbon dioxide and nitrous oxide in salt solution, J. Amer. Chem. Soc., *63*, 449, (1941).

Matsubara, T. & Mori, T., Studies on denitrification, J. Biochem., *64*, 863 (1968).

Schuetz, K., Junge, C., Beck, R. & Albrecht, B., Studies of atmospheric N_2O, J. Geophys. Res., *75*, 2230 (1970).

Wijler, J. & Delwiche, C. C., Plant and Soil, *5*, 155 (1954).

Vaccaro, R. F., in Riley, J. P. & Skirrow, G., Chemical Oceanography, Vol. 1, 3rd Edition, p. 390–403, Academic Press, London/New York 1970.

Verhoeven, W., Aerobic spore forming nitrate reducing bacteria, Dissertation, Delft, Netherl., p. 1–160 (1952).

Discussion 2. Nitrous Oxide. Carbon Monoxide

Duursma

How is N_2O placed in the "chemical" or bacterial reactions in nature between the other nitrogen compounds present in water, air and soil?

Hahn

The nitrogen cycle is very complex. We today do not know more about it as was published by Cooper already before World War II. The cycle is something like this:

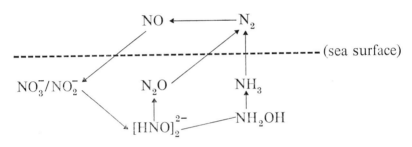

This is a very abbreviated form of Cooper's nitrogen cycle. For the whole and more detailed nitrogen cycle reference is made to the literature. [L. H. N. Cooper, The nitrogen cycle in the sea, J. Mar. Biol. Assoc., U.K., *22*, 183 (1937)].

Duursma

Did you check the experiments on soil-CO production and decomposition with blank experiments at the temperature you have used but with sterilized soil and air? These should show whether microorganisms or photo-chemical reactions are the cause of the processes.

Did you do the experiments in dark or with light?

Seiler

The experiments were done in dark, so photo-chemical reactions were excluded. We did not use blank-sterile experiments but other investigators (Inman et al., Science *172*, 1229–1231) have proved that under sterile conditions there is no CO production and/or reduction.

Grasshoff

According to the surface profiles and the clear dependence of the CO concentration of the irradiation there should be a good correlation of the CO formation and primary production. In order to get more reliable figures of natural CO formation in the Oceans it should be advantageous to set up the correlation of p.p. and calculate the CO formations on the basis of the large number of existing p.p. data from all parts of the world ocean.

Seiler

This has not been done yet. The presented data of total natural CO production are based on values from the North, Tropical and South Atlantic, Pacific and Iceland–Faeroe region.

Steele

The graphs presented suggest that the decrease in CO concentration just below the sea surface is almost exponential in character. Is this always the case?

Seiler

Most of the vertical CO-profiles show an exponential decrease of dissolved carbon monoxide. But we have also found some vertical profiles with a maximum in 2–3 m depth and some cases with a constant CO-mixing ratio between surface layer and a depth of about 10 m. We think that the constant CO-mixing ratio is caused by the movement of the propeller of the ship.

Sorokin

The shape of the curve of the vertical profile of the distribution of CO in the water column presented by Seiler is well known to me. It is quite similar to the vertical profiles of the distribution of biomass and activity of microbial population in the ocean and I will demonstrate it in my lecture. The same form of curve was published by Holm-Hansen from Scripps Institution. It described the vertical distribution of the living microflora in a water column at the Eastern Pacific as indicated by ATP. This correlation can be accepted as an indirect proof of the participation of planktonic microflora in the formation of CO in sea water.

Dyrssen

Is CO consumed by oxidation to CO_2 and does this function as a sink?

Seiler

The reaction rate between CO and O_2 is so small at the normal temperature in the troposphere that this sink is not to take into account.

Waldichuk

"Spikes" of nitrite concentration are often seen at one or two depths. The upper, major one at about 75 m in the Pacific during summer appears to be associated with the top of the pycnocline where organic matter tends to hang up and bacterial attack occurs. There are sometimes other secondary nitrite maxima below this layer, although I have not seen any at 500 m. Were any nitrite data collected along with carbon monoxide data at any of the stations?

Seiler

No, we have not done such nitrite measurements. But perhaps this will be a good idea to do so.

Impact of Natural and Man-Made Surface Films on the Properties of the Air-Sea Interface

By William D. Garrett

Introduction

Areas of the ocean surface calmed by oil or smoothed due to the presence of natural surface films have intrigued observers since man first went to sea. The earliest scientific attention to this phenomenon was a study by Benjamin Franklin (1773) which was inspired by mariners observations of the effects of oil on rough water. He described his experiments in a letter to a scientific acquaintance as follows: "At length being at Clapham, where there is, on the common, a large pond, which I observed one day to be very rough with the wind, I fetched out a cruet of oil, and dropped a little of it on the water. I saw it spread itself with surprising swiftness upon the surface; but the ef ect of smoothing the waves was not produced; for I had applied it first on the leeward side of the pond, where the waves were largest, and the wind drove my oil back upon the shore. I then went to the windward side where they be- gan to form; and there the oil, thought not more than a teaspoonful, produced an instant calm over a space several yards square, which spread amazingly, and extended itself gradually till it reached the lee side, making all that quarter of the pond, perhaps half an acre, as smooth as a looking-glass."

This inquiry constituted man's first controlled attempt to modify his en- vironment through the use of surface films; and if one calculates the ultimate thickness of the spread oil from Franklin's observations, a value of 24 Ang- stroms is obtained, about the thickness of a compacted surface film of mono- molecular dimensions. The correspondence between this precocious observa- tion and the current picture of sea surface films is remarkably good as we shall discover later in this introduction.

The field of surface chemistry blossomed in 1917 under the leadership of Irving Langmuir, but this discipline was not applied intensively to organic surface-active films on the sea until the middle of this century when natural films were collected, analyzed chemically, and characterized with respect to surface properties. The present chemical model of a natural oceanic film reveals that it is a mixture of organic compounds which are highly surface active, i.e., they possess a strong tendency to adsorb at the air-sea interface and lower its surface energy. This property arises from a chemical structure which causes the molecule to anchor its hydrophilic functional groups ($-COOH$, $-COH$,

–COOR, etc.) in the water surface while its hydrophobic segment, a nonpolar hydrocarbon chain, is oriented away from the polar seawater.

Under the influence of surface convergent forces, the adsorbed molecules are compacted into films which damp capillary waves and produce light reflectance anomalies known commonly as "slicks" or Glattwasser. These films are composed primarily of water-insoluble organic materials and exhibit film pressures (surface tension decreases) of from 2 to 10 dynes/cm (Garrett, 1965). The film pressures usually found in natural slicks are somewhat less than the maximum or collapse pressures which can be sustained by mono-molecular films of sea surface molecules (Jarvis, et al., 1967). Natural surface films are truly monomolecular in thickness as opposed to the multilayer character of oil slicks which contain a large percentage of unadsorbed hydro-carbons. Natural surface films are observed most frequently in the biologically active coastal water near continents or island groups (Dietz and LaFond, 1950). In the open ocean, the dispersive forces of waves and breaking water together with a lower concentration of surface active material reduce the prob-ability of coherent monolayer formation. However, in relatively calm weather of several hours duration, a large percentage of the sea can become slick in appearance due to the adsorption of film-forming materials.

To determine the chemical constitution of the sea surface a 150 μm thick upper skin was collected from a number of ocean sites and analyzed for speci-fic organic compounds by gas chromatography (Garrett, 1967a). The major water-insoluble components of the sea surface are a complex mixture of fatty esters, free fatty acids, fatty alcohols, and variable quantities of hydrocarbons. Although proteins and carbohydrates have been identified qualitatively in surface water, their contribution to surface effects is small because of their greater water solubility. Surface active material was found in all locations, but the largest yields were recovered from surface waters which were ob-viously slick covered. Although the same classes of chemicals were found in all samples, the relative distribution of the specific fatty compounds was de-pendent upon localized events taking place in the marine environment (e.g., the presence of certain organisms). In addition, the higher-molecular-weight and less soluble species were strongly adsorbed at the air-water interface while the more soluble or less surface active compounds were forced out of the sur-face film by the more active molecules as a film aged or when surface con-vergences operated on the slick. Thus, the alternating surface compressions and dilations caused by passing waves progressively decreased the solubility of the film.

While most slicks are composed of products from the marine biosphere, increasing human activity is certainly adding surface active and water-in-soluble contaminants to the sea from ship discharges, ocean industry, polluted rivers, and atmospheric fallout. An assessment of the influence of surface films on the character of the sea surface and the resulting impact upon the adjacent marine environment requires an understanding of the boundary processes which are altered by this complex mixture of chemicals. The problem is multi-disciplinary and involves an evaluation of the effects of an organic layer on a dynamic water surface whose chemical composition is constantly being modified by physical, chemical and biological processes. The net effect of a natural or pollutant film is determined by its chemical and physical character, areal coverage and its response to the dispersive forces of the marine environment which selectively remove portions of the film from the sea surface.

Influence of Surface Films on the Properties of the Air-Sea Interface

Most existing information on the impact of organic films at the air-sea interface deals with natural sea slicks which are monomolecular films composed of adsorbed organic molecules. However, extrapolations from thin films to thicker oil layers can be made on the basis of laboratory measurements and field observations of the properties of organic films and thin petroleum layers on seawater. An initially fluid petroleum spill is modified by exposure to the marine environment and eventually attains a semisolid condition, either as tarry lumps or as a stable water-in-oil emulsion. Between the time of the spill and that of the final, almost refractory state, the oil exists as a thick layer, a thinner iridescent film and a monomolecular film of surface active petroleum constituents surrounding the thicker layers. To obviate repetition, the influence of both natural slicks and thicker oil films on the properties of the air-sea interface will be considered simultaneously.

Wave Damping

Visibility of natural slicks at sea arises from a light reflectance anomaly produced by the capillary-wave damping properties of the otherwise invisible one-molecule-thick film. Simultaneous measurements of wave-damping characteristics and film pressure on freshly collected seawater indicated that adsorbed films of natural surface active material damped capillary waves at very low film pressures (Garrett, 1967b), where film pressure F is the difference in surface tension between a clean seawater surface and that covered by the organic film. The damping coefficient increased from 0.08 cm^{-1} for a clean seawater surface to a maximum of about 0.43 cm^{-1} at a film pressure of only one dyne/cm using 60 Hz waves (Fig. 1). With a further increase in film pressure, the damping coefficient decreased to a value of 0.24 cm^{-1} becoming constant at 2 dynes/cm film pressure. The damping coefficient k was calculated from the expression

$$a = a_0 e^{-kx}$$

which describes the decay of the linear capillary waves used in the laboratory experiments, where a_0 is the wave amplitude at its source and a is the amplitude at distance x from the source. Fig. 1 is a composite plot of k vs. F for surface films formed from the constituents in freshly collected seawater and from three pure fatty acids commonly found in sea surface films. The shapes of these curves reflect the influence of chemically unsaturated fatty compounds (linoleic and linolenic acids) which produce pronounced maxima in k at low F. Furthermore, these data are in accord with the observation that sea slicks can exist at low film pressures, and that the surface molecules need not be greatly compressed to damp capillary waves. Since extremely small quantities of surface active materials at a low state of molecular compression produce easily visible patterns on the sea surface, extensive pollution of the sea surface by oil or other contaminants can be detected readily. However, only in the vicinity of local oil spills or in areas of chronic pollution are such damped conditions prevalent. The majority of the world ocean surface is capillary active indicating almost no surface tension reduction and a relatively clean surface condition.

Adsorbed surface active material not only attenuates existing waves, but also inhibits wave formation (Keulegan, 1951; Van Dorn, 1953). According to Miles (1967), the addition of a sufficient quantity of a soluble surface active agent (detergent) to produce an inextensible film can increase by almost an

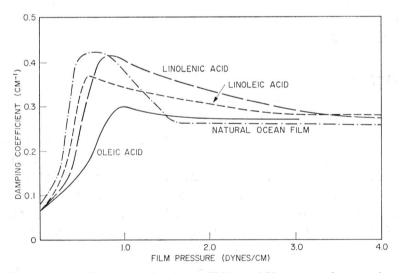

Fig. 1. Relationship between damping coefficient and film pressure for natural sea surface films, and three fatty acids which are common constituents of such films.

order of magnitude the minimum wind velocity necessary to produce waves. A recent experiment performed in the open ocean has demonstrated that a large areal coverage by a surface film will also decrease the amplitudes of wind-driven gravity waves by reducing the form drag of the atmosphere upon the ocean through the elimination of capillary waves (Barger, et al., 1970).

In a similar manner, monomolecular films which surround an oil spill and separate windrows of oil will damp waves and resist their formation. Capillary-wave damping coefficients of thicker layers of oil may be calculated from

$$k = \frac{8\pi\eta f}{3\gamma}$$

where f is the ripple frequency, η the bulk viscosity expressed in poises and γ the surface tension of the fluid. At this laboratory an experimental determination of k for pure hexadecane using 60 Hz waves at 25°C gave a value of 0.53 cm^{-1}, a damping coefficient greater than that for seawater covered with a coherent surface film. Furthermore, if we assume values of η and γ for an average crude oil, k is 1.8 cm^{-1} for 60 Hz capillary waves. Thus, capillary wave attenuation on a pollutant oil is somewhat greater than that of a monolayer-covered surface and about 22 times that for clean seawater at this frequency of wave generation where $\lambda = 0.52$ cm, a typical capillary wavelength. The low incidence of ripples on the oily surface coupled with its higher viscosity will also diminish wind-driven gravity waves of longer wavelength when the areal coverage of the spill is large. Thus, the uncoupling of air-water interactions by an oil film and its attendant monolayer would produce a halcyon condition at and near the sea surface.

Gas Transport

Numerous studies of evaporation retardation by monomolecular films have been reviewed by La Mer (1962) and Frenkiel (1965). Only those films containing linear molecules which are capable of close packing are effective in reducing gas transport across the air-water interface by acting as a molecular barrier. In addition to slowing evaporation of water, closely packed monolayers can reduce the mass transfer flux of other gases such as carbon dioxide, methane, nitrogen and oxygen by as much as 25–40% (Sada and Himmelblau, 1967). Films of linear molecules under high film pressure constitute a thin diffusion barrier to the adsorption of oxygen, carbon dioxide and nitrous oxide by water (Blank, 1962). Monolayer permeabilities were found to be of the same magnitude for all of these gases.

In large bodies of water depletion of oxygen beneath an impermeable surface film is unlikely because dissolved oxygen levels are near or above saturation due to wind-induced mixing. Trapped oxygen produced by marine organisms during photosynthetic periods would compensate for oxygen losses (Wiltzius, 1967). The most important factor which will serve to maintain normal oxygen levels beneath a surface film is the dilation of the surface caused by waves. These surface expansions reduce the close-packed character of the molecules and allow periodic gas exchange. With winds above 7 m/s, it is virtually impossible to maintain a highly adlineated molecular structure in a surface film and it essentially loses all resistance to gas exchange.

It is sometimes mistakenly assumed that any monomolecular surface film would interfere with the rate of gas transport to or from the sea. However, only compounds capable of forming rigid films in which the molecules are adlineated demonstrate the ability to retard the evaporation of water. The molecules must be linear in structure so that they may form a close-knit structure when forced together under high surface compression (Garrett, 1971). The surface-active substances responsible for the spreading and film-forming characteristics of petroleum products include aromatic, condensed-ring and branched-chain structures, and cycloparaffin carboxylic acids in addition to the more linear polar molecules. A monolayer formed from such a mixture does not meet the structural requirements of films which retard gas transport. Consequently, the portion of an oil spill which is of monomolecular dimensions should have an inconsequential effect upon gas exchange. A similar case can be made for natural sea slicks since they are usually not highly compressed and contain significant quantities of nonlinear molecules.

On the other hand, it has been demonstrated experimentally that a 5 μm thick duplex film of paraffin oil and surface-active material may reduce the evaporation rate of water to 15% of that from a clean water surface (Gilby and Haymann, 1948). The relative efficiency of evaporation inhibition with multilayered oil films increases with wind velocity, and it was concluded that the effect was due to the diffusional resistance of the oil and its interfacially oriented film rather than that of the stagnant diffusion-controlled air layer above the oil. Above 10 μm the evaporation resistance increased with film thickness and depended upon the nature of the spreading agent in the oil. Under nonturbulent air flows, films thicker than 50 μm decreased evaporation rates to less than one percent of that for clean water. Powell (1943) investigated the influence of films of oxidized oils up to 2.5 cm in thickness on the evaporation of water and determined that a maximum retardation occurred between 0.6 and 1.0 cm film thickness. At greater oil-film thicknesses the efficiency of evaporation retardation decreased. This result was attributed to convective effects in the thicker films which overcame the diffusion barrier effect. The lower rate of diffusion of water through oil as opposed to that in air accounts for the evaporation retardation; the diffusion coefficient for water being about 10^4 greater in air than in oils. It was observed that under the influence of wind it was difficult to maintain a uniform oil film in the micron range. These surface films broke up into lenses which were in equilibrium with their supporting monomolecular films, a factor to be considered for any oil spill. In such instances, wind-wave effects break continuous films into discontinued puddles of oil surrounded by thin films and monolayers.

It is unlikely that oxygen depletion by an oil slick would reach disastrous proportions near the sea surface unless the oil spill uniformly covered a vast area. Uniform coverage is rare because of wave-induced dilations which thin the film, drive it into windrows and consequently create open sea surface areas for gas exchange. Furthermore, horizontal transfer beneath the slick from saturated water masses can resupply oxygen-deficient zones. Only in small bodies of water with little mixing should oil films cause abnormal oxygen levels. Of course, this relatively clean bill of health with regard to oxygen depletion at sea only relates to effects at the sea surface. If large quantities of petroleum products are submerged into the bulk water, the biological and chemical oxygen utilization which will result could create a situation critical to marine life.

Exchange of Solids and Liquids

The transfer of solids and liquids from sea to air is effected by sea spray and bursting bubbles. These processes are modified by organic films, oil layers and the existence of emulsions at the air-sea boundary. Free gas bubbles may be produced in the sea by the decomposition of detrital matter, the impact of raindrops and the breaking of waves. By scavenging surface-active material and foam-stabilizing particulate substances, bubbles promote the formation of foams. In addition, bursting air bubbles generate salt-containing aerosols through the disintegration of the thin film of water which separates the air in the bubble from the atmosphere. When surface films are present, fragments from bursting bubbles transfer organic components into the marine atmosphere. In fact, the ejected portions of the bubble crown (film drops) and the jet drops produced by collapse of the bubble cavity may remove any sea-surface matter, animal, vegetable, or mineral, which is attached to the bubble fragments. Oil films are also readily stripped from the water surface by this process.

The longevity of air bubbles and foam at the air-water interface is dependent upon both the surface activity of the seawater and the physical nature of sea-surface films (Garrett, 1967c). In the absence of a surface film, the lifetime of a bubble is determined by the surface-active material adsorbed during its passage upwards through the ocean. The existence of a sea slick of monomolecular dimensions at the point of bubble emergence will significantly reduce

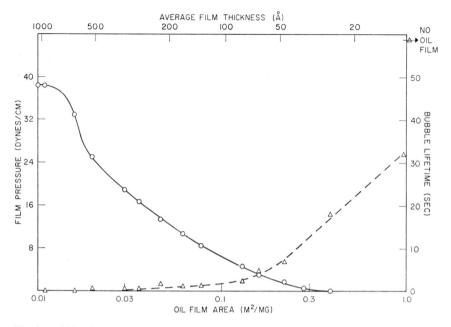

Fig. 2. Bubble lifetime (dashed line) and film pressure (solid line) vs. thickness of a spread film of crude oil.

bubble stability and act as an antifoaming agent even though the bulk sea-water may be rich in foam-stabilizing substances. Similar circumstances prevail for oil films up to 1 000 Å thickness as indicated by recent data presented in Fig. 2. Bubble lifetimes (58 sec. average value) were first measured at the surface of freshly collected seawater contained in a glass hydrophil tray. Single bubble duration was then measured as a function of the film pressure of a crude oil film spread onto the seawater substrate from a dilute chloroform solution. The oil layer which was initially of monomolecular dimensions was compressed in stages, and bubble lifetime and film pressure were measured at each film area. Before compression of the oil film was initiated, the bubbles were stable since they were influenced by soluble surface active material which they had collected by adsorption on their rise to the surface. This stability was due to the rapid repair of the protective surface film by the available supply of foam stabilizing compounds from the bulk seawater. Upon compression of the oil film, bubble lifetime decreased substantially to values of zero at high film pressures at which the oil film behaved like a brittle, solid sheet, and the air bubbles burst instantaneously upon reaching the surface. The compressed, water-insoluble oil film then became the controlling factor in determining bubble duration and foam stability. Especially at high film pressure there was an increased instability in the embrittled film, and the probability of film rupture was large. Conversely, we have observed that somewhat thicker oil films have an opposite effect when they are as thick as the diameter of the air bubble. The mm-thick multilayers of oil appear to contain sufficient foam-enhancing, surface-active material to stabilize clusters of bubbles at the air-oil interface.

The foaming characteristics of the sea surface determine the rate of transfer of liquids and solids by breaking air bubbles. The addition of water-insoluble monomolecular surface films to bubbled seawater increased the concentration of bubble-generated salt nuclei by as much as three-fold (Garrett, 1968). No increases in nuclei concentration resulted when these films were spread onto the surface of clean aqueous systems which did not contain surface-active foam-forming materials. Consequently, the increased salt nuclei concentration resulted from a modification of the bubble bursting process by the surface film. The water-insoluble film decreased the degree of foaming at the seawater surface and enhanced the immediate breaking of bubbles. There was a greater rate of fragmentation of the air-water interface which increased the concentration of bubble-generated salt particles over that produced from a foamy surface. On the other hand, it is to be expected that a thick oil film will not only decrease the production of bubbles and spray by inhibiting breaking water, but also will retard the bubble bursting through stable emulsion formation. Thus, a thick oil layer will cause a decreased rate of transport of matter from sea to air while μm-thick oil layers and monomolecular films should cause increased transport under identical environmental conditions associated with bubble bursting processes.

In addition to phlegmatizing physical processes at the air-sea interface, an oil spill may also affect physical processes in the marine atmosphere. Bubbles which burst at an oil-covered surface eject water drops coated with oil film which retards drop evaporation. The evaporation rates of distilled water drops, and drops coated with 1-hexadecanol and various pollutant oils are compared in Fig. 3. Oil-coated drops were produced by the rupture of 2 mm air bubbles at a water surface covered by a 10-μm-thick oil film. The evaporation rates, expressed as $-2r\,dr/dt$, were up to 25 times larger for distilled water than for the oily drops. It is interesting to note that the evaporation rate for the oil-coated drops was sometimes less than that for the drops whose surface was covered with a monomolecular film of 1-hexadecanol, an effective agent for the retardation of evaporation. Under windy conditions at sea, considerable oil would be transferred into the marine atmosphere where it could retard droplet evaporation and perpetuate an oily mist.

The air to sea pathway, atmospheric fallout and precipitation scavenging, may constitute a significant source of both hydrocarbons and surface-active substances. Goldberg (1970) has estimated that the hydrocarbon input into the oceans via atmospheric transport could be five times as great as the massive contribution from ship and land sources. The movement of matter from the

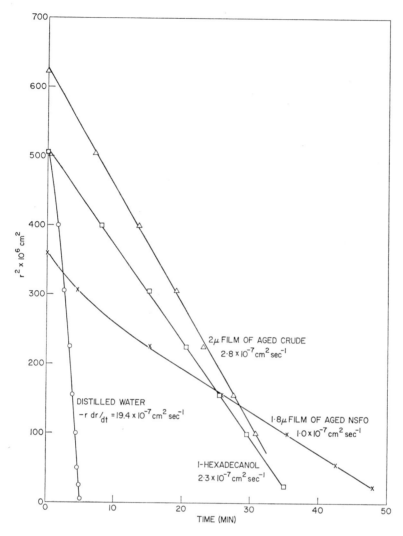

Fig. 3. Evaporation characteristics of distilled water drops coated with 1-hexadecanol or oil films at 25±0.2 C and 50±2 % relative humidity.

atmosphere into the bulk ocean is also impeded by slicks and oil spills. Oleophilic aerosol fallout from the atmosphere (e.g., organic pesticides) can be concentrated in sea slicks (Seba and Corcoran, 1969). The concentration effect is due to the preferential solubility of the very water-insoluble pesticides in nonpolar organic materials. Pesticide fallout will be concentrated first in organic films and oil layers, then distributed into the sea by dispersive processes including biological feeding which can further accumulate and concentrate the pollutant.

Dispersion of Oceanic Surface Films by Natural Forces

It is nature's compound attack on films at the sea surface that has thus far prevented the ocean from becoming wholly covered with natural slicks or films formed from the products of human activity. There are a number of dispersive processes which act upon this adsorbed or floating organic material (Fig. 4) to partially destroy and disperse it into the subsurface water and to a lesser extent into the marine atmosphere. Volatile constituents of an oceanic film evaporate quickly, leaving a more permanent and durable surface layer. The evaporative process is enhanced by both winds and thinning of the film due to spreading. In addition to evaporation, organic film-forming material or oil may be transported into the marine atmosphere by wind-generated sea spray or by fragments from bursting bubbles (Blanchard, 1964; Garrett, 1970).

Pathways for sea-slick components into the sea include dissolution of water-soluble substances, adsorption into nonbuoyant particulate matter and emulsification caused by the physical action of waves and breaking water. Heavy crude oil may sink when the loss of volatile constituents causes the density of the remaining oil to exceed that of the surface water. In addition, constituents of the sea surface are forced into the sea by sinking water motions beneath wind-driven film streaks or windrows (Kraus, 1967). Emulsification of oil spills is enhanced by the presence of emulsion-stabilizing, surface-active species in the oil. This process may take two forms; oil-in-water emulsion where the sea is the continuous phase, or water-in-oil, a stable floating emulsion containing 30–80 % water. The emulsification of crude oil may also be promoted by surface-active materials produced during degradation of the oil by certain microorganisms (Miget et al., 1969). In fact, it is the highly surface-active compounds which enhance the physical mixing of water and oil, a mutually insoluble two-fluid system.

Decomposition and chemical alteration of portions of a sea surface slick can result from atmospheric oxidation and actinic attack. Paraffins and aromatic hydrocarbons with tertiary C–H bonds are most readily attacked by oxygen through an autooxidative process (Berridge et al., 1968). In thin films and monolayers, chemically unsaturated species are prime subjects for oxidation catalyzed by ultraviolet radiation. This photochemical oxidation ultimately breaks the unsaturated molecule into smaller, more soluble organic fragments which are easily lost from the surface film by dissolution or evaporation (Timmons, 1962). The various oxidative modes which lead to soluble species are relatively slow compared to the physical dispersive forces in operation in a rough sea. Under calm conditions, after a slick has aged and lost its volatile components, oxidation will play a more dominant role.

Biological utilization and decomposition of oil at sea is as yet an incomplete and controversial story. A somewhat rosy picture has been portrayed by some investigators who conclude that biodegradation of oil will ultimately decompose a large portion of oil spilled at sea. Bacteria, yeasts and fungi may oxidize hydrocarbon oils, thereby providing a natural biological clean-up process for beaches and coastal areas. Microbial attack is most effective against thin films of oil adsorbed at the air-sea interface or on solid particles while being relatively ineffective against massive spills, particularly in the open ocean where oil-oxidizing microorganisms are scarce. A less optimistic story emerges when one considers recent reports of extensive quantities of tar-like lumps of oil with varying consistency on beaches and in the open ocean. Horn et al. (1970) found such lumps in abundance in the Mediterranean Sea and the eastern North Atlantic Ocean. Some were estimated to be at least two months old, while others of lesser age at sea contained low-boiling fractions which had been trapped in the bulk of the oily mass. Similar observations of oil-tar lumps at sea were reported by Blumer (1969) who estimated three times as much tar-like material as Sargasso weed in "Neuston" net catches from the Sargasso Sea. Dennis (1959) reported oil in varying degrees of hardness on beaches of the Florida coast where incoming oil was present in the surf on 341 out of 355 days of observation. Such information suggests that weathered petroleum products may become quite resistant to decomposition and have long lifetimes in the sea, at its surface, and on its shore.

Extent of Oil in the Oceans and on Its Surface

A first approximation to the extent of oil pollution of the seas can be obtained from the solution of two problems. The input of oil from ships, oil production operations, accidental spills and river discharges for 1969 is estimated to be 2.08×10^6 metric tons (SCEP, 1970). This figure does not include atmospheric fallout of petroleum products onto the sea, estimated by Goldberg to be five times greater than the fluid input. Dividing the volume of the world ocean, 1.4×10^{21} liters, into 2.08×10^{15} mg of oil, we obtain an average input concentration rate of about 1.5×10^{-6} mg/l per year if it assumed that the oil is uniformly distributed throughout the oceans. This value is small when compared to the average dissolved organic content of seawater of 0.5 to 1.0 mg/liter (Williams, 1969). Of course, this comparison is subject to many qualifications since most petroleum products are entering the seas in specific areas of the Northern hemisphere and in small localized areas when accidentally spilled. The oil is not uniformly distributed but tends to be concentrated at surfaces or in ocean sediments. Furthermore, a local spill of large proportions can produce significant effects on the marine environment since its concentration would far exceed the natural organic level for a period of time in the vicinity of the injection point.

The second problem deals with the concern that the ocean surface may become covered with an oil film whose influence on air-sea interactions could cause environmental alterations on a global scale. The annual oil input may be expressed as 2.08×10^{12} cm^3 if a density of one is assumed. Dividing by 3.6×10^{18} cm^2, the surface area of the seas, we obtain 5.8×10^{-7} cm or 58 Angstroms for the thickness of this quantity of oil spread uniformly onto the ocean's surface. This figure is about double the thickness of a monomolecular layer, indicating that the annual oil loading would be sufficient to paint the sea with a film composed of hydrocarbons and surface-active material. Again, however, the results of the calculation are misleading for many obvious reasons. The chemical physical and biological factors which disperse surface films into air and water and modify its character (Fig. 4) would remove much of the film and prevent it from forming an intact ubiquitous layer. The end product of weathered oil on the sea surface appears to be floating lumps of tar-like petroleum or stable water-in-oil emulsions. Most of the film-forming constituents have been lost from the surface or are contained within the weathered petroleum products so that they do not contact the water surface and no further spreading occurs.

The concentration of surface-active molecules in a large portion of the sea surface must still be less than 0.57 mg/m^2. This value is the minimum concentration of oleic acid required to initiate capillary wave damping. Since most of the sea surface is covered with capillary waves when wind is blowing and slicks of any kind are rare away from coastal areas, it appears that the likelihood of a world-wide sea slick is remote at present. Capillary-wave damping by surface films provides a sensitive indicator of the onset of serious surface contamination.

We still do not know how much organic pollution the seas can accept before they become burdened to the extent that climatic, ecological, and other natural imbalances result. Certainly local overloadings are occurring with increasing frequency, and damage to marine life, recreational facilities, the fishing industry, and the esthetics of the coastal zones have resulted. A disturbing case in point is the Viareggio phenomenon occurring along the west coast of Italy adjacent to the Ligurian Sea, a portion of the Mediterranean (Cornwell, 1971). Industrial and municipal organic pollutants pouring into the sea from nearby rivers produce vast areas of film-covered coastal water. Onshore winds carry petroleum and surface-active constituents of this film inland where they are coating the needles of coastal pine trees. Serious interferences with transpiration results and vast numbers of trees are dead or dying. This phenomenon is directly related to sea-surface pollution, and certainly

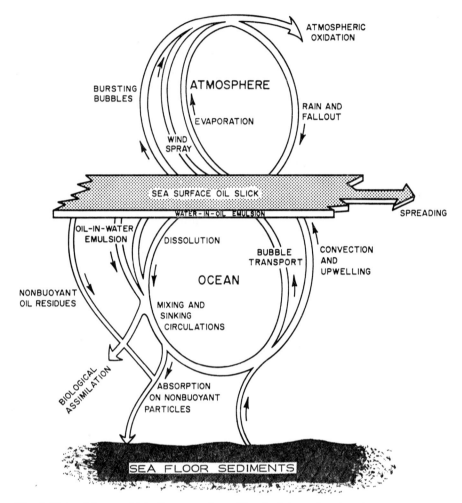

Fig. 4. Natural forces which disperse and modify oil slicks and surface films on water.

presages further disasters along coastal areas affected by industrial and urbanized regions.

Sequel

Surface films on the ocean are influenced by many forces which operate at the dynamic air-water boundary to modify their composition and produce weathered, more durable films. If they are not totally dispersed by winds and waves, selective adsorption occurs, and the film constituents become more water insoluble and more strongly adsorbed at the air-sea interface. Whether from natural or man-made sources, these films will blend and thin with time into monomolecular layers of mixed surface-active material. The original source of their surface-active ingredients can be ascertained only by detailed chemical analysis of the specific constituents of the film. Whatever the source, the effects of a water-insoluble monomolecular film on the properties of the air-sea interface will result in diminished wave energy, decreased bubble stability, slight decreases in surface water temperature, etc.

Contaminant films with thicknesses greater than monomolecular dimensions occur in local ocean areas as chemical scums or slicks of petroleum products. For example, spilled oil spreads rapidly under the influence of wind, surface currents, and hydrostatic forces. Eventually, the oil layer thins and attains a crude equilibrium with thinner films containing large quantities of surface-active constituents. Additional spreading is then governed by surface forces. The time required to reach this condition is dependent upon the spill volume, meteorological conditions and the character of the oil. A number of natural forces operate on the slick to disperse its constituents, partly into the marine atmosphere, but largely into the sea. The relative influence of the various dispersive forces changes as the oil ages and spreads. Weathering, dispersion, and air-sea dynamics ultimately degrade the spill to tar-like lumps and/or stable water-in-oil emulsions with long and as yet undetermined lifetimes at the sea surface. When conditions are suitable, the dispersed surface-active material may readsorb at the sea surface and become a part of an ocean film indistinguishable in appearance from natural slicks.

Oceanic surface films influence various properties of the air-sea interface and modify exchange processes between the atmosphere and the ocean. Small waves are resisted and attenuated and the interaction between wind and waves is uncoupled through the elimination of form drag. Gas exchange is inhibited by films of oil, but not to a serious extent in the open ocean. Liquid-solid exchange is altered, organic fallout is concentrated at the surface by organic films, and a mechanism exists whereby oil is transported into the marine atmosphere where it may influence atmospheric processes. In general, it may be concluded that a large sea slick or oil film serves to damp its environment by replacing a high-surface-tension, dynamic water surface with a more phlegmatic, less mobile, organic-air interface.

Although the ratio of contaminant to natural film-forming material in the sea is increasing, the natural oceanic background of organic matter is still large in comparison to the man-made input. However, spills of oil, river inputs or ocean dumping can create localized conditions where the resulting surface films are predominantly a result of human activity. Severe damage to the marine environment occurs in these areas affected by man. However, a worldwide ocean surface film is unlikely in the near future, but weathered lumps of petroleum products and chemical scums floating on and near the water surface will increase if biological degradation and physical dispersion do not keep pace with the world loading of these contaminants. Should a ubiquitous film one day cover the seas there would be a sensible modification to the marine environment although the magnitude of such alterations is difficult to predict at the present time.

References

Barger, W. R., Garrett, W. D., Mollo-Christensen, E. L. & Ruggles, K. W., J. App. Met., *9*, 396 (1970)

Berridge, S. A., Dean, R. A., Fallows, R. G. & Fish, A., J. Inst. Pet., *54*, 300 (1968).

Blanchard, D. C., Science, *146*, 397 (1964).

Blank, M., The permeability of monolayers to several gases, in Retardation of Evaporation by Monolayers (ed. V. K. La Mer). Academic Press, New York. 1962.

Blumer, M., Oceanus, *15*, 3, (1969).

Cornwell, J., Is the Mediterranean Dying?, The New York Times Magazine. February 21, 1971.

Dennis, J. V., Oil pollution survey of the United States Atlantic Coast, American Petroleum Institute Report. Washington, D. C., May 15, 1959.

Dietz, R. S. & LaFond, E. C., J. Mar. Res., *9*, 69 (1950).

Franklin, B., Effect of oil on water (letter to William Brownrigg, Nov. 7, 1773), in The Ingenious Dr. Franklin, N. G. Goodman, Univ. Pennsylvania Press, Philadelphia, 1931.

Frenkiel, J., Evaporation Retardation, UNESCO, Paris 1965.

Garrett, W. D., Limnol. Oceanogr., *10*, 602 (1965).

Garrett, W. D., Deep-Sea Res., *14*, 221 (1967a).

Garrett, W. D., J. Mar. Res., *25*, 279 (1967b).

Garrett, W. D., Deep-Sea Res., *14*, 661 (1967c).

Garrett, W. D., J. Geophys. Res., *73*, 5145 (1968).

Garrett, W. D., J. Atm. Sci., *28*, July, 1971 (in press).

Gilby, A. R. & Heymann, E., Aus. J. Sci. Res. (A), *1*, 197 (1948).

Goldberg, E. D., Atmospheric transport of petroleum hydrocarbons, summarized in Man's Impact on the Global Environment. MIT Press, Cambridge, Massachusetts, pp. 140–141, 1970.

Horn, M. H., Teal, J. M. & Backus, R. H., Science, *168*, 245 (1970).

Jarvis, N. L., Garrett, W. D., Scheiman, M. A. & Timmons, C. O., Limnol. Oceanogr., *12*, 88 (1967).

Keulegan, G. H., J. Res. Nat. Bur. Stand., *46*, 358 (1951).

Kraus, E. B., Phys. Fluids (Supplement), *10*, S294 (1967).

La Mer, V. K., Retardation of Evaporation by Monolayers. Academic Press, New York 1962.

Miget, R. J., Oppenheimer, C. H., Kator, H. I. & LaRock, P. A., Proc. Joint Conf. on Prevent. and Control of Oil Spills, New York City, pp. 327–331, 1969.

Miles, J. W., Proc. Roy. Soc., *A297*, 459 (1967).

Powell, R. W., Trans. Faraday Soc., *39*, 311 (1943).

Sada, E. & Himmelblau, D. M., AIChE J., *13*, 860 (1967).

SCEP, Man's Impact on the Global Environment. MIT Press, Cambridge, Mass., pp. 266–267, 1970.

Seba, D. B. & Corcoran, E. F., Pest. Monitor. J., *3*, 190 (1969).

Timmons, C. O., Stability of plankton oil films to artificial sunlight. U. S. Naval Research Laboratory Report 5774, 1962.

Van Dorn, W. G., J. Mar. Res., *12*, 249 (1953).

Williams, P. M., The distribution and cycling of organic matter in the ocean, in Proc. Rudolf's Conf., Rutgers Univ., New Brunswick, N. J., June 30–July 2, 1969.

Wiltzius, W. J., Effects of monolayers on insects, fish and wildlife, Research Report 7, Bureau of Reclamation, U. S. Dept. of the Interior, 1967.

Some Aspects of the Geochemistry of Marine Aerosols

By Roger Chesselet, Jacques Morelli and Patrick Buat Menard

Introduction

The chemistry of the sea/air interface is receiving increasing attention today. This has, however, mainly been in terms of meteorology, macro-hydrodynamics, energetics and gaseous-exchange-chemistry, and condensed-phase chemistry has received only indirect attention. Nevertheless, microscopic physicochemical hydrodynamic processes at this interface, during the transfer of material from sea to air, exert a profound effect on macroscopic geophysical phenomena.

Conway (1943) showed that a considerable proportion of the salts dissolved in rivers has a marine origin. These salts arise from the injection of particles into the atmosphere, at the surface of the oceans, fall out, subsequently, onto the continents, and are then carried back to the oceans by rivers.

Then, the atmosphere must be involved in the geochemical cycle for such major elements as chlorine, sodium, potassium, calcium and magnesium, and for other elements associated with these elements.

Later, Barth (1952) and Goldberg (1963) demonstrated the validity of the "cyclic salts" hypothesis. A salinity at a steady state for the oceans, over a long geological period, required that a large fraction of the salts carried by rivers should be of cyclic origin. This cyclic salt phenomenon appeared as one of the numerous cyclic processes on which the present status of the biosphere depends.

However, an accurate evaluation of the fraction of salts of cyclic origin is somewhat obscured by a rather complicated situation.

In fact, following the work by Sugawara (1949), numerous determinations have shown that the virtually constant relative proportions of the principal ionic constituents in sea water are never found in the atmosphere or in precipitations.

Thus, the absence of any univocal characteristic, such as identical ratios of alkaline salts in sea water and in the atmosphere, makes it far from easy to demonstrate the marine origin of a substantial fraction of the relevant elements found in the atmosphere and to accurately evaluate the amounts of salts recirculated by oceans.

Very controversial positions are hold in attempting to explain "non-sea-

water ratios". These are often attributed: a) to experimental errors, b) to contamination of samples due to the very low concentrations involved, or c) to the
presence in the atmosphere and in precipitations of minute amounts of terrigenous dust, since the relative proportions of cations are closer to those found
in the soil than in sea water (Junge, 1963; Lazrus et al., 1970).

Actually, there seems to exist among workers a concensus to accept the
existence of a "chemical fractionation process" which controls the cation ratios in particles originating from either of two processes: jet drop and film
drop ejection by whitecap bubbles (Komabayasi, 1962; Mac Intyre, 1966;
Bloch et al., 1966; Morelli, 1968; Brujewicz and Korzh, 1970). Some mechanisms involved are known; others remain highly controversial (Mac Intyre,
1970). Moreover, the tropospheric distribution of these particles is still questionable (Junge et al., 1969; Pötzl, 1970; Bressan and Wilkin, 1971).

It is here necessary to point out that the acceptance of a "fractionated" or
"not fractionated" model for ions in sea-borne salt particles, often called
marine aerosols, plays an important role when trying to set an accurate
budget for terrigenous, marine and extra-terrestrial contributions, in some
critical areas such as polar caps or the stratosphere. The controversy arises
when "non-seawater ratios" are taken as an index for terrigenous contributions (Vosters et al., 1970; Murozimi et al., 1969; Shedlowski and Paisley,
1966; Morelli and Chesselet, 1971).

From the point of view of environmental studies, weather modification and
air pollution are critically dependent upon further understanding of sea surface events such as the production of marine particles (Chesselet, Duce, Mac
Intyre, Prospero, 1971).

Organic materials on the sea surface seem to coat particles as they are
ejected (Barger and Garrett, 1970). If sufficiently hydrophobic, such a film
might significantly alter the properties of condensation and precipitation
nuclei, of which an indubitable source is sea-borne salt particles (Woodcock
and Blanchard, 1955; Blanchard, 1970). Through this could oil spills indirectly
influence the weather?

It is, moreover, urgent to determine in the atmosphere, on a pollution-free
baseline, levels of trace-metals. There may be a chemical fractionation of these
metals when particles are injected from the sea to the air. This has to be much
better understood in order to be able to evaluate the global transport of me-
tallic air pollutants.

Also, when excess atmospheric SO_4 is sought as a measure of fossil fuel
contribution, the naturally occurring SO_4/Cl ratio of marine aerosols must
be understood with respect to the parameters that determine it.

Moreover, as mentioned recently by Blanchard (1970), an injection of bacteria into the atmosphere is associated with the drop ejected from the bubbles.

The concentration of bacteria may be 10 to 1 000 times that of the water in which the bubbles burst.

All these problems require new efforts in interpreting the physico-chemical processes which control the composition of marine aerosols and their geochemical behaviour in our environment.

In the course of our study on exchange of matter between oceans, atmosphere and continents, we carefully measured the weight ratios Cl/Na, Na/K, Na/Ca, Na/Mg in particles collected in diverse open-sea conditions and in the lower troposphere. Meanwhile, in various areas and periods of time, we evaluated the rate of wet and dry deposition of these elements. Samples were analysed by neutron activation (for chlorine, sodium and potassium) and by atomic spectrophotometric absorption (for sodium, potassium, calcium and magnesium).

Marine Aerosols

Production and Chemistry of Marine Aerosols

The production mechanisms of salt particles depend upon the action of the wind on the surface of the sea (Woodcock, 1953).

As indicated by Fig. 1, our results show a linear relation between the logarithm of the chlorine and sodium concentrations, collected as particles in air, and the wind speed. This relation, checked at a given level of 8 m, both over the North Atlantic (25° W, 43° N and 5° W, 63° N) and over the Mediterranean Sea (7°30 E, 42°47 N) is identical to that observed by Woodcock (1953) in the Hawaii region. It clearly indicates the marine origin of the col-

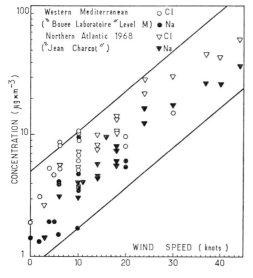

Fig. 1.

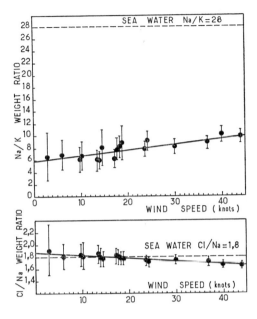

Fig. 2.

lected salts, which are produced both by sprays and, mainly, by the bubbling of the sea, according to Blanchard (1957).

Fig. 2 shows the Na/K weight ratios found in *all* these samples.

They are always very much smaller than the values existing in sea water (Na/K = 28), although the Cl/Na ratio remains practically identical to the sea water ratio (Cl/Na = 1.8).

These observations strongly support the existence of a "chemical fractionation mechanism", affecting the cations, when the particles are produced.

The similarity of the Cl/Na ratio to that which exists in bulk sea water and its constancy, compared to the Na/K ratio variability is of importance in the interpretation of this mechanism. Indeed, it seems to indicate that there is not a "depletion" of sodium relative to potassium when the Na/K ratio is smaller than that of sea water, but, on the contrary, it denotes the existence of a true enrichment of potassium. We know that this finding does not seem to be in agreement with a depletion of sodium ions required by recent computations on the structure of the "vicinal water layer" from which the film of water forming the aerosols should be drawn (Horne and Courant, 1970).

We point out here that the boundary values shown in Fig. 2 were worked out by making allowance for the maximum inaccuracies in our measurements of the weight of chlorine, sodium and potassium collected on filters:

$$Na/K_{(max)} = \frac{Na_{(max)}}{K_{(min)}} \qquad Na/K_{(min)} = \frac{Na_{(min)}}{K_{(max)}}$$

(same for Cl/Na ratios).

At a wind speed of 20 knots, a slight decrease in the Cl/Na ratio is observed. This has to be attributed to the local release of chlorine in the form of HCl gas, at the expense of chlorine in the particulate state (see below).

The number of chlorine equivalents in aerosols is then no longer sufficient to maintain the electro-neutrality existing in sea water, if allowance is made for the enrichment of potassium and also of calcium (as will be demonstrated later in this paper), and for the presence of magnesium. This equilibrium is probably achieved by means of enrichments observed in sulfates (Eriksson, 1960), phosphates (Mac Intyre, 1966), nitrates (Morelli, 1970) associated with surface active organic material (Garrett, 1967, 1968; Blanchard, 1968; Barger and Garrett, 1970).

The Na/K ratios in aerosols are close to the mean value ($\simeq 2$) found in the insoluble fraction of soils. However, it is not possible to attribute the values found in aerosols to an incorporation in our samples of terrigenous dust sufficient to provide such a shift in the Na/K ratios. As a matter of fact, the weight of terrigenous dust over the oceans represents, at most 0.1 to 10 micrograms per cubic meter of air (Delany et al., 1967; Prospero and Bonatti, 1969; Hoang Chi Trach, 1969; Ferguson et al., 1970). The mean contents of the insoluble fraction of these dust particles in sodium and potassium is in of the order of 2%, (Prospero and Bonatti, 1969) and thus the contribution of sodium and potassium of terrigenous origin would be far too small to account for the observed concentrations and the Na/K ratios in marine air.

The trend to higher values for the Na/K ratios with increasing wind speed, as shown by Fig. 2, is explained by a higher production rate of particles less enriched in potassium. This indicates the existence of a broad range of Na/K values associated with different types of particles. Their distribution in space and time is studied in the next part.

Distribution of Marine Aerosols in the Vicinity of the Sea Surface

The spatial distribution of marine aerosols in the vicinity of the sea surface was studied from the Cousteau floating buoy laboratory.

Fig. 3 shows for three levels above the sea surface (B = 2m, M = 8m, H = 15m), the Na/K weight ratios observed at the "Bouée Laboratoire", moored in the Occidental Mediterranean. From level B upwards, we found, for particles collected very near the sea surface, an enrichment in potassium identical to that which we observed in our laboratory experiments (Buat-Ménard, 1970) and over the Atlantic. Between levels B and M, the Na/K ratio decreases rapidly and becomes practically constant between levels M and H.

To explain the contour of this profile, we have made the hypothesis of a distribution of particles in several size classes, having different sodium and potassium proportions (Morelli et al., 1971). Owing to their size, the smaller

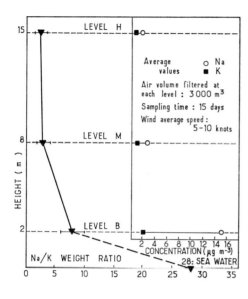

Fig. 3.

particles, very much enriched in potassium, rapidly escape the intense cleaning processes which involve primarily the largest particles occurring in the lowest atmospheric layers (Toba, 1964; Monahan, 1968), and are then able to remain relatively long periods of time in the atmosphere.

To test the validity of this hypothesis, we used a 6-stage cascade impactor (Scientific Advanced Co.), which separates particles according to their size (Duce, 1967). The sampling was carried out recently over the Norwegian Sea at an altitude of 12 m, and we included the calcium content of the particles in our analyses.

Fig. 4 gives the Na/K and Na/Ca weight ratios in three main size classes of particles collected. The calculated distribution of the number of particles with size is identical to that observed by Woodcock (1963) from optical counting on glass plates. This shows that the theoretical separating efficiency of the cascade impactor was obtained for each size class of marine particles.

The following observations are worth to be noted:

1. Whatever the size class is, the Na/K sea-water value was never observed.

2. The enrichment extends to calcium (in sea water, Na/Ca = 26). The enrichment factor for calcium is comparable to that observed for potassium. This seems to exclude the enrichment in potassium to be only due to the presence of a K-rich organic matter film at the sea surface, an explanation often given to explain the shift of the Na/K ratio. It is hard to believe that the calcium enrichment, which strictly follows the potassium one, would be only of organic origin. Then, the Na/K and Na/Ca ratios seem to have their origin in physico-chemical processes occuring at the formation of particles, presumably associated with the presence of a surface active film (Barger and Garrett,

SIZE CLASSES	A	B	C	A + B + C
SIZE INTERVALS ($\emptyset$ in μ)	>16	16–1	1–0,4	
% OF TOTAL WEIGHT	34	61	5	100
CALCULATED NUMBER OF PARTICLES by m³ of air	100	90 000	600 000	690 000
THEORETICAL RESIDENCE TIME (DAYS) from JUNGE	< 1	1 – 220	> 220	
WEIGHT RATIOS — Na/K	4,5±0,5	8± 2,5	3 ± 1,5	6 ±1,5
Na/Ca	7± 1	6±1,5	2,5±1	6 ± 1
OBSERVATIONS	HEIGHT OF SAMPLING : 12 m SAMPLING TIME : 13 DAYS AVERAGE SPEED OF WIND : 5–15 KNOTS			

Fig. 4.

1970), and belonging to some identical properties of K and Ca ions. But all this, is still quiet unclear for us. The "high ionic potential theory" (MacIntyre, 1970) could explain the enrichments for calcium and magnesium but not simultaneously the one for potassium.

3. The enrichment is high for particles of small size (i.e. class C:0.4 to 1 μm size). The same dependence of the enrichment on size was observed by Kombayasi (1964) in his laboratory experiments. It was also found, for iodine, bromine and chlorine, in tropical oceanic air, by Duce et al. (1967).

Therefore, this dependence should be considered as providing an important clue in the debated question of the origin of the ionic fractionation process. Moreover, its existence supports the explanations given for Figs. 2 and 3.

This "size effect" appears to be of extreme importance when tracking particles of marine origin in the whole atmosphere.

Distribution of Marine Aerosols in the Low Troposphere

In Fig. 4, we see that, whereas class C particles form 5% of the total mass of collected salts, they represent 90% of the total number of collected particles. The residence time in a theoretical atmosphere computed by Junge (1953) for such particles is of the order of several months, whereas observed values for this parameter, as worked out from radioactive aerosols of comparable size, is of the order of a few weeks (Burton and Stewart, 1960; Lambert and Nezami, 1965; Ba Cuong, 1968).

Since the mixing rate of the atmosphere on a tropospheric scale is about one month (Lal and Rama, 1966), there is a very high probability of finding these particles over the whole atmosphere. It would be true even in the un-favourable case where a high percentage of them is eliminated as a conse-quence of capture processes of fine aerosols by association with larger particles.

It is then reasonable to accept the idea that marine particles of chemical composition widely different from that of sea water, may be carried to very great distances from their place of origin and may circulate in the whole tro-posphere.

To check this hypothesis, aerosol samplings by air filtration have been car-ried out, from aeroplanes and helicopters, at altitudes from 500 m up to 5 000 m. Vertical samplings were completed by a latitudinal profile made be-tween Paris and Madagascar, with sampling altitudes ranging from 3 000 m to 5 000 m. We analysed the filters for sodium and potassium by neutron activation. Unfortunately, blank corrections for the filters used were too high to permit an accurate determination of the chlorine content. The volumes of filtered air were always obtained by volucounters (the value in cubic meters expresses the real volume of air filtered).

The profiles obtained (Figs. 5, 6, 7 and 8) show that, above regions which are geographically far apart, 1) the atmospheric concentrations of sodium and potassium are very close, within the same order of magnitude; 2) above 500 to 1 000 m, sodium and potassium concentrations become practically constant, and 3) the Na/K ratio is always smaller than in sea-water.

Again, by the same arguments as given above, it is not possible in these cases to attribute the observed sodium and potassium concentrations to a large enough incorporation of terrigenous dust in our samples. The observed con-centrations of sodium and potassium may therefore be explained by the pres-

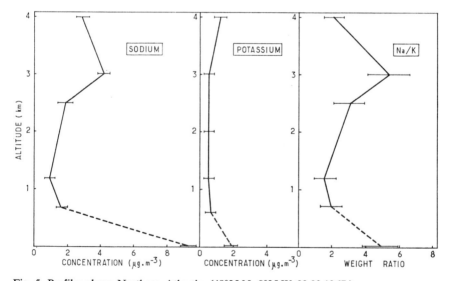

Fig. 5. Profiles above Northern Atlantic. (48°25 N, 8°25 W–02.03.1967.)

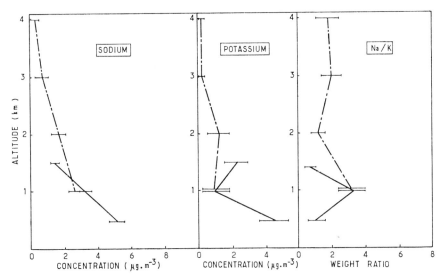

Fig. 6. Profiles above Kerguelen Islands. (49°20 S, 70°13 E–13.01.1969 and 15.01.1969.)

ence of particles of marine origin whose Na/K ratios are very much smaller than those of sea water.

In the lowest layers of the marine atmosphere, the variations in the overall Na/K ratio were explained above by a settling process affecting the salt particles according to their size (Fig. 3). A similar process could be detected again at the scale of sampling we are dealing with here. Indeed, analysis of the figures shows:

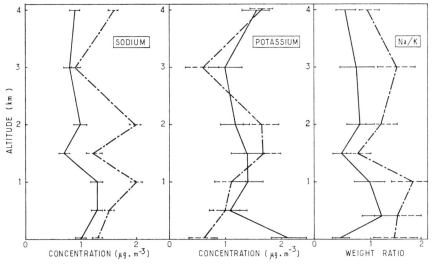

Fig. 7. Profiles above "Terre Adelie" Station (Antarctic). (60°30 S, 144° E–30.01.1969 and 02.03.1969.)

102   *R. Chesselet et al.*

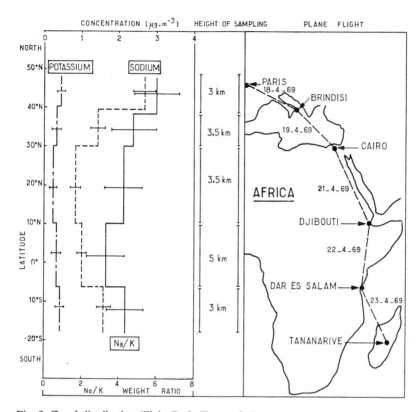

Fig. 8. Zonal distribution (flight Paris–Tananarive).

a) the Na/K ratio tends to increase when sampling is made in the cloudy layer (e.g. in our case, 3 000 m over the North Atlantic and 1 000 m over the Kerguelen Islands). The presence of such a moist layer would have the property of altering the size distribution of particles by changing the settling process (Eriksson, 1965). The largest particles, i.e. the least enriched in potassium, would be trapped inside the cloudy layer, by association with droplet formation.

b) at the vertical profile over "Terre Adélie" Station (Antarctica), meteorological data show that, between ground level and about 2 000 m to 3 000 m, we were sampling in an air mass which is very likely to have slowly drifted over the Antarctica continent. In the absence of a renewed production of salt particles, as indicated by the low concentrations observed, the very small Na/K ratio would indicate the survival, in the air mass, of particles highly enriched in potassium and having a long residence time in the atmosphere. This explanation holds again for the profiles obtained in the eastern part of France (Alpine region), Fig. 9. In this case, the Na/K ratios (<1) could not, however, be entirely explained by highly enriched marine particles, only.

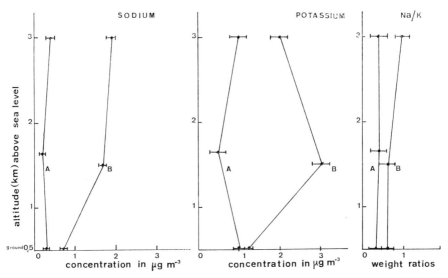

Fig. 9. Profiles above France (Gap. Hautes Alpes) June, 1970. (A 10–11 June, B17 June.) Airplane Whatman 41 filter.

c) at 5 000 m over the African continent, there remains 1 $\mu g/m^3$ of sodium and 0,3 $\mu g/m^3$ of potassium. The fact that, in this case too, we are dealing with aerosols very enriched in potassium seems to confirm the hypothesis put forward for the interpretation of Fig. 7. We note that these profiles are in agreement with the few profiles of the number of salt particles observed above North America by Byers et al. (1957).

These data seem to demonstrate the amplitude of vertical and horizontal circulation patterns in the atmosphere for particles having a marine origin (Chesselet et al., 1971). Besides sodium and potassium, numerous other constituents of sea water are present in these particles.

The validity of the model for a large scale circulation of fractionated aerosols is also substantiated by the values given in Table 1. These show interesting similarities for the Na/K and Na/Ca ratios. Looking at values observed in open-sea conditions, the similarities cannot be the result of a casual mixture of terrigenous dust plus sea-salt particles with the sea-water ratio. The values found in ice from Antarctica are also in agreement (Vosters et al., 1970).

The enrichment factor for cations, fE (fE is given by: aerosols ratio/sea-water ratio normalized to sodium) in all our samples, follows fairly well the relation with atomic weight of elements first described by Kombayasi (1962), as shown in Fig. 10. This relation has recently been discussed by Mac Intyre (1970), using the isotopes of calcium, and could simply be a coincidence.

In Figure 10, the shift to higher enrichment values from aerosols to continental precipitations also seems to confirm the fact that cations in rain are provided by marine salt particles of small size.

Table 1

Sea water	Cl/Na 1.8	Na/K 28	Na/Ca 26	Na/Mg 8
All size class of marine aerosols collected above ocean	1.75±0.2	6±1.5	6±1	6±4
Oceanic rain collected at the surface of the sea	1.75±0.3	10±4	11±5	8±4
Marine aerosols collected above ocean class C (1 μm)	1.75±0.2	3±1.5	2.5±1	9±7
Continental rain	1.75±0.5	2±1	1.5±1	3±2
Average of marine aerosols collected in coastal zone	1.75±0.2	6±2	n.d.	n.d.
Aerosols collected in land at ground level	1.3±0.3	2±0.5	n.d.	n.d.
East Antarctica Plateau averaged[a]	n.d.	6	5.2	5.7
Corrected for terrigenous contribution[a]	n.d.	7.2	9.2	8.2

N.B. Upper and lower limits observed are given.
[a] Vosters (1971). (See also Lorius et al., 1969.)

It must be noted here that Na/Mg ratios are always very erratic (see Table 1), whatever the sampling procedure or the analytical technique. The explanation of this enigma should contribute to the understanding of the enrichment process.

This population of particles originating from the sea, and for which we have observed very constant concentrations at each level in various regions of the

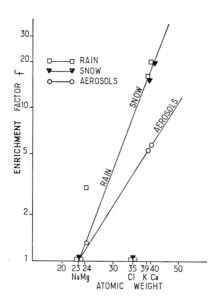

Fig. 10. Relation between enrichment factor and atomic weight in rain, snow and atmospheric particles (aerosols).

lower troposphere, seems to constitute a quasi-stationary system, as was first pointed out by Eriksson (1961).

Large Scale Circulation

In the troposphere, losses in the form of fallout, both over the oceans and continents, either in a "dry" state or associated with precipitations, are balanced by the quantities of aerosols which are produced by the continuous bubbling which takes place over vast marine areas (0.3 to 3 % of the total surface of the oceans, according to Blanchard, 1963).

Marine aerosols are then an evident supply of easily assimilable hydrosoluble salts which fall onto the soils of the continents and are later sent by rivers to the oceans. This was predicted by Conway in 1943, with profound foresight.

Using special sampling devices, we were able to measure, with accuracy, the "dry fraction" of salts falling on our regions. This has to be taken into account to establish a true budget (Table 2).

By extrapolating, over the land surface, our observations on the local fallout of particles originating from the sea (Morelli, 1968), the total yearly fallout may be estimated to be 10^9 tons. This value is in complete accordance with recent data from Zverev (1970).

Within some evident uncertainties, this value agrees fairly well with the data of Livingstone (1963) for the sodium cycle. Taking the enrichment process as true, it is then possible to compute models for the circulation of potassium, calcium and other elements of marine origin.

As a consequence of the enrichment concept for potassium and calcium, the previous calculations for their residence time in the ocean (Goldberg, 1963) have to be re-evaluated, when calculated from river inputs only.

Let us point out here that a more accurate evaluation of the fraction of salts of cyclic origin in rivers is necessary when estimating the present rate of the chemical erosion (Eriksson, 1960, Buat-Menard, 1970).

Table 2

Element M	Na	K	Ca	Mg
$RS°$ in $mg \times m^{-2} \times d^{-1}$	10	0.8	2	1.2
RS^c	0.5 to 0.75	0.4 to 0.5	0.6 to 1.1	0.09 to 0.11
RP^c	1.5 to 3.2	0.8 to 1.2	1.1 to 2.2	0.2 to 0.5

$RS°$ = Dry fallout above oceanic surfaces (over-estimated as they are collected near the surface)
RS^c = Dry fallout above continental soils (France)
RP^c = Fallout by precipitations (France)
Sampling duration: 3 months (August–October 1968)

The Atmospheric Sodium Cycle

Taking into account all available evaluations we can build a simplified model for the circulation of the "cyclic" sodium. This is displayed in Fig. 11. In this, values and symbols are:

R_c^h: observed fallout by precipitation above continents: 1.5 mg $\times$ m^{-2} $\times$ d^{-1}

R_c^s: observed fallout in the "dry" fraction above continents: 0.7 mg $\times$ m^{-2} $\times$ d^{-1}

R_o^t 1, R_o^t 2, R_o^t 3: total fallout at a given level above the oceans

R_o^t 2: is observed: $\sim$ 20 mg $\times$ m^{-2} $\times$ d^{-1}

R_o^t 3: is extrapolated: $\sim$ 10 mg $\times$ m^{-2} $\times$ d^{-1}

I_1, I_2, I_3: inputs of sodium in particles at different levels above the sea surface

C_1, C_2, C_3: averaged concentrations of sodium observed in different compartments in air above the sea.

D: fraction of sodium available for deposition onto the continents.

Q: 2 μg/m^3 $\times h$ = 20 mg; h being taken as 10 km as supported by recent high altitude samplings. Q is the quantity of sodium in an air column of 1 m^2.

At steady state, $Q = I_3 - (R_o^t 3 + D)$, then D is about 1 to 10 mg per day per m^2 of oceanic surface. The global values for D are:

$1 \times 10^8 < D < 1 \times 10^9$ tons/year

D has to be compared with the global fallout onto the continents:

$Q_c = 1.2 \times 10^8$ tons/year (extrapolated from measurements).

Q_o being about 50 % of the value of the yearly sodium input to the oceans: 2.6.10^8 tons/year (Livingstone, 1963).

It is of importance to note that, as particles, marine aerosols, according to their rapid circulation above oceans and continents (mg per day per square meter in troposphere), could have a strong scavenging effect on all the other particles in the atmosphere.

The Gaseous Chlorine Problem

Presence of Gaseous Chlorine of Marine Origin above the Sea

The problem of chlorine of marine origin in the atmosphere must receive much attention, especially because, as we have shown above, the Cl/Na ratio plays an important role in showing the sea origin of salts in the atmosphere (Eriksson, 1959, 1960; Seto et al., 1969; Duce et al., 1969).

The problem is complicated by the fact that in the atmosphere chlorine exists in a gaseous state whose origin is debatable (Duce, 1969).

Cauer first suggested (in 1951), that gaseous chlorine (HCl or Cl$_2$) may be released to the atmosphere from salt particles, with a change in the Cl/Na ratio.

Measurements in marine atmospheres at Hawaii and on the coast of Florida have shown that some chlorine was present in a phase which could pass through filters able to retain more than 99 % of chlorine in the particulate state. The chlorine found in this phase was called "gaseous chlorine" of marine origin (Junge, 1957, Duce et al., 1965). Yet, the marine origin of such chlorine, as thus detected, appeared uncertain in some aspects. The possibility of local production due either to the volcanic environment of Hawaii Island, or to industrial pollution on the coast of Florida, could not in fact be discarded. Moreover, Valach (1967) has since strongly disputed the validity of the marine origin hypothesis.

During our work on marine aerosols, we have tried, in open ocean conditions, using sampling techniques similar to those used by Junge and Duce, to confirm the existence of gaseous chlorine in the atmosphere and its marine origin. At the same time, we measured concentrations of gaseous chlorine in a coastal sampling station located in the peninsula of Quiberon (Atlantic coast of France) and in a station situated in the central part of France (Beauce plain).

Chlorine was collected by bubbling (1 m³/h) carefully filtered air through a 0.01 N K_2CO_3 solution. The measured collection efficiency was 80 %. The low concentrations expected led us to use neutron activation analysis for our measurements.

Fig. 12 shows the simultaneous variations of wind speed and chlorine concentrations in the particulate and in the gaseous state in air. The concentration in the particulate state is then related to the production processes of marine aerosols (Fig. 1). During the same period of sampling, one will observe

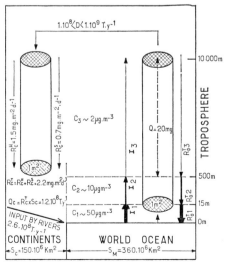

Fig. 11. Simplified model for sodium circulation in the ocean–atmosphere–continents system.

a constant base line of 2 to 3 $\mu g/m^3$ of gaseous chlorine, on which are super-posed strong variations of gaseous chlorine concentrations when the wind speed increases.

Returning to Fig. 2, we see a slight decrease in the Cl/Na ratio in particles when the wind reaches 20 knots. Thus, the two phenomena seem to be cor-related. When stronger turbulent conditions occur, gaseous chlorine is produced at the expense of particulate chlorine. The average ratio between gaseous-chlorine/particulate-chlorine is then small: 0.2. Later, during quiet conditions, this ratio reaches 1. This is due to the greater residence time for the gaseous fraction than for the bulk of the particulate fraction. Our Cl/Na ratio in par-ticles is 1.72 ± 0.03, equal to a depletion in chlorine of about 3% referred to the sea water value. The same argument as the one given by Duce (1969) shows that with this 3% of particulate chlorine released in gaseous form, a residence time for the gaseous fraction nine times greater than that for the particulate fraction would give a ratio between gaseous and particulate con-centrations of 0.3. This is exactly the value we found for the same conditions of sampling as Duce and Junge.

All these considerations seem to demonstrate the existence of a local pro-duction of gaseous chlorine which is superposed on concentrations at steady state. Results from a complementary program in a different sampling area in the Atlantic (black dots in Fig. 12) show, for identical wind speed conditions, concentrations of gaseous chlorine very similar to those observed in the prev-ious cruise.

The quasi-simultaneous variations in concentrations of marine aerosols and gaseous chlorine concentrations near the sea surface indicate that the two phenomena are closely linked together (Buat-Menard and Chesselet, 1971).

Our laboratory experiments have confirmed this strong dependence (Buat-Menard, 1970). During these experiments, we were able to identify one forma-tion mechanism which seems to be responsible for at least 90% of the gaseous

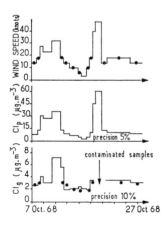

Fig. 12. Concentration of particulate chlorine (Cl_p) and gaseous chlorine (Cl_g) above Northern Atlantic. (45° N, 20° W).

chlorine produced. This part was generated at the expense of the particulate phase only in common atmospheric air and thus could be present as HCl vapour following the mechanism predicted by Eriksson (1960) and supported by Duce (1969), which depends upon the interaction of SO_3 or H_2SO_4 with the particulate chlorine.

Gaseous Chlorine of Marine Origin in Continental Environment

To check the existence of a steady state situation which controls gaseous chlorine concentrations in the atmosphere, we measured concentrations of gaseous chlorine in an air mass coming from the sea, at a sampling station situated at the end of the peninsula of Quiberon.

We then observed a decrease in concentration as the air mass gradually passes over land with wind veering from W to NNW In Fig. 13, this decrease is plotted against the distance travelled by the air over land. The variations in the concentration of gaseous chlorine may be then expressed in the form of an exponential relation:

$$C_{vx} = C_{v\sigma} \exp - K_v x \tag{1}$$

$C_{v\sigma}$ being the value 2 m above the ground level along the shore, for a given wind speed v and C_{vx} the value for the same altitude of sampling and wind speed at a distance x inland; K_v is then the "scavenging coefficient" above ground level for the marine air mass, with gaseous chlorine concentration C, circulating over the land at speed v. In the case of our sampling, we have:

$K_v = 0.011$ km^{-1} with $C_{v\sigma} = 3$ μg/m^3 and $v = 3$ m/s.

Concentrations observed at an inland station (Beauce plain) for an air mass of marine origin, endowed with the same wind speed as at Quiberon, were in agreement with those predictable by Eqn. (1).

The presence of gaseous chlorine in two different regions of the North Atlantic, together with observations made at Hawaii, in Florida and in France, demonstrates the existence of a production phenomenon ranging all over the oceans, as is the case for marine aerosols.

This production may slightly alter the Na/Cl ratio in particulate matter in the atmosphere. But this gaseous chlorine does not seem to be incorporated

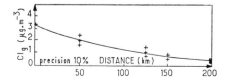

Fig. 13. Variation of gaseous chlorine concentrations with the distance covered by the mass of air over the land (height of sampling 2 m, constant wind speed).

Table 3

Global Production of Chlorine	Tons/year
Total quantity of chlorine injected into the atmosphere	6×10^9
Total production of gaseous chlorine by ocean	2×10^8
Estimated production of gaseous chlorine of volcanic origin (Eriksson, 1960)	9×10^6

in rain because the Cl/Na ratios observed are not greater than the ratio in particles (Table 1). For aerosols and rainwater collected close to the ground, the reduction in the Cl/Na ratio, as compared to that of sea water (Table 1) is sometimes due to a slight incorporation of terrigenous dust of about 30 μg/ m³ (Buat-Menard, 1970).

From our study, we can estimate the minimum fraction of particulate chlorine converted above the oceans into gaseous chlorine as 3%. This gives a gaseous chlorine production at the ocean surface equal to 2×10^8 tons/year. It should be noted that this quantity is only three times smaller than that given by Duce (1969). This rate of production may be compared to values computed for volcanic sources (Table 3).

Gradual losses in gaseous chlorine over land, probably connected with the combination of this chlorine with the constituents of the terrestrial environment, then come into play to balance the oceanic production.

Conclusions

Observations described here, made mainly in open-sea conditions, confirm the existence of a chemical fractionation process when particles of salt originate from the sea. The weight ratios between chlorine, sodium, potassium, and calcium seem to reflect a "true" enrichment process for cations, such as potassium and calcium, with respect to sodium. Similarity between enrichments of calcium and potassium, as first demonstrated in *in situ* conditions, appears to be important for the approach of the still unknown mechanism of the enrichment. The sodium/magnesium ratios show significant variations whose origin is not yet clearly understood. The chlorine/sodium ratio is only slightly affected by the relase of chlorine in a "gaseous" form.

The effect of enrichment must be taken into account for a true understanding of the geochemistry of marine aerosols. Indeed, owing to their observed very small size, the circulation in the whole of the troposphere of marine particles, highly enriched in potassium and calcium, is evident. The settling processes, which differently affect particles having various sodium/potassium and sodium/calcium ratios, may greatly shift the ratios observed in air masses with different circulation patterns. As time and distances from the oceanic source are longer, greater will be, in the air, the importance of the residual fraction of particles of very small size with high enrichment factors and a long residence time.

This concept should be accepted when one desires to track particles of marine origin and to differentiate the cations from contributions of dust of various origins.

With recent data put into the model, the circulation pattern for sodium of marine origin on a global scale, shows complete agreement with the previous hypothesis of a large fraction of salts of "cyclic" origin carried back annually to the oceans by the rivers.

In the debated problem of the source of gaseous chlorine in the atmosphere, the release above the ocean of gaseous chlorine, probably as HCl, at the expense of particulate chlorine, seems to be demonstrated. For the present, the oceanic source exceeds the others. In the meantime, it has been shown that concentrations of gaseous chlorine of marine origin above the lands seem to be controlled by a slow combination of this chlorine with the terrigenous environment. This loss balances a supply of oceanic gaseous chlorine of about 2×10^8 tons/year.

More generally speaking, in view of the data mentioned in this work, it seems of importance that the injection into air of particulate matter at the air/sea interface should be regarded as being undoubtedly significant, among all the processes by which the ocean exerts its profound influence on the biosphere. A better understanding of all the processes involved is still urgently needed.

We wish to thank Doctors Jacques Labeyrie, Claude Lalou, Gérard Lambert, Jean Servant, Marcel Vosters, and Professor E. Picciotto for their helpful discussions and criticisms during this work. We are gratefully indebted to the staff of the Laboratoire d'Analyse par Activation "Pierre Sue" and his Earth Science Group for their helpful cooperation.

References

Barth, T F. W., in Theoretical Petrology, John Wiley, New York 1952.

Barth, F. W., Abundance of the elements, areal averages and geochemical cycles. Geochim. et Cosmochim. Acta, *23*, 1 (1961).

Barger, W. R. and Garrett, W. D., Surface active organic material in the marine atmosphere. J. Geophys. Res., *75*, 4561–4566 (1970).

Blanchard, D. C. and Woodcock, A. H., Bubble formation and modification in the sea and its meteorological significance. Tellus, *9*, 145–158 (1957).

Blanchard, D. C., The electrification of the atmosphere by particles from bubbles in the sea. In Oceanography, M. Sears Ed., Pergamon Press, Oxford 1963.

Blanchard, D. C., Positive space charge from the sea. J. Atmosph. Sci., *23*, 507–515 (1966).

Blanchard, D. C., Surface active organic material in airborne salt particles. Proceedings of the Int. Conf. on Cloud Physic, Toronto, August 26–30, pp. 25–29 (1968).

Blanchard, D. C., The oceanic production rate of cloud nuclei. J. Rech. Atmosph., 4, (1969).

Blanchard, D. C. & Syzdek, L., Mechanism for the water-to-air transfer and concentration of bacteria. Science, 170, 626 (1970).

Bloch, M. R., Kaplan, D., Kertes, V. & Schnerb, J., Ion separation in bursting air bubbles: and explanation for the irregular ion ratios in atmospheric precipitations. Nature, 209, 802 (1966).

Bloch, M. R. & Luecke, W., Uneinheitliche verschiebungen der ionenverhaltnisse zwischen meereswasser und niederschlagen durch gischtbildung. Naturwissenschaften (55, Jahrgang) 9, S-441, ppl-3 (1968).

Bressan, D. J. & Wilkniss, P. E., F. Cl, Na and K ratios in Atlantic coast aerosols (abstract). 52nd Annual Amer. Geophys. Union Meeting (to be published) (1971).

Brujewicz, S. W. & Korzh, V. D., Some principles of the salt exchange between ocean and atmosphere (abstract), International Symp. Hydrogeochemistry and Biochemistry, Tokyo, Japan, 6–12 September (1970).

Buat-Menard, P., Contribution à l'étude du cycle géochimique du chlore d'origine marine. Thèse de 3ème cycle. Faculté des Sciences Paris (1970).

Buat-Menard, P. & Chesselet, R., Sur la présence de chlore "gazeux" d'origine marine dans l'atmosphère. Comptes Rendus Acad. Sci., Paris, 272, 1330 (1971).

Burton, W. M., & Stewart, N. G., Use of long lived natural radioactivity as an atmospheric tracer. Nature, 186, 584 (1960).

Cauer, H., Some problems of atmospheric chemistry, in Compendium of Meteorology, American Meteorological Society, Boston, USA (1951).

Chesselet, R., Duce, R. A., MacIntyre, F. & Prospero, J. M., Preliminary proposal for a Symposium on sea/air chemistry: non gaseous chemical transport from ocean to atmosphere (1971).

Chesselet, R., Morelli, J. & Buat-Menard, P., Sur la distribution d'aérosols d'origine marine dans la basse atmosphere. Comptes Rendus Acad. Sci. Paris, 272, 1221 (1971).

Conway, E. J., 1943, The chemical evolution of the ocean. Proceedings Roy. Irish Acad., 48 B, 161 (1943).

Delany, A. C., Parkin, D. W., Griffin, J. J. & Goldberg, E. D., Airborne dust collected at Barbados. Geochim. et Cosmochim. Acta, 31, 885 (1967).

Duce, R. A., Winchester, J. W. & Van Nahl, T. W., Iodine, bromine and chlorine in the Hawaian marine atmosphere. J. Geophys. Res. 70, 1775 (1965).

Duce, R. A., Winchester, J. W. & Van Nahl, T. W., Iodine, bromine and chlorine in winter aerosols and snow from Barrow, Alaska. Tellus, 18, 238 (1966).

Duce, R. A., Woodcock & Moyers, J. L., Variation of ion ratios with size among particles in tropical oceanic air. Tellus, 19, 369 (1967).

Duce, R. A., On the source of gaseous chlorine in the marine atmosphere. J. Geophys. Res., 74, 4597 (1969).

Duce, R. A., Seto, Y. B. & Moyers, J. L., Variation of sodium and chlorine concentrations with rainfall intensity in Hawaian trade wind showers. Pacific Science, 23, 483 (1969).

Eriksson, E., The yearly circulation of chloride and sulfur in nature, meteorological, geochemical and pedological implications. Part I. Tellus, 11, 375 (1959).

Eriksson, E., The yearly circulation of chloride and sulfur in nature, meteorological, geochemical and pedological implications. Part II. Tellus, 12, 63 (1960).

Eriksson, E., The exchange of matter between atmosphere and sea, in Oceanography, M. Sears Ed., Pergamon Press (1961).

Eriksson, E., Technical note no. 68, W. M. O. no. 169, TP 83, Genève, 117 (1965).

Ferguson, W S., Griffin, J. J. & Goldberg, E. D., Atmospheric dusts from the North Pacific, a short note on a long-range eolian transport. J. Geophys. Res., *75*, 1137 (1970).

Garrett, W. D., The organic chemical composition of the ocean surface. Deep Sea Res., *14*, 221 (1967).
and Stabilization of a bubble at the air-sea interface by surface active material. Deep Sea Res., *14*, pp. 661 (1967).

Garrett, W. D., 1968, The influence of monomolecular surface films on the production of condensation nuclei from bubbled sea water. J. Geophys. Res., *73*, 5145 (1968).

Goldberg, E. D., The ocean as a chemical system. In The Sea, vol. 2, John Wiley and Sons, New York (1963).

Hoang Chi Trach, Etude de la retombée de fer 55 artificiel. Application à l'estimation de la retombée de fer naturel stratosphérique. Thèse de doctorat d'Etat, Paris (1969).

Horne, R. A., "Marine Chemistry" Wiley–Interscience (1969).

Horne, R. A. & Courant, R. A., I) The structure of sea-water at the air/sea interface (abstract). II) Ionic fractionation at the air/sea interface (abstract). International Symp. on Hydrogeochemistry and Biochemistry, Tokyo, Japan, 6–12 September (1970)

Junge, C. E. & Gustafson, P. E., On the distribution of sea salt over the United States and its removal by precipitation. Tellus, 9, 164 (1957).

Junge, C. E., "Air Chemistry and Radioactivity", Acad. Press, New York (1963).

Junge, C. E., Robinson, E. & Ludwig, F. L., A study of aerosols in Pacific air masses. J. Applied Meteorology, *8*, pp. 340 (1969).

Komabayasi, M., Enrichment of inorganic ions with increasing atomic weight in aerosol, rainwater and snow in comparison with sea water. J. Met. Soc. Japan, *40*, 25 (1962).

Komabayasi, M., Primary fractionation of chemical components in the formation of submicron spray drops from sea salt solution. J. Met. Soc. Japan, *42*, 309 (1964).

Lal, D. & Rama, Characteristics of global tropospheric mixing based on man-made ^{14}C, ^{3}H and ^{90}Sr. J. Geophys. Res., *71*, 2865 (1966).

Lambert, G. & Nezami, M., Determination of the mean residence time in the troposphere by measurement of the ratio between the concentration of lead 210 and polonium 210, Nature, *206*, 1343 (1965).

Lazrus, A. L., Baynton, H. W. & Lodge, J. P., Trace constituents in oceanic cloud water and their origin. Tellus, *22*, 106 (1970).

Livingstone, D. A., The sodium cycle and the age of the ocean. Geochim. et Cosmochim. Acta, *27*, 1055 (1963).

Lorius, C., Baudin, G., Cittanova, J. & Platzer, R., Impuretés solubles contenues dans la glace de l'Antarctique. Tellus, 21, 136 (1969).

Mac Intyre, F., Fractionation in chemical transport from sea to air of phosphate, organic matter and bubbles. In abstract of papers, 2nd International oceanographic congress, 30 May–9 June, NAUKA, Moscow (1966).

Mac Intyre, F., Geochemical fractionation during mass transfer from sea to air by breaking bubbles. Tellus, *22*, 451 (1970).

Monahan, E. C., Sea spray as a function of low elevation wind speed. J. Geophys. Res., *73*, 1127 (1968).

Morelli, J., Contribution à l'étude de la composition des aérosols formés à la surface de la mer; leur rôle dans les échanges de matière entre l'océan, l'atmosphère et le continent. Thèse 3ème cycle, Faculté des Sciences, Paris (1968).

Morelli, J., Observation sur les facteurs d'enrichissement en nitrates dans les aérosols marins du Pacifique Sud (to be published) (1970).

Morelli, J., Buat-Menard, P. & Chesselet, R., Mise en évidence dans l'atmosphere marine d'aérosols enrichis en potassium et calcium ayant la surface de la mer pour origine. Comptes Rendus Acad. Sci. Paris, 272, 812 (1971).

Morelli, J. & Chesselet, R., Sur la pénétration des aérosols marins dans la stratosphère. To be published in Comptes Rendus Acad. Sci. Paris (1971).

Murozumi, M., Chow, T. J. & Patterson, C., Chemical concentrations of pollutant lead aerosols, terrestrial dusts and sea salts in Greenland and Antarctic snow strata. Geochim. et Cosmochim. Acta, 33, 1247 (1969).

Nguyen Ba Cuong, Etude par les traceurs radioactifs des échanges entre les diverses de l'atmosphère au-dessus des continents et des océans. Thèse doctorat d'Etat, Paris (1968).

Pötzl, K., Inorganic chemical analyses of non polluted aerosols sampled at 1800 meters altitude. J. Geophys. Res., 75, 2347 (1970).

Prospero, J. M. & Bonatti, E., Continental dust in the atmosphere of the Eastern Equatorial Pacific. J. Geophys. Res. 74, 3362 (1969).

Seto, V. B., Duce, B. A. & Woodcock, A. A., Sodium to chlorine ratio in Hawaian rains as a function of distance and of elevation. J. Geophys. Res., 74, 1101 (1969).

Shedlovsky, J. P. & Paisley, S., On the meteoritic component of stratospheric aerosols. Tellus, 18, 499 (1966).

Sugawara, K., Oana, S. & Koyama, T., Separation of the components of atmospheric salt and their distribution. Bull. Chem. Soc. Japan, 22, 47 (1949).

Sugawara, K., Chemistry of ice, snow and other water substances in Antarctica. International Assoc. Sci. Hydrology, General Assembly of Helsinki, 1960, Symp. on Antarctic Glaciology, 55, The Antarctic record no. 11, Ministry of Education, Tokyo, Japan, 836 (1961).

Toba, Y., On the giant sea-salt particles in the atmosphere, I, II, III, Tellus 17, 131 and 365 (1965). Tellus 18, pp. 132 (1965).

Valach, R., The origin of the gaseous form of natural atmospheric chlorine. Tellus, 19, 509 (1967).

Vosters, M., Hanappe, F. & Buat-Ménard, P., Determination of Cl, Na, Mg, K, and Ca in firn sample 66-A-6 from New Byrd Station, Antarctica—Comparison with the work of Murozumi, Chow and Patterson. Geochim. et Cosmochim. Acta, 34, 399 (1970).

Vosters, M., Hanappe, F. & Picciotto, E., Contribution to the hydrochemistry of the Antarctic ice-sheet (abstract). International Symp. on Hydrogeochemistry and Biogeochemistry, Tokyo, Japan, 6–12 September (1970).

Vosters, M., Contribution à la chimie des neiges antarctiques. Composition et origine des aérosols atmosphériques. Thesis U. L. B., Bruxelles (to be published) (1971).

Woodcock, A. H., Salt nuclei in marine air as a function of altitudes and wind force. J. Meteor. 10, 363 (1953).

Woodcock, A. H., Kientzler, C. F., Arons, A. B. & Blanchard, D. C., Giant condensation nuclei from bursting bubbles. Nature, 172, 1144 (1953).

Woodcock, A. H. & Blanchard, D. C., Test of the salt nuclei hypothesis of rain formation. Tellus, 7, 437 (1955).

Zverev, V. P., The role of atmospheric precipitation in redistribution of substance between atmosphere, hydrosphere and lithosphere. (abstract), International Symp. on Hydrogeochemistry and Biochemistry Tokyo, Japan, 6–12 September (1970).

Discussion 3. Surface Films. Marine Aerosols

Stig Friberg, The Swedish Institute for Surface Chemistry, S-114 28 Stockholm

I would like to show some results of determinations of water transport through surface layers with regard to two factors. The first factor is the formation of multilayers of surfactants. A double layer may form from ethylstearate as shown by Fig. 1. Fig. 2 shows that the resistance to water evaporation to a double layer is of the same order as a monolayer. Multiple layers actually show less resistance due to a higher degree of disorder.

The influence of specific bonds between metal ions and surface layers is demonstrated by the difference in surface pressure as area per molecule of monohexadecyl-phosphate monolayers on sodium chloride solution (0.46 M) and on sea water (Fig. 3, 4). The latter is a typical curve of a phosphate ester the phosphate group of which has formed a strong bond with a metal ion. The

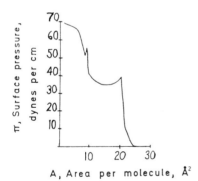

Fig. 1.

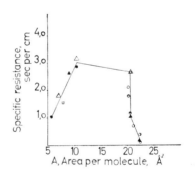

Fig. 2.

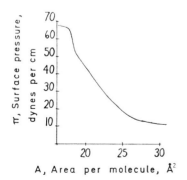

Fig. 3.

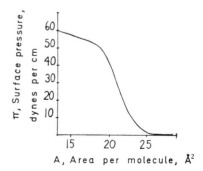

Fig. 4.

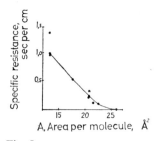

Fig. 5.

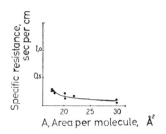

Fig. 6.

resistance to water transport is in that case lower (Fig. 5, 6). This shows that the high valence metal ions in the sea water form strong bonds with phospholipids in the surface layer. It is my opinion that this has some importance for the transport of heavy metal ions from the surface to aerosols.

Stewart

With respect to the effect of surface active films on wave generation: recent measurements by Dobson, remarkably supported by observations in an international program reported by Hasselmann, have shown that most wave momentum and energy goes not into the shortest waves, but into waves little shorter than the longest wind-waves present. Further, almost all of the momentum lost by the air goes into wave generation. It is thus at least strongly indicated that surface slicks may have little effect on either wave generation or on wind stress—although some dissipation effects may be important, and slicks certainly inhibit the *initial* formation of waves on calm surfaces.

Garrett

The very recent information that you have cited is interesting in that it may clarify mechanisms related to air-sea interactions. As you have stated, if these data represent reality, the concept that capillary waves are most influential in momentum transfer from wind to water is no longer valid, and that the influence of surface films would only be significant in inhibiting initial wave formation and in preventing capillary wave formation on gravity waves under dynamic conditions.

   In contrast to this idea, the results of Barger et al. (1970) indicate that a coherent, monomolecular surface film did in fact uncouple wind-wave interactions resulting in a decrease in gravity wave energy within an area of the sea surface under the influence of the artificial sea slick. Capillary waves were eliminated and the frequency of breaking waves was diminished. It was concluded from this experimental study that major interactions between wind and waves in a wind-driven sea appears to depend on the existence of the capillary wave system. Obviously, additional field experimentation of this kind using artificial sea surface films will be essential to resolve these diametric models and mechanisms for the interaction of atmosphere and ocean under dynamic conditions.

Reference
Barger, W. R., Garrett, W. D., Mollo-Christensen, E. L. and Ruggles, K. W., J. Appl. Meteorol. *9*, 396 (1970).

Namias

Would you care to make any comment on the possible effects of these films on macroscale meteorological systems of the dimensions of cyclones and anti-cyclones—or even hurricane formation and development?

Garrett

In order for a surface film to influence a meteorological system of this magnitude it must cover a very large area and remain intact in spite of wind-wave disturbances. Artificial monomolecular films have been sustained at wind velocities as great as 9 m/sec, and the influence of a 0.5 km² slick on waves, breaking water and ripples indicates that the interaction between the atmosphere and the ocean can be uncoupled (Barger et al., 1970). A similar wave-calming effect by natural surface films is unlikely when winds exceed 6 m/sec, since they are fragile and their constituents readily dispersed under such dynamic conditions. Disturbances such as tropical storms derive energy from a warm sea and the heat released by condensation of water vapor. It is also possible that a large artificial slick or oil spill would reduce the water flux from sea to air. It has recently been postulated that fluid, monomolecular films could retard evaporation, not as a molecular barrier to gas transport, but by diminishing wave parameters which normally promote the sea-to-air flux of water (Garrett 1971). While these findings suggest that a *surface film* could modify macroscale atmospheric processes, the creation of a sufficiently large artificial slick is a difficult logistical problem.

References
Barger, W. R., Garrett, W. D., Mollo-Christensen, E. L. & Ruggles, K. W., J. Appl. Meteorol. *9*, 396 (1970).
Garrett, W. D., J. Geophys Res. *76*, 5122 (1971).

Waldichuk

The one photograph you showed with a slick in Chesapeake Bay is very similar to what we often see in Burrard Inlet, British Columbia, when Fraser River water intrudes in a thin layer over the surface of the sea water. Is there any analogy of the damping process of waves by such fresh water layers to that caused by oil films?

Garrett

There are two possible answers to the reflection anomaly which you have described. The first is that the capillary waves have been eliminated by a hydrodynamic type of wave damping due to the rapid surface flow of the intruding river water. This first form of damping is often seen in a boat wake and no organic surface films are involved.

The second possible explanation would require a surface-film damping mechanism. If there was sufficient film-forming organic matter in the river water, surface compression, occurring as it advanced into the sea water, would create a coherent organic film capable of damping and resisting the formation of waves. The surface film acts like a two-dimensional rigid sheet which also immobilizes a relatively thick layer of underlying water (0.03 mm) and resists deformations into waves or turbulent cells.

Goldberg

What are the SO_4^{2-}/Cl^- ratios in your particles and in rains?

Chesselet

In particles, the values found for SO_4^{2-}/Cl^- ratios are very much varying, but sometimes reach 1, which means a strong enrichment. But this could be a consequence of an adsorption process occurring in the air as pointed out by Eriksson, instead of a physico-chemical process of enrichment during the formation of marine aerosols at the air/sea interface. Nevertheless, as I point out in the introduction of my paper, the natural occurring ratio SO_4^{2-}/Cl^- has to be much more well understood when excess atmospheric SO_4^{2-} is sought as a measure of fossil fuel contribution.

Patterson

Observed concentrations of Na, K, Ca, Mg, and Si in uncontaminated firn on the costs of NW Greenland and on the plateau near Byrd Station in Antarctica do not indicate fractionation of sea salts. The mechanisms which inject these salts into the atmosphere must be different than those which may produce the effects you observe.

Chesselet

We have yet to realize that Na/K, Na/Ca ratio variations, in the atmosphere and in the fallout, are:

a) function of the sizes of the particles, then

b) function of their specific residence time in the atmosphere,

c) function of the circulation patterns of the masses of air,

d) function of the relative population of particles that could be present in the air at a given time and at a given altitude.

I guess that, under certain conditions (i.e. regions under the influence of heavy storms, ice shelves, etc.), "non fractionated" and relatively large particles, mainly produced by fast dehydration process of sea-water droplets blown in the atmosphere—what we observe in strong wind conditions on board of a moving ship—may be carried and found much further away than in normal conditions of transportation of marine aerosols occurring in the troposphere.

Odum

Is it known that hydrogen chloride derives from the acid forest soils of the land? If so the balance of chloride may be important in terrestrial nutrition —for example—the animals of the rainforest. The runoff of chloride in Puerto Rico rainforest may be less than in the rain.

Chesselet

We should measure this.

Ui

What is the proportion of Cl_2 in gaseous chlorine?

Chesselet

I must point out that we have for the present *no clear* evidence for a fraction of the gaseous chlorine in the Cl_2 form. We are still carrying experiments on that, because we have found in laboratory experiments that 10–20% of the total gaseous chlorine we observe, cannot be explained by the mechanism which produce the gaseous chlorine by interactions of atmospheric air components such as SO_3 or H_2SO_4 on the chlorine associated with the particles. One must realize that this unexplained fraction could represent a global production rate of about 1×10^7 tons/year.

Johnson

What experimental evidence do you have supporting your claim of the exi-
stance of Cl_2 as a measurable fraction of the gaseous chlorine of marine aerosols?

Chesselet

In open sea conditions (Norwegian sea), the air was filtered through double
0.1 μm porosity membranes, heated up to 500°C to destroy the ozone, cooled
and passed through an ERBA gas extractor unit containing KI solution. In
that solution, quantities of I_2 formed were then measured on board, by micro-
coulometry. If we express the I_2 formed in terms of quantities of Cl_2 we had
about 0.2 μg/m³ which was between 1 and 10% of the amount of "gaseous
chlorine" measured in the air. But, I do repeat that it is the only evidence we
have for a supposed fraction of Cl_2. Of course, we cannot rule out the possibility
of an interference of the I_2 that was measured by Myake in the marine atmosphere.

The Role of the Oceans and Biosphere in the Carbon Dioxide Cycle

By Lester Machta

Part I. Prediction of Future Atmospheric Concentrations

Introduction

Carbon dioxide is known to play a role in the radiation budget of the atmosphere. The future growth and fluctuations of this gas, due either to natural or man-made causes, must be predicted and understood before forecasts of climate modification can be undertaken.

The three reservoirs through which carbon exchanges are: the atmosphere, the biosphere and the oceans. The prediction of future atmospheric carbon dioxide depends on: 1. The input of carbon dioxide from the combustion of fossil fuels; 2. The exchange between reservoirs; 3. The exchanges within parts of each reservoir; and 4. The stability of each reservoir. The present analysis considers a very simple set of reservoirs; assigns exchange rates between and within all reservoirs except between air and ocean; and employs certain estimates of the growth rate in the consumption of fossil fuels. It also makes the usual assumption, which can be challenged, that the characteristics of neither the oceans nor the biosphere alter with time. First, we shall examine the basis for calculating the exchange rates between air and sea surface; the one exchange left unspecified in the model.

Man Made $C^{14}O_2$

Nuclear weapon tests increased $C^{14}O_2$ over that present due to cosmic ray production. The U.S. Atomic Energy Commission and other U.S. organizations have monitored the troposphere and stratosphere for $C^{14}O_2$; the monitoring data have been analyzed and published (Telegadas, 1971). A sample analysis appears as Fig. 1, a vertical cross section from pole to pole. The heavy solid and dashed lines are schematic (or average) tropopause locations. The analysis consists of a series of isolines of concentration (thin solid and dashed lines) based on measurements at the position of the dots and crosses. The difference between dots and crosses simply reflects the organizations performing the $C^{14}O_2$ analyses in laboratories; only the dots have concentrations listed to their right in units of $10^5 C^{14}$ atoms/gram air in excess of the natural background

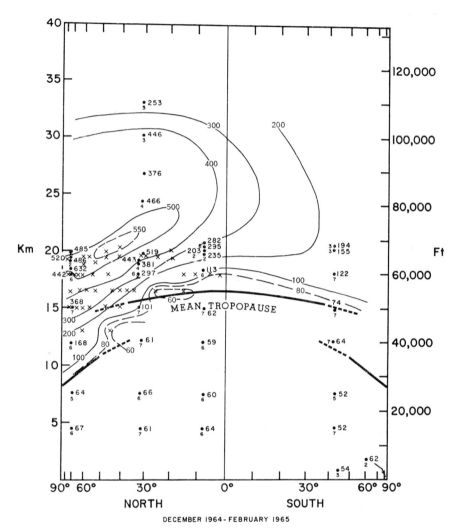

Fig. 1. A cross section from pole to pole showing concentrations of man made $C^{14}O_2$ (Telegadas, 1971). Heavy solid and dashed lines are schematic or average tropopause positions. Dots and crosses indicate locations near which samples have been collected. The difference between crosses and dots reflects the laboratory performing the radiocarbon analysis. Concentrations are expressed in 10^5 C atoms/gram air. The samples at altitudes above about 20 km were collected aboard balloons. All samples collected in the time interval December 1964 to February 1965 have been averaged. The thin lines (solid and dashed) are subjectively interpolated and extrapolated isolines of C^{14} concentration from the observed data.

from cosmic rays. The smaller numbers give the number of samples during the period represented by the figure (December 1964 through February 1965).

Fig. 1 contains slightly more information than is typical for the period 1955–1969 but is representative of the more important 1963–1969 interval. From a series of charts such as illustrated by Fig. 1, a time history of the tropospheric and entire atmospheric $C^{14}O_2$ is given in Fig. 2. The horizontal bars are the

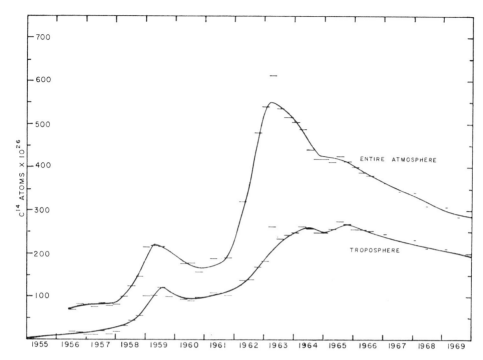

Fig. 2. The time history of C^{14} atoms produced by nuclear tests in the troposphere and in the whole atmosphere (up to about 30 km) as derived from a graphical intergration of the analysis in Fig. 1 assuming no change in the height of the troposphere and a non-varying concentration of atmospheric $C^{12}O_2$ (Telegadas, 1971).

actual numbers for given time intervals; the heavy lines, subjective best fits to the data.

Two periods of increasing C^{14} atoms can be recognized. The first ends in 1959 and the second in 1961 and 1962 although the troposphere continues to reflect increasing C^{14} atoms for several years after 1962. The decrease of the C^{14} in the entire atmosphere after say, 1962, implies its transfer to other reservoirs. Thus, it will be possible to select appropriate exchange rates to best fit the decrease in atmospheric $C^{14}O_2$.

Table 1 presents in the first four columns, the mean annual C^{14} content of the troposphere and entire atmosphere as taken from the smoothed curve in Fig. 2. The column labelled "corrected" reduces the atmospheric C^{14} content for the few large nuclear tests which took place in 1967–69. Note that only those periods have been chosen in the analysis which have no or only small injections of man-made C^{14}.

The lack of regularity in the observed annual changes in atmospheric C^{14} reflects the uncertainty and errors in the inventories of C^{14} due mainly to imperfect sampling by aircraft and balloons. No effort was made to reanalyze the cross sections such as shown in Fig. 1 to improve the smoothness in the

Table 1. *Man-Made $C^{14}O_2$*

Expressed in units of 10^{26} atoms of Carbon-14. (Telegadas, 1971)

Year	Troposphere	Selected years		Observed yearly decrease	Predicted yearly decrease
		Entire atmosphere			
		Observed	Corrected		
1955	5				
1956	15				
1957	24				
1958	50				
1959	110	220	220	50	29
1960	95	170	170		
1961	112				
1962	155				
1963	230	533	533	63	56
1964	255	470	470	55	58
1965	260	415	415	30	49
1966	250	385	385	39	41
1967	238	352	346	42	32
1968	220	318	304	30	24
1969	201	294	274		

trend of year to year changes. Rather, as will be seen later, a best fit minimizes the discrepancies between observed and predicted values over the entire period of selected years. The final column represents the predicted best fit which will be discussed later.

A Simple Model

Fig. 3 shows the elements of the simple model used below. It represents the ideas of many scientists (Dr George Woodwell, Brookhaven National Laboratory; Dr Jerome Olson, Oak Ridge National Laboratory, the present writer, Jonathan Machta, and most particularly, Dr C. David Keeling, Scripps Institution of Oceanography).

Two physical processes are employed. First order kinetics are used between troposphere and stratosphere, between troposphere and mixed layer of the ocean, and between mixed and deep layers of the oceans. This states that a fixed fraction, λ, of the content of one reservoir transfers to a neighboring reservoir in a unit of time. We assume that in the equilibrium state the mass of carbon dioxide (expressed in grams of carbon or atoms of C^{14}) times the exchange rate, in one reservoir equals the product of the same properties in the adjacent reservoir for which the exchange coefficient, λ, is applicable. The second process is the biospheric exchange which employs the concept of the net primary production, NPP. A mass of carbon equal to the NPP is transferred from troposphere to biosphere (or mixed layer to marine biosphere) in a year. This mass of carbon is tied up in the biosphere for a specified number of years,

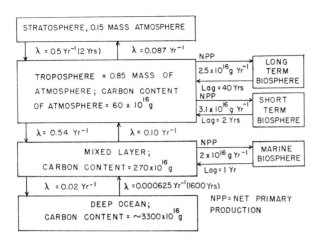

Fig. 3. The model of the three reservoirs of CO_2. The quantity, λ, denotes the fraction of the CO_2 in one reservoir being transferred to an adjacent reservoir according to the sense of the arrow. The transfer between troposphere and mixed layer is calculated from the history of the C^{14} data; all others are pre-assigned. The carbon content of the mixed layer and the exchange constant from mixed layer to deep ocean is derived from other assumed and computed parameters.

the lag, after which it returns completely to the reservoir from which it was initially taken, that is the troposphere or marine layer.

All but two of the exchange rates are assumed in advance. The exchange coefficients between troposphere and stratosphere are based on a stratospheric residence time of 2 years. The exchange coefficient from the deep ocean to the mixed layer derives from an age of 1 600 years of the deep ocean relative to the mixed layer. The exchange coefficient from the mixed layer to the deep ocean uses the assumption of equilibrium noted above. The carbon mass of the mixed layer is obtained when the two exchange rates between air and oceans are calculated from the man-made $C^{14}O_2$ data assuming that the oceans (both mixed and deep layers) contain about 60 times as much carbon as the atmosphere.

The net primary production and the lags represent the judgement of ecologists Woodwell and Olson. Their estimate of the total NPP is slightly larger than given by Leith (1970). It is recognized that the decay of forest organic material occurs over a range of years rather than the single value in Fig. 3 but the choice of these numbers will not be important for predicting the carbon dioxide concentrations in the year 2000. The NPP in the oceans follows Leith. The lag should be even smaller than one year, on the average, but this overestimate is also not significant to the present purposes. The mathematical formulation and the constants required for the calculations appear in the appendix. Two items deserve special attention, however, since they may not be obvious to the non-specialist.

The first item is the increased photosynthesis for certain parts of the land biosphere in the presence of higher carbon dioxide concentrations. Ecologists Woodwell and Olson estimate that very roughly half of the land biosphere is carbon dioxide limited. Further, they suggest (SCEP, 1970) that for each 10 % increase in atmospheric carbon dioxide, the photosynthetic uptake of the carbon dioxide limited land biosphere will increase by about 5 %. These biospheric estimates are provisional and very uncertain at this time.

The second factor is the dependence of the partial pressure of carbon dioxide on other carbon molecules in the sea. Thus the fractional change in the carbon dioxide partial pressure is ten times greater than the fractional change in the inorganic carbon content of the mixed layer. This buffering effect has the following consequences: Assume for the sake of explanation that the mixed layer has a carbon content equal to that of the atmosphere and that the mixed layer does not exchange with the deep ocean. Then if 11 units of carbon dioxide are added to the atmosphere, the equilibrium partition between air and mixed layer will not be 5.5 in air and 5.5 in ocean but rather 10 in air and only 1 in oceans. This 10 to 1 ratio may, according to Keeling, be as low as 6 to 1 or as high as 14 to 1.

Determining the Exchange Rates Between Troposphere and Mixed Layer

The model given in Fig. 3 and stated mathematically in the appendix permits prediction of the man-made $C^{14}O_2$ once the exchange between troposphere and mixed layer is specified. A trial and error procedure uses an assumed exchange rate and predicts the $C^{14}O_2$. Each year (1959–1960 and 1963–1969) the predicted change is subtracted from the observed change and the resultant difference is squared. The difference from 1959–60 is given a weight of one half because the $C^{14}O_2$ information in that period is inferior to that in the 1963–69 interval. All the squared differences are summed. The minimum value of the summation is selected.

The upper portion of Table 2 shows the results. The minimum squared error is achieved when 0.54/yr. transfers from troposphere to mixed layer and 0.10/yr in the reverse direction. Values near the best fit exchange rates give rise to errors almost as small as the minimum but, far removed, the squared errors are clearly larger.

The last column of Table 1 lists the year to year changes in man-made $C^{14}O_2$ given by the best fit calculations. Some of the discrepancies, such as the 1959–60 change are large but may not be entirely due to the errors produced by the model; that is, the observed changes also have an uncertainty.

The lower part of Table 2 describes some of the implications of the table. The exchange rate is the reciprocal of the mean residence time, so that 0.54/yr.

Table 2. *Squared error in predicted annual change of man-made C^{14}, 10^{26} atoms 1959–60 and 1963–69*

$\lambda_{OCEAN \rightarrow TROP}$, per year	$\lambda_{TROP \rightarrow OCEAN}$, per year				
	0.40	0.52	0.54	0.56	0.64
0.02	1 100	2 776	3 252	3 784	6 476
0.08	1 147	807	856	935	1 557
0.10	1 439	803	784	790	1 077
0.12	1 777	949	883	838	868
0.20	3 174	2 115	1 977	1 850	1 451

Minimum error occurs with:

$\lambda_{TROP \rightarrow OCEAN} = 0.54$ yr.$^{-1}$, mean residence time = 1.85 yr. for trophosphere or 2.15 yr for whole atmosphere.

$\lambda_{OCEAN \rightarrow TROP} = 0.10$ yr.$^{-1}$, mean residence time = 10 yr. for mixed layer.

Mass of carbon in mixed layer $= \dfrac{\lambda_{TROP \rightarrow OCEAN}}{\lambda_{OCEAN \rightarrow TROP}} \times$ Mass of carbon in troposphere (50×10^{16} g)

$$= 270 \times 10^{16} \text{ g.}$$

Depth of mixed layer $= \dfrac{\lambda_{TROP \rightarrow OCEAN}}{\lambda_{OCEAN \rightarrow TROP}} \times$ Depth of mixed layer with equivalent carbon mass

of troposphere (50 m)

$$= 270 \text{ m}$$

is the same as a mean tropospheric residence time of 1.85 yrs. Since the literature usually deals with the whole atmosphere, one can convert 1.85 yrs to an equivalent mean residence time for the whole atmosphere of 2.15 yrs; since the troposphere contains 85 % of the mass of the whole atmosphere. This residence time is smaller than found by previous authors who usually quote values closer to 5 years. Because of the assumption that the same number of carbon atoms cross the air-sea interface in equilibrium conditions, the mass of carbon and the depth of the mixed layer can be estimated; the latter turns out to be 270 meters since 50 meters of the ocean has the same carbon mass as the troposphere.

Prediction of C^{12}O$_2$

The model now permits prediction of the changes in C^{12}O$_2$ due to the injection of fossil fuel C^{12}O$_2$ into the atmosphere.

Table 3 gives the latter information. Please note that the numbers in Table 3 should be 10 % greater than shown. The implications of this correction will be discussed further. However, the values in Table 3 have been used in the calculations shown in the subsequent tables and figures. The conversion of fossil fuel carbon into C^{12}O$_2$ is due to Keeling (1971 a) who has modified a similar analysis (U. S. Government, 1965).

Table 3. *Annual release of fossil fuel Carbon Dioxide to the atmosphere*

Year	10^{16} gC	Year	10^{16} gC	Year	10^{16} gC	Year	10^{16} gC
1860	0.008	1900	0.048	1040	0.102	1980	0.512
61	0.008	01	0.050	41	0.106	81	0.530
62	0.008	02	0.052	42	0.110	82	0.548
63	0.008	03	0.054	43	0.114	83	0.566
64	0.010	04	0.056	44	0.120	84	0.586
65	0.010	05	0.056	45	0.124	85	0.608
66	0.010	06	0.058	46	0.128	86	0.628
67	0.012	07	0.060	47	0.134	87	0.650
68	0.012	08	0.062	48	0.140	88	0.674
69	0.012	09	0.064	49	0.144	89	0.696
70	0.012	10	0.072	50	0.148	90	0.722
71	0.012	11	0.072	51	0.158	91	0.746
72	0.014	12	0.074	52	0.160	92	0.772
73	0.014	13	0.076	53	0.162	93	0.800
74	0.016	14	0.076	54	0.168	94	0.828
75	0.016	15	0.078	55	0.182	95	0.856
76	0.016	16	0.078	56	0.196	96	0.886
77	0.018	17	0.080	57	0.202	97	0.918
78	0.018	18	0.080	58	0.214	98	0.950
79	0.020	19	0.082	59	0.224	99	0.982
80	0.020	20	0.086	60	0.238		
81	0.020	21	0.088	61	0.232		
82	0.022	22	0.088	62	0.244		
83	0.024	23	0.088	63	0.260		
84	0.024	24	0.088	64	0.278		
85	0.024	25	0.090	65	0.286		
86	0.026	26	0.090	66	0.300		
87	0.026	27	0.090	67	0.304		
88	0.028	28	0.092	68	0.320		
89	0.028	29	0.092	69	0.332		
90	0.028	30	0.084	70	0.346		
91	0.030	31	0.086	71	0.360		
92	0.030	32	0.088	72	0.376		
93	0.032	33	0.092	73	0.388		
94	0.034	34	0.094	74	0.404		
95	0.036	35	0.096	75	0.420		
96	0.038	36	0.098	76	0.436		
97	0.040	37	0.100	77	0.454		
98	0.040	38	0.104	78	0.473		
99	0.044	39	0.106	79	0.492		

(Fossil Fuel Production from U.N. Statistical Papers)

Conversion to atmospheric CO_2 as follows:

  1860–1949, U.S. Gov't × 0.8
  1950–1968, Keeling, 1971*a*
  1969–1979, Annual growth rate of 4 %
  1980–1999, Annual growth rate of $3^{1}/_{2}$ %

All annual releases of Carbon Dioxide listed in this table should be increased by 10 % because of computational error. In 1970, for example, the reported value of 0.346×10^{16} gC should be 0.381×10^{16} gC.

The changes in $C^{12}O_2$ predicted by the model should in principle be added to the natural background concentration prior to the industrial era, arbitrarily chosen to begin in 1860. However, the value of $C^{12}O_2$ concentration in the last century is known very imperfectly so that a prediction of future CO_2 concentra-

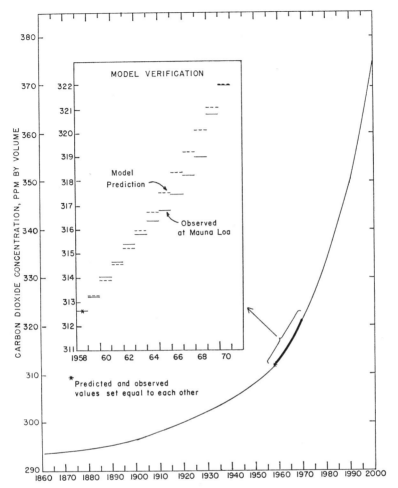

Fig. 4. The predicted time history of global atmospheric $C^{12}O_2$. Because of the 10 % error in the amount of fossil fuel consumed correct prediction in the year 2 000 should be raised to 380 ppm and the value in 1860 reduced to about 290 ppm. Intermediate values should be corrected by a proportionate amount. The observed $C^{12}O_2$ concentrations at Mauna Loa are due to Pales and Keeling (1965) and Keeling (1971).

tions might better use a modern value from which to add or subtract the fossil fuel $C^{12}O_2$. The year 1958 has been chosen and the Mauna Loa value of about 313 ppm is taken as the world value (Pales and Keeling, 1965).

The results appear as the large graph in Fig. 4, the bold portion between 1958 and 1971 being amplified in the inset. Due to the 10 % underestimate of the fossil fuel CO_2, the predicted value in the year 2000 should be raised by about 5 ppm to 380 rather than the plotted value of 375 ppm and the 1860 value decreased to about 290 ppm. The inset shows that over the 13 year period the average fit between the model prediction and the Mauna Loa record is almost perfect. But the year to year changes in the predicted values are, as might be expected, more regular than for the Mauna Loa changes. This irregularity in the Mauna Loa record will acquire significance later when the uncertainty in the prediction for the year 2000 is assessed.

The prediction for the year 2000 agrees with that made in the SCEP report even though the latter did not have the benefit of the $C^{14}O_2$ data. The value in 1860 of 290 ppm is also reasonable.

Further Consequences

Both the man-made $C^{14}O_2$ and the man-made fossil fuel $C^{12}O_2$ were added initially to the atmosphere but with time transferred to other reservoirs. Table 4 shows the partition of these gases among the three reservoirs in 1970 according to the model calculation. More than half of the $C^{12}O_2$ remains airborne; the majority of the rest going into the oceans and only 15 % tied up in the biosphere. In contrast, 60 % of the man-made $C^{14}O_2$ is found in the oceans and less than a third remains airborne; this despite the fact that the $C^{14}O_2$ has had less than 20 years to transfer out of the atmosphere while the $C^{12}O_2$ has been added to the atmosphere since 1860. The reason for the different behavior lies in the buffering action of the ocean for $C^{12}O_2$ while $C^{14}O_2$, being present in trace quantities, exerts no buffering effect. It is also possible to predict future $C^{14}O_2$ (assuming no further injections) as shown in Fig. 5. The scale is given as the C^{14}/C^{12} ratio taking into account the fact that $C^{12}O_2$ will also change with time as in Fig. 4. It is usual to measure the C^{14}/C^{12} ratio rather than the $C^{14}O_2$ concentration. The curve labeled "natural plus man-made" shows what may be found in say, future tree rings corrected for fractionation. The man-made C^{14}/C^{12} ratio appear as crosses and long dashes as a matter of interest and should be read on the right-hand scale.

Table 4. *Partition of man-made C^{14} and fossil fuel $C^{12}O_2$ in 1970 according to model calculations*

	$C^{14} \times 10^{26}$ atoms	%	$C^{12} \times 10^{16}$ g	%
Atmosphere	172	29	5.6	55
Stratosphere	82	14	4.8	47
Troposphere	90	15	0.8	8
Biosphere	66	11	1.5	15
Long term land	49	8	1.3	13
Short term land	13	2	0.2	2
Marine	4	1	0	0
Oceans	359	60	3.0	30
Mixed layer	345	58	2.5	25
Deep layer	14	2	0.5	5
Total	597	100	10.1	100

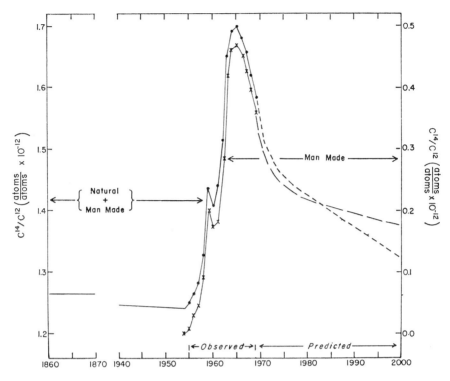

Fig. 5. Time history of the C^{14}/C^{12} ratio in tropospheric air according to the model calculations. The curve entitled "Natural + Man made", read on the left hand scale, should describe the actual measured ratios while the curve entitled "Man made" only reflects the ratio of man-made C^{14} atoms to man-made C^{12} atoms in the troposphere. The decrease from 1860 to 1950 is usually called the "Suess Effect". The ordinate scale shows that radiocarbon constitutes only a very small fraction ($\sim 10^{12}$) of the total carbon atoms in the atmosphere.

The portion of the graph between 1860 and 1954 reflects the dilution of cosmogenic $C^{14}O_2$ by man-made $C^{12}O_2$, the Suess effect. The curve beyond 1970 indicates that the consequences of adding $C^{14}O_2$ to the air by nuclear testing will not be compensated by increasing $C^{12}O_2$ up to the year 2000.

Deletion of the Biosphere

One can readily remove the biosphere from the model by setting the NPP equa to zero and ask for the best fit to a new set of air-ocean exchange parameters. The results of this exercise appear in Table 5 in which some of the features of the original model are compared with a two reservoir (air and ocean) system. Since the biosphere is unavailable, the transfer of carbon dioxide to the ocean must be faster (0.64/yr. vs. original 0.54/yr.) although the reverse coefficient (0.10/yr.) does not change. The squared error, the measure of how well the observed changes in $C^{14}O_2$ are reconstructed, becomes slightly but not significantly

Table 5. *Comparison of models with and without a biosphere*

	Biosphere + Oceans	Oceans only
$\lambda_{\text{TROP}\to\text{OCEAN}}$ Mean air residence time	0.54 y.$^{-1}$ 2.15 y.	0.64 y.$^{-1}$ 1.80 y.
$\lambda_{\text{OCEAN}\to\text{TROP}}$ Mean ocean residence time	0.10 y.$^{-1}$ 10 y.	0.10 y.$^{-1}$ 10 y.
Squared error	784	824
Depth of mixed layer	270 m	320 m
Man-made C^{14} atoms in mixed layer in 1969	342×10^{26}	410×10^{26}

Fixing 1958 CO_2 concentration
 as 313 ppm in atmosphere
    Concentration in 1860
    Concentration in 1970
    Concentration in 2000
	
	295
	 322
	 375
		
		293
		 322
		 381

$\left[\left(\dfrac{C^{14}}{C^{12}}\right)_{1950} \Big/ \left(\dfrac{C^{14}}{C^{11}}\right)_{1860} - 1 \right] \times 100$	-1.8%	-1.1%

larger when the biosphere is deleted. The mixed layer of the ocean must also increase slightly to 320 meters depth. There are small changes in the predictions for the year 2000 which will be discussed below. Finally, the Suess effect drops from -1.8% to -1.1%. On the whole, however, there is nothing which derives from the model without the biosphere which looks more unreasonable (except that we know there is a biosphere) than the original formulation. Perhaps if the depth of the mixed layer is too large and the atmospheric mean residence time too short then these parameters become even less acceptable for a model without a biosphere.

Sensitivity Tests

Just as one may run the case with no biosphere, so have we run other cases changing model parameters. These appear in Tables 6a and 6b. Table 6a treats those items in which the ocean is affected; a repeat of the no biosphere case, a decrease in the age of the deep ocean and changing the buffering factor both up and down. Each variation provides detectable changes in the reported parameters but, focusing on the prediction in the year 2000, no number is more than 10 ppm below or above the original model prediction.

The first four columns in Table 6b (with the second column of Table 6a) show the role played by biospheric parameters including reducing the biosphere to zero and doubling the NPP. Only the change in growth limitation reduced to 0.05 rather than 0.25 produces a change more than 10 ppm in the year 2000 and that by only 11 ppm.

Table 6*a. Variation of model parameters*

Property	Model	No Biosphere	Deep ocean 400 y. not 1600 y. old	Buffering factor 6 not 10	14 not 10
$\lambda_{\text{TROP}\rightarrow\text{OCEAN}}$, y.$^{-1}$	0.54	0.64	0.56	0.54	0.54
$\lambda_{\text{OCEAN}\rightarrow\text{TROP}}$, y.$^{-1}$	0.10	0.10	0.12	0.10	0.10
Squared error	784	824	770	780	788
Average fraction fossil fuel CO_2 in troposphere	50 %	54 %	44 %	40 %	52 %
Assuming 313 ppm in 1958, the predicted concentration in					
1860	295	293	297	298	293
1970	322	322	321	321	323
2000	375	381	370	365	380

Thus it is concluded that changing parameters in the original model by even a very large amount still produces errors in the prediction for the year 2000 of about 10 ppm or less.

The final column adds a different dimension to the prediction; namely it questions the initial $C^{14}O_2$ data upon which the calculations are based. It is argued that the years soon after nuclear tests may have more irregular gradients of atmospheric $C^{14}O_2$ so that the inventories are less reliable. These years have

Table 6*b. Variation of model parameters*

Property	Model	Doubled net primary production	Growth limitation 0.05 not 0.25	Long term biosphere lag 20 y. not 40 y.	Omitting 1959–1960 1963–1964
$\lambda_{\text{TROP}\rightarrow\text{OCEAN}}$, y.$^{-1}$	0.54	0.40	0.50	0.54	0.32
$\lambda_{\text{OCEAN}\rightarrow\text{TROP}}$, y.$^{-1}$	0.01	0.08	0.08	0.10	<0.02
Squared error	784	749	788	786	Not comparable
Average fraction fossil fuel CO_2 in troposphere	50 %	43 %	52 %	50 %	34 %
Assuming 313 ppm in 1958, the predicted concentration in					
1860	295	297	293	294	300
1970	322	321	323	323	319
2000	375	369	386	377	357

been removed from the analysis in the least squares fit. The resulting transfer to the oceans is slower giving rise to what may be a more reasonable mean residence time of a CO_2 molecule in the atmosphere (over 3 years) but allowing only 34 % of the fossil fuel $C^{12}O_2$ to remain airborne in contrast to the model's 55 %. During the 1958–1968 period about 50 % of the fossil fuel remained airborne if one accepts the Mauna Loa record as representative of the whole atmosphere. The observed airborne fraction thus agrees better with the original model using all the changes in $C^{14}O_2$ rather than the selected years in the last column of Table 6b.

Conclusion

A simple model of the exchange of CO_2 between air, ocean, and biosphere has, in part, been calibrated by new $C^{14}O_2$ data. The results using the 1958 value Mauna Loa as the base, predict concentrations of 380 ppm in the year 2000. Uncertainties in the parameters create errors generally below 10 ppm. But unevaluated uncertainties in future combustion of fossil fuels may produce changes larger than 10 ppm. Larger potential errors may follow from the imprecision in the world-wide inventories of the man-made $C^{14}O_2$.

Perhaps more serious, from a fundamental viewpoint, than the uncertainties and errors just noted, is the lack of full understanding of the transfer between air and ocean and the integrity of the biosphere. These comments are prompted by the unexplained changes in the growth rate of atmospheric $C^{12}O_2$ seen in Fig. 4. Relatively small changes in the sea surface temperature or in the net primary production (due to variable rainfall or sunshine in say, equatorial forests) may alter the future predictions. Thus, it is not known whether the 1960's, the period of the present analysis, is necessarily representative of longer time periods or of the future 30 years.

Part II. Seasonal Variations in Atmospheric Carbon Dioxide
Introduction

The most conspicuous feature of atmospheric carbon dioxide observations at clean-air locations, particularly in the northern hemisphere, is a seasonal variation. A pronounced decrease occurs during the summer five months with a somewhat slower recovery during the remaining seven months. There is little disagreement that the explanation for the decrease lies in photosynthetic uptake during the summer season. Nevertheless, the sea surface temperatures warm during the summer, and this should raise the air carbon dioxide in opposition to the sense of changes caused by photosynthesis.

Junge and Czeplak (1968) have made the first attempt to relate the seasonal variations of biospheric uptake (photosynthesis) and release to the air (decay and respiration) to atmospheric changes in carbon dioxide via a simple north-south mixing process for the northern hemisphere. Earlier Bolin and Keeling (1963) had derived source and sink information, in part, from the seasonal variation in observed atmospheric carbon dioxide.

In the present analysis, a more sophisticated diffusion model and more recent estimates by Leith of the seasonal variation in biospheric use of carbon dioxide than was available to previous investigators will aim to see if the land biosphere alone can account for the observed seasonal variation. The limited and imperfect Antarctic monitoring will be compared with that expected from the land biosphere because the ratio of land to oceans in the southern hemisphere is much smaller than in the northern hemisphere. If the oceans play a role in controlling the seasonal variation of atmospheric carbon dioxide, it should be most apparent in high southern latitudes such as in Antarctica.

Leith has provided an estimate of the seasonal variation in uptake and release of carbon dioxide by the land biosphere at about 50° N based on conditions over Europe. He also has mapped the world-wide distribution of net primary production. These two sets of data permit quantitative calculation of the seasonal source and sink functions near latitude 50° N. The growing season north of 50° N becomes shorter and, in winter with snow cover, even the decay largely ceases. Further, both the net primary production and geographical area decrease toward the pole. On the other hand, these latter properties increase toward low latitudes but the more uniform temperature and solar radiation throughout the year will result in more constant photosynthesis, decay and respiration throughout the year. While Junge and Czeplak used estimates of rainfall to judge the differences in summer over winter uptake and decay in low latitudes, this analysis has employed the amount of solar radiation. In practice, there is general agreement between the two approaches.

Table 7 lists the monthly source and sink strength in 20° bands for the land biosphere from 90° N to 50° S. Note that in the tropical rain forests between 10° N and 10° S, it is assumed that the decay and respiration approximately balance photosynthetic uptake of atmospheric carbon dioxide each month so that there is no entry in the table. While the values between 30° and 70° derive directly from Leith's data, all other numbers represent the author's judgment based on the principles stated in the previous paragraph and on Leith's map of net primary production.

Meteorological Diffusion Model

The meteorological diffusion model employs a flux-gradient process of transfer with the constant of proportionality called the eddy diffusion coefficient. Mixing

Table 7. *Carbon Dioxide release (+) to or uptake (−) from the atmosphere, $10^{14}\,gC$ month^{-1}*

	Biospheric sources and sinks					
	70°–90° N	50°–70° N	30°–50° N	10°–30° N	10°–30° S	30°–50° S$_2$
Jan.	0.0	1.00	1.56	1.12	−0.98	−1.64
Feb.	0.0	1.00	1.56	0.75	−0.61	−1.40
Mar.	0.08	1.20	1.84	0.0	0.0	0.60
Apr.	0.12	1.28	2.00	−0.75	0.61	0.80
May	0.12	0.44	0.68	−1.12	0.98	0.60
Jun.	−0.24	−3.16	−4.92	−1.49	1.22	0.40
Jul.	−0.20	−4.80	−7.48	−1.19	0.92	0.36
Aug.	−0.16	−4.16	−6.44	−0.75	0.61	0.36
Sep.	0.20	1.84	2.88	0.0	0.0	0.40
Oct.	0.08	2.40	3.72	0.75	−0.61	0.44
Nov.	0.0	1.76	2.76	1.19	−0.92	0.16
Dec.	0.0	1.20	1.84	1.49	−1.22	−1.08

is permitted in north-south and vertical directions. This is common practice in global transport problems since the west-east advection usually creates zonal homogeneity much sooner than mixing produces meridional or vertical uniformity.

The grid spacing in the north-south direction is 20° latitude, with the grid values at 80° (70–90°), 60° (50–70°) and so forth. In the vertical direction, the grid spacing is 2 kilometers centered at 0 km (0–1 km), 2 km (1–3 km), 4 km (3–5 km), ... 36 km (35–37 km), 38 km (37–39 km) and 40 km (39–40). The tropospheric horizontal eddy diffusion coefficients are about $1–5 \times 10^{10}$ cm²/s, with slightly lower values at the 0–1 km interface. Winter values exceed those in summer, southern hemisphere values exceed those in the northern hemisphere and values near the equator are smaller than to the north or south. The tropospheric vertical eddy diffusion coefficients are in the range $4–8 \times 10^4$ cm²/s. Values are smaller near the earth's surface than in the free air and, over the

Table 8. *Change in partial pressure of CO_2 at sea surface from end of winter to end of summer*

	% change due to			
	Biospheric uptake		Warming of sea surface	Temperature change, °C
Depth of mixed layer	270 m	60 m		
60° N	−6.5	−30	+17	+5
40° N	−2.2	−10	+20	+6
20° N	−0.4	−1.5	+ 7	+2
20° S	−0.5	−2	+13	+4
40° S	−2.2	−10	+13	+4
60° S	−5.0	−22	+ 6	+2

polar winter area they are especially small. The summertime values exceed those in winter and are highest in the temperate northern hemisphere (with its large heated land surface). After passing through a transition zone in the vicinity of the troposphere, the vertical eddy diffusion coefficient is less than 10^4 cm²/s everywhere in the stratosphere. The depth of the troposphere varies with latitude and season according to classical climatology.

The numerical calculation is a time iteration process with a time step of one day. During each step, the appropriate amount of carbon dioxide is added to or taken from the bottom boxes in which the biosphere resides. A background value of about 320 ppm is given initially to every grid point. The program is run for five years but after the first year the seasonal variation is virtually identical for each of the other four years.

The Results

The results appear in Fig. 6 for both northern and southern hemisphere in the 0–1 km layer. The amplitude of the seasonal variation is significantly smaller, at all latitudes, in the southern than northern hemisphere. The amplitude of the seasonal variation has a maximum at 50–70° N. These amplitude changes with latitude and hemisphere are qualitatively in accord with observations, as far as is currently known. The eddy diffusion coefficients change abruptly each three months to accommodate their seasonal variability in the program. These abrupt changes in horizontal and vertical mixing partially account for the lack of smoothness in the calculated time history of the atmospheric carbon dioxide in Fig. 6.

Fig. 7 shows a few relevant quantitative comparisons between the month-to-month calculated and observed change in atmospheric carbon dioxide. The lower part of the figure compares predictions in the 70–90°S region with data at the South Pole. The amplitudes agree well while the phase is moderately good; the minimum is properly timed but the calculated maximum occurs two months earlier than observed.

The upper part of the figure compares Scandinavian aircraft data (Bolin & Bischof, 1970) with calculations at two different altitudes. At both altitudes, the phase is well represented but predicted amplitudes are about one-half of the predicted values. The reduction in amplitude with height is correctly modelled.

Discussion

It is argued that the relatively good fit between the model prediction of carbon dioxide from the biosphere and the observations at the South Pole suggests

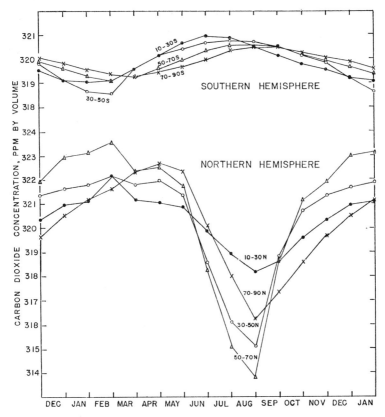

Fig. 6. Seasonal variation in ground level carbon dioxide concentration based on the uptake and release of carbon dioxide by the land biosphere and an atmospheric diffusion model. The absolute value of the concentration is arbitrary and has been fixed to reproduce conditions in the late 1960's.

negligibly small oceanic contributions to the seasonal variation despite the predominance of water in that hemisphere.

The poorer fit in the northern hemisphere cannot be used to argue that the seasonal variation is accounted for by the seasonal changes in biospheric uptake and release of carbon dioxide. Nevertheless, a significant fraction is so explained. Assuming the Scandinavian measurements to be characteristic of the 50–70° N band, two likely explanations for the imperfect fit are suggested. First, and more likely, the information on biospheric release and uptake of carbon dioxide may be in error. This information is admittedly uncertain.

The amplitude of the observed seasonal variation at Mauna Loa, 19° N (Pales and Keeling, 1965) is also greater by almost a factor of two over that calculated. Thus, if the discrepancy between the calculated and observed seasonal amplitudes is ascribed to a larger seasonal amplitude in the biospheric uptake and release of carbon dioxide, the correction to Table 6 must be both large and widespread.

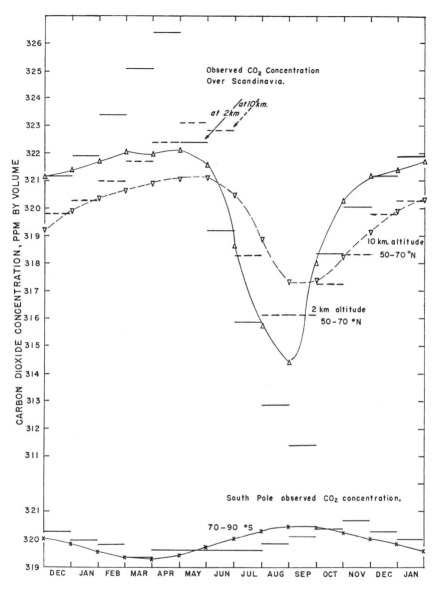

Fig. 7. Comparisons of the observed seasonal variations over Scandinavia (Bolin and Bischof, 1970) and at the South Pole (Brown and Keeling, 1965; Keeling, 1971) with those calculated by a diffusion model and land biospheric uptake and release of carbon dioxide.

Should the input data in Table 6 for the northern hemisphere be in error, it is probable that the same increase in seasonal amplitude ought to be applied equally to the southern hemisphere; the calculated amplitude of the 70–90° S band would also double. In that case, a compensating seasonal variation such as would occur from change in ocean temperature would be required to fit the calculated and observed data. The oceans would then play a role in reducing the southern hemisphere seasonal variation over that which would take place from the land biosphere alone.

A second possible explanation for the discrepancy in amplitudes in the northern hemisphere is the seasonal variation in the consumption of fossil fuels. It is estimated that this can only add, at most, one or two ppm to the calculated amplitudes since the total annual increase if confined to the northern hemisphere troposphere would amount to only about 3.5 to 4.0 ppm. The seasonal component will be only a fraction of the annual increase.

It is unlikely that changes in the treatment of atmospheric transport can account for the difference in the computed and observed seasonal variation of carbon dioxide.

The apparent absence or near absence of any contribution of the oceans to a seasonal variation in atmospheric carbon dioxide may have one of two likely explanations. First, the response time of carbon dioxide release to or from the ocean surface may be too slow to permit a seasonal response (Bolin, 1960).

The second reason is a compensating effect of the marine biosphere. The latter will extract more carbon from the upper layers of the water in the spring or summer when the solar radiation is more intense and the sea surface slightly warmer. Table 8 shows a comparison of the change in partial pressure of carbon dioxide in the mixed layer due to one estimate of photosynthetic uptake and decay using Leith's maps of annual net primary production in the sea and due to changes in sea surface temperature through the summer. The latter has been calculated on the assumption that a one degree Celsius warming increases the partial pressure of carbon dioxide in the sea by a little over 3 %. The fractional reduction of inorganic carbon due to its transfer to organic carbon by photosynthesis creates a tenfold greater fractional decrease in partial pressure of sea water carbon dioxide. To compute the fractional reduction of inorganic carbon requires knowledge of the amount of carbon initially in the reservoir. The table uses two examples, one for a mixed layer 270 m deep (as in Part I) and a second more realistic summertime depth of 60 m.

The comparison of fractional changes in partial pressure for biospheric seasonal variation is seen to be of the same order of magnitude but of opposite sign to that due to the warming of the surface waters. This may also contribute to the explanation of a lack of significant contribution to the atmospheric seasonal variation of carbon dioxide by the oceans.

Conclusion

Despite uncertainties in the true seasonal variation of biospheric uptake and release of carbon dioxide to the atmosphere, the present analysis confirms, in a semi-quantitative way, its dominant role in observed seasonal variation. More important, the analysis suggests the lesser role of the oceans even in the southern hemisphere with its large water area. In fact, the oceans, if important for this purpose, would produce the opposite changes in atmospheric carbon dioxide than have been observed because of its temperature variations. The reasons for the lesser role of the oceans may be its slow response time to temperature changes and the compensating effects of the marine biosphere.

The support of the Fallout Studies Branch, Division of Biology and Medicine, US Atomic Energy Commission is gratefully acknowledged. The assistance of many others including Mr Milton Smith, who programmed the several mathematical models, and Miss Y. Causey and Jonathan Machta who helped in the computations, is appreciated. Above all, I thank Dr. C. David Keeling of Scripps Institution of Oceanography without whose guidance much of the work could not be performed.

References

Bolin, B., Tellus, *XII*, 274 (1960).

Bolin, B. & Keeling, C. D., J. Geophys. Res., *68*, 3899 (1963).

Bolin, B. & Bischof, W., Tellus, *XXII*, 431 (1970).

Brown & Keeling, C. D., J. Geophys. Res., *70*, 6077 (1965).

Junge, C. E. & Czeplak, G., Tellus, *XX*, 422 (1968).

Keeling, C. D. Private Communication (1971).

Keeling, C. D. "Carbon Dioxide and other Carbonaceous Emissions from Fossil Fuels", To be published (1971 a).

Lieth, H., "Phenology in Productivity Studies in "Ecological Studies", 4 (ed. J. Jacobs *et al.*). Springer Verlag, New York, Heidelberg, Berlin, 1970.

SCEP "Man's Impact on the Global Environment", Report of the study of Critical Environmental Problems, MIT Press, Cambridge, Mass., 1970.

Telegadas, K., U. S. Atomic Energy Commission Report, HASL-243 (1971).

United Nations "World Energy Supply", Statistical Papers, Series J., United Nations, New York, many years up to 1968.

U. S. Government, "Restoring the Quality of Our Environment", Appendix Y 4, p. 114, Washington, D. C. (1965).

Appendix

The transfer equations between troposphere, stratosphere, biosphere, mixed and deep layers of the oceans are applied to three kinds of carbon dioxide. The first is $C^{12}O_2$ due to the combustion of fossil fuels starting in 1860. The second is cosmogenic $C^{14}O_2$ which is in quasisteady state and the third is man-made $C^{14}O_2$ due to weapon's testing beginning in 1954.

The transfer between troposphere and stratosphere, between troposphere and the mixed layer of the oceans and between the mixed and deep layers of the oceans obeys first order kinetics; that is a fixed fraction of the content of each reservoir is transferred to its adjacent reservoir during a given time step. On the other hand, the transfer to and from the several biospheric reservoirs depends on the net primary production or the fraction of carbon converted to living matter during a growing season. For simplicity, the return of living carbon back to the reservoir with which it is in contact also occurs in a single year with the following lags: short-term land biosphere, 2 years; longterm land biosphere, 40 years; and marine biosphere, 1 year.

The predictive equations for the troposphere are:

$$T(t) = T(t-1) - \lambda_{T\to M} T(t-1) + b\lambda_{M\to T} M(t-1) - \lambda_{T\to S} T(t-1) + \lambda_{S\to T} S(t-1) - \\ - fP_L T(t-1)/T_0 + fP_L T(t-41)/T_0 - fP_S T(t-1)/T_0 + fP_S T(t-3)/T_0 \\ + I(t) \tag{1}$$

$$T^{14}(t) = T^{14}(t-1) - \alpha_2 \lambda_{T\to M} T^{14}(t-1) + \frac{1}{\alpha_2} \lambda_{M\to T} M^{14}(t-1)$$

$$+ b\lambda_{M,T} \frac{M(t-1)}{M_0 + M(t-1)} [M_0^{14} + M^{14}(t-1)] - \lambda_{T,S} T^{14}(t-1)$$

$$+ \lambda_{S\to T} S^{14}(t-1) - \alpha_1 P_L \frac{T^{14}(t-1)}{T_0 + T(t-1)} - \alpha_1 P_S \frac{T^{14}(t-1)}{T_0 + T(t-1)}$$

$$+ \alpha_1 P_L \frac{T^{14}(t-41)}{T_0 + T(t-41)} + \alpha_1 P_S \frac{T^{14}(t-3)}{T_0 + T(t-3)} \tag{2}$$

No predictive equation for the transfer of man-made $C^{14}O_2$ from the troposphere. Rather its transfers from and to the troposphere are computed and stored.

$$TBR(t) = - \alpha_2 \lambda_{T\to M} TB(t-1) + \frac{1}{\alpha_2} \lambda_{M\to T} MB(t-1) + b\lambda_{M\to T} \frac{M(t-1)}{M_0 + M(t-1)}$$

$$\times MB(t-1) - \alpha_1 P_L \frac{TB(t-1)}{T_0 + T(t-1)} + \alpha_1 P_L \frac{TB(t-41)}{T_0 + T(t-41)}$$

$$- \alpha_1 P_S \frac{TB(t-1)}{T_0 + T(t-1)} + \alpha_1 P_S \frac{TB(t-3)}{T_0 + T(t-3} \tag{3}$$

For the mixed layer, the transfer equations are:

$$M(t) = M(t-1) + \lambda_{T\to M} T(t-1 - b\lambda_{M\to T} M(t-1) - \lambda_{M\to D} M(t-1) + \lambda_{D\to M} D(t-1) \tag{4}$$

$$M^{14}(t) = M^{14}(t-1) + \alpha_2 \lambda_{T\to M} T^{14}(t-1) - \frac{1}{\alpha_2} \lambda_{M\to T} M^{14}(t-1)$$

$$- b\lambda_{M\to T} \frac{M_0^{14} + M^{14}(t-1)}{M_0 + M(t-1)} \times M(t-1) - a_1 P_M \frac{M_0^{14} + M^{14}(t-1)}{M_0 + M(t-1)}$$

$$+ \alpha_1 P_M \frac{M_0^{14} + M^{14}(t-2)}{M_0 + M(t-2)} - \lambda_{M\to D} M^{14}(t-1) + \lambda_{D\to M}(t-1) \tag{5}$$

$$MB(t) = MB(t-1) + \alpha_2 \lambda_{\text{T}\to\text{M}} TB(t-1) - \frac{1}{\alpha_2} \lambda_{\text{M}\to\text{T}} MB(t-1)$$

$$- b\lambda_{\text{M}\to\text{T}} \frac{MB(t-1)}{M_0 + M(t-1)} \cdot M(t-1) - \alpha_1 P_{\text{M}} \frac{MB(t-1)}{M_0 + M(t-1)}$$

$$+ \alpha_1 P_{\text{M}} \frac{MB(t-2)}{M_0 + M(t-2)} - \lambda_{\text{M}\to\text{D}} MB(t-1) + \lambda_{\text{D}\to\text{M}} DB(t-1) \qquad (6)$$

The predictive equations for the deep ocean are:

$$D(t) = D(t-1) + \lambda_{\text{M}\to\text{D}} M(t-1) - \lambda_{\text{D}\to\text{M}} D(t-1) \qquad (7)$$

$$D^{14}(t) = D^{14}(t-1) + \lambda_{\text{M}\to\text{D}} M^{14}(t-1) - \lambda_{\text{D}\to\text{M}} D^{14}(t-1) \qquad (8)$$

$$DB(t) = DB(t-1) + \lambda_{\text{M}\to\text{D}} MB(t-1) - \lambda_{\text{D}\to\text{M}} DB(t-1) \qquad (9)$$

The predictive equations for the stratosphere are:

$$S(t) = S(t-1) + \lambda_{\text{T}\to\text{S}} T(t-1) - \lambda_{\text{S}\to\text{T}} S(t-1) \qquad (10)$$

$$S^{14}(t) = S^{14}(t-1) + \lambda_{\text{T}\to\text{S}} T^{14}(t-1) - \lambda_{\text{S}\to\text{T}} S^{14}(t-1) \qquad (11)$$

The predictive equations for the short-term biosphere are:

$$B_{\text{S}}(t) = B_{\text{S}}(t-1) + fP_{\text{S}} \frac{T(t-1)}{T_0} - fP_{\text{S}} \frac{T(t-3)}{T_0} \qquad (12)$$

$$B_{\text{S}}^{14}(t) = B_{\text{S}}^{14}(t-1) + \alpha_1 P_{\text{S}} \frac{T^{14}(t-1)}{T_0 + T(t-1)} - \alpha_1 P_{\text{S}} \frac{T^{14}(t-3)}{T_0 + T(t-3)} \qquad (13)$$

$$BBS(t) = BBS(t-1) + \alpha_1 P_{\text{S}} \frac{TB(t-1)}{T_0 + T(t-1)} - \alpha_1 P_{\text{S}} \frac{TB(t-3)}{T_0 + T(t-3)} \qquad (14)$$

The predictive equations for the long-term biosphere are:

$$B_{\text{L}}(t) = B_{\text{L}}(t-1) - fP_{\text{S}} \frac{T(t-1)}{T_0} - fP_{\text{S}} \frac{T(t-41)}{T_0} \qquad (15)$$

$$B_{\text{L}}^{14}(t) = B_{\text{L}}^{14}(t-1) + \alpha_1 P_{\text{L}} \frac{T^{14}(t-1)}{T_0 + T(t-1)} - \alpha_1 P_{\text{L}} \frac{T^{14}(t-41)}{T_0 + T(t-41)} \qquad (16)$$

$$BBL(t) = BBL(t-1) + \alpha_1 P_{\text{L}} \frac{TB(t-1)}{T_0 + T(t-1)} - \alpha_1 P_{\text{L}} \frac{TB(t-41)}{T_0 + T(t-41)} \qquad (17)$$

The predictive equations for the marine biosphere are:

$$B_{\text{M}}^{14}(t) = B_{\text{M}}^{14}(t-1) + \alpha_1 P_{\text{M}} \frac{M_0^{14} + M^{14}(t-1)}{M_0 + M(t-1)} - \alpha_1 P_{\text{M}} \frac{M_0^{14} + M^{14}(t-2)}{M_0 + M(t-2)} \qquad (18)$$

$$BBM(t) = BBM(t-1) + \alpha_1 P_{\text{M}} \frac{MB(t-1)}{M_0 + M(t-1)} - \alpha_1 P_{\text{M}} \frac{MB(t-2)}{M_0 + M(t-2)} \qquad (19)$$

The predictive equations for the world atmosphere

$$(\Delta W)_P(t) = TBR(t) + [T^{14}(t) - T^{14}(t-1)] + [S^{14}(t) - S^{14}(t-1)] \tag{20}$$

The definition of symbols follows:

T =carbon content in 10^{16} g of the troposphere due to the carbon dioxide from the man-made combustion of fossil fuels

S =same—for the stratosphere

M =same—for the mixed layer of the oceans

D =same—for the deep layer of the oceans

B_s =same—for the short-term land biosphere

B_L =same—for the long-term land biosphere

B_M =same—for the marine biosphere

Each of the above symbols with a "14" superscript represents the cosmic ray C^{14} content of each reservoir in 10^{26} atoms of C^{14}.

TB $= C^{14}$ content in 10^{26} atoms of the troposphere due to the $C^{14}O_2$ from the man-made production of C^{14}

MB =same for mixed layer of the oceans

DB =same for deep layer of the oceans

BBS =same for short-term land biosphere

BBL =same for long-term land biosphere

BBM =same for marine biosphere

TBR =the net amount of man-made C^{14} in 10^{26} atoms resulting from the transfer out of and into the troposphere in one unit of time end at time t.

t =time; $t-1=$ one unit of time before t.

T_0 =total quantity of carbon as $C^{12}O_2$ in the troposphere in 1860; taken as 50.68×10^{16} g based on an atmospheric concentration of CO_2 of 290 ppm by volume.

T_0^{14} =total quantity of C^{14} atoms as $C^{14}O_2$ in the troposphere in 1950; taken as 323.3×10^{26} atoms of C^{14} based on an atmosphere C^{14} concentration of 74×10^5 atoms g^{-1} (air).

$M_0 + D_0$ =total carbon content of the oceans in 1860, taken as about 60 times the carbon content of the troposphere.

λ_{ij} =fractional transfer of the contents of reservoir i to reservoir j in one year. The reservoirs are: T=troposphere; S=stratosphere; $M=$ mixed layer of the oceans and D=deep layer of the oceans.

M_0 is obtained from the assumption of a steady state transfer across the sea surface:

$$M_0 = T_0 \frac{\lambda_{T \to M}}{\lambda_{M \to}}$$

$M_0^{14} = C^{14}$ content of the mixed layer of the ocean in units of 10^{26} atoms due to cosmic ray production and is obtained from:

$$M_0^{14} = 0.95 \, \frac{\lambda_{T \to M}}{\lambda_{M \to T}} \, T_0^{14}$$

$$\lambda_{T \to S} = 0.087 \text{ yr.}^{-1}$$

$$\lambda_{S \to T} = 0.5 \text{ yr.}^{-1}$$

$$\lambda_{D \to M} = 0.000625 \text{ yr.}^{-1}$$

$$\lambda_{D \to M} = \frac{61 \, T_0 - M_0}{M_0} \cdot \lambda_{D \to M}$$

P_S = net primary production into the short-term land biosphere; taken as 3.1×10^{16} gC/yr.

P_L = net primary production into the long-term land biosphere; taken as 2.5×10^{16} gC/yr.

P_M = net primary production into the marine biosphere; taken as 2.0×10^{16} gC/yr.

α_1 = fractionation factor for carbon transferring from air or water to the biosphere; $(C^{14}/C^{12})_B/(C^{14}/C^{12})_{T,M} = 0.964$ where the subscripts T, M refer to either the tropospheric air or the ocean water.

α_2 = fractionation factor for carbon transferring from air to water; $(C^{14}/C^{12})_M/(C^{14}/C^{12})_T = 0.984$

f = fraction of land biosphere whose growth is assumed to be CO_2 limited, taken as 0.5, times a factor representing the fractional growth of the CO_2 limited land biosphere from a given fractional increase in atmospheric CO_2, taken as 0.5. The value of f is therefore 0.25.

b = buffering factor which accounts for the change in partial pressure of CO_2 in the mixed layer resulting from changes in the carbon content of the mixed layer; taken as 10.

The Chemical Stability of the Oceans and the CO$_2$ System

By Ricardo M. Pytkowicz

Introduction

Sillén (1961, 1967) proposed an equilibrium model as an approximation to explain the relatively stable composition of the oceans. This model is an important contribution because, as a tendency towards equilibrium drives natural systems, equilibria control the direction of most chemical reactions in the oceans and may have been nearly achieved for some sea water solutes. The equilibrium constants and activity coefficients needed to test this model are still poorly known as functions of temperature, pressure, ionic strength, and complexing.

Little attention has been given to the alternative mechanism for chemical stability, the steady state, which will be shown to be a reasonable one in stationary open systems with gradients of chemical potential. Equilibria and steady states may coexist in the oceans. Steady states only require that the net input and output rates of reservoirs be equal and are, therefore, less restrictive than equilibria for which the net rates must be zero.

Simple first order models will be used to deduce the general conditions which lead to an equilibrium or to a steady state ocean and to suggest more complex models and the types of data needed to treat geochemical systems quantitatively.

Model 1

Let A, B, and C be the amounts of a given chemical in the weathering reservoir on land, the oceans, and the submarine sediments. The simplest rate model, which may apply to removal by biological uptake and physical adsorption, is

$$\frac{dA}{dt} = -k_A A \tag{1}$$

$$\frac{dB}{dt} = k_A A - k_B B \tag{2}$$

$$\frac{dC}{dt} = k_B B \tag{3}$$

for which the solution is

$$B = A_0 \frac{k_A}{k_B - k_A} (e^{-k_A t} - e^{-k_B t}) \tag{4}$$

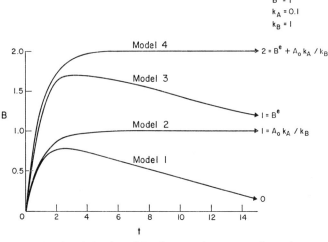

Fig. 1. The time behavior of B, the oceanic content of an element, for the open models.

It can be seen from Fig. 1 that this model does not yield a non-zero stationary state.

Model 2

A is kept essentially constant in model 1, either because $dA/dt \ll A$ or because of replenishment, which may be due to cyclic processes. Then,

$$B = A_0 \frac{k_A}{k_B}(1 - e^{-k_B t}) \tag{5}$$

and the system tends towards the steady state $A_0 k_A/k_B$ (see Fig. 1). In this model the amount B of a solute in the oceans increases and so does the exit rate from the oceans, until the input and output fluxes become equal.

Model 3

The equilibrium state B^e enters the equations for the case of removal of solutes by mineral-sea water equilibria and it can easily be shown, for the first order case, that

$$\frac{dB}{dt} = k_A A - k_B (B - B^e) \tag{6}$$

The solution is

$$B = B^e(1 - e^{-k_B t}) + A_0 \frac{k_A}{k_B - k_A}(e^{-k_A t} - e^{-k_B t}) \tag{7}$$

which tends towards the equilibrium value B^e.

Model 4

If A is not significantly depleted in model 3, then B tends towards the steady state $B = B^e + A_0 k_A/k_B$.

Cyclic Model

The cyclic counterpart of model 1 is:

$$\frac{dA}{dt} = k_C C - k_A A \tag{8}$$

$$\frac{dB}{dt} = k_A A - k_B B \tag{9}$$

$$\frac{dC}{dt} = k_B B - k_C C \tag{10}$$

and has the solution

$$B = C_0 \beta_1 + C_2 \beta_2 e^{p_2 t} + C_3 \beta_3 e^{p_3 t} \tag{11}$$

and it can be shown (M. S. Longuet-Higgins, personal communication) that it tends towards the steady state $B = C_1 \beta_1$. This is an important result because many natural systems are cyclic.

The general equations for open or cyclic systems with n reservoirs and with or without an internal tendency towards equilibrium have solutions of the type

$$X_i = X_i^e + K_1 \alpha_{i1} e^{p_1 t} + \ldots + K_n \alpha_{in} e^{p_n t} \tag{12}$$

This solution will tend either to X_i^e or to $X_i^e + K_j \alpha_{ij}$ depending upon the extent of reservoir depletion.

Conclusions

Several conclusions may be drawn from these models:

1. There is not enough information available for most natural systems to decide which models apply to specific chemical systems. Still, these models indicate the types of data needed for such decisions and for a quantitative description of geochemical systems. The sizes of reservoirs, the fluxes, and the rate constants k must be estimated. The cyclic versus open nature of the systems and the extent to which the systems are driven by biological or adsorption versus equilibrium reactions need to be ascertained. The rate laws which govern the fluxes and the time changes of A must be determined.

2. A steady state ocean will occur for chemical systems for which the weathering reservoir on land is not seriously depleted within the time scale of interest,

whether the systems in the oceans are controlled by biological or by mineral equilibration processes. The rough constancy of A is a likely possibility as cyclic replenishment of the weathering reservoir may occur for several elements.

3. Depletion of the continental reservoir and mineral-sea water interactions in sea water lead to the equilibrium ocean proposed by Sillén.

4. A description of the time behavior of geochemical systems requires as many relaxation times $(T=1/k)$ as there are reservoirs. The use of only two reservoirs, such as the atmosphere and the ocean, is only permissible if the relaxation time for exchange is short relative to the other relaxation times for the system.

The Stability of the CO_2 System

The CO_2 system is complex and cannot yet be solved quantitatively as most reservoir sizes and rate constants and some of the fluxes are unknown. Still, the first steps in the model approach, the deduction of pathways and the estimate of fluxes, yield useful insights into control mechanisms.

Fig. 2 represents a flow chart for the CO_2 system through and within the recent oceans. The fluxes are in 10^{15} g CO_2/year, for the species in parentheses,

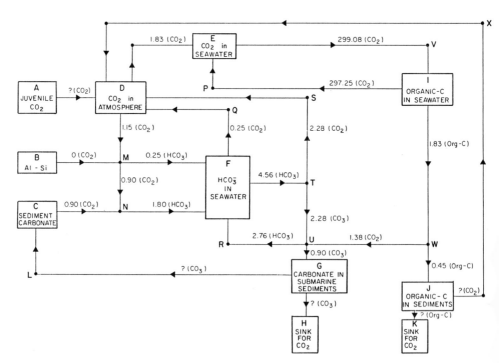

Fig. 2. Fluxes of the CO_2 system expressed in 10^{15} g CO_2/year, for the species shown in parentheses.

and were estimated by the procedures of Pytkowicz (1967, 1968). The eventual quantitative description of the system will involve a large number of differential equations and relaxation times.

Juvenile CO_2 enters the atmosphere and part of it is used to weather aluminium silicates (M in Fig. 2) and carbonates (N). HCO_3^- is produced and brought to the oceans by rivers. This HCO_3^- is used in reverse weathering (Garrels, 1965) and in the formation of calcareous organisms. The settling calcareous tests are partly dissolved (U) and the remainder is incorporated into the sediments from which they may be recycled to the weathering environment (Mackenzie and Garrels, 1966) or they may be removed to sink H. Photosynthesis occurs at V and biological oxidation at P. Some of the CO_2 produced by oxidation is used in the solution of calcareous tests (W). That part of the organic carbon which is not oxidized is incorporated into the sediments (J) and some of it may reach sink K.

Conclusions

Several conclusions are suggested by this model:

1. The stability of atmospheric pCO_2 over geologic time may result from the biological removal of juvenile CO_2 into the two sedimentary sinks as $CaCO_3$ and as organic carbon. It should be noted that the weathering of $CaCO_3$ does not remove atmospheric CO_2 permanently as this CO_2 is released during the formation of calcareous organisms. Rather, it is that part of the bicarbonate formed during the weathering of aluminium silicates and not taken up in reverse weathering which, when utilized by calcareous tests, would lead to removal of juvenile CO_2. This is the mechanism by which calcareous sediments were first formed. The data in Fig. 2 are not accurate enought to test this mechanism.

2. There are features of all the models described earlier in the figure and equilibria and steady states may coexist. The steady state, however, plays an important role. In effect, I have shown in earlier work that dissolved $CaCO_3$ is not at equilibrium with the solid phase and that the removal of alkalinity is biogenic (Pytkowicz, 1965a, 1965b). Therefore, the alkalinity of the oceans appears to be in a steady state. The pCO_2 of sea water, below the thin wind mixed layer, is controlled by oxidation rather than by near equilibrium with the atmosphere. The pH is determined by any two relevant quantities. Thus, if the alkalinity and the pCO_2 of sea water are at a steady state controlled by life processes, then so is the pH.

3. It has been proposed that, if the CO_2 system does not have the buffer capacity to cope with the injection of acid volatiles, then pH-stating is achieved by the titration of aluminium silicates. This is a likely mechanism but, in addi-

tion, the removal of juvenile CO_2 into sinks H and K by biological processes may contribute to the pH-stating.

4. pH fluctuations within a time scale of a few thousand years have been shown (Pytkowicz, 1967) to be taken care of by the alkalinity already present in sea water. About 88 % of this alkalinity in the recent oceans results from the weathering of $CaCO_3$ and the remainder from the weathering of aluminium silicates (fluxes NF and MF). The dissolution of tests enhances the alkalinity level of the oceans. The actual pH, within the buffer capacity of the bicarbonate present, is determined by the pCO_2 and the alkalinity which result from photosynthesis, oxidation, formation and dissolution of calcareous tests.

Afterthoughts

Simple linear relations such as $dA/dt = -k_A A$, mean that a straight line is drawn between the points $dA/dt = 0$ for $A = 0$ and some value dA/dt when the content of the land reservoir is A. The actual curve between the two points, when known, will probably be quite complex but will have in common with the simple model the monotonic feature of increasing with increasing A. It is this feature of reservoirs which is pertinent to a general study of their behavior.

I would also like to point out, as another afterthought, that if indeed organisms now play a major role in the control of the pH of the oceans then this is an interesting illustration of the biota preventing the environment from varying in a way that would damage life.

This work was done while the author was a National Science Foundation Senior Postdoctoral Fellow at the University of Cambridge and was also supported by the National Science Foundation Grant GA-17011.

References

Garrels, R. M., Science, *148*, 69 (1965).
Mackenzie, F. T. & Garrels, R. M., Am. J. Sci., *264*, 507 (1966).
Pytkowicz, R. M., Limnol. Oceanogr., *10*, 220 (1965a).
Pytkowicz, R. M., J. Geol., *73*, 196 (1965b).
Pytkowicz, R. M., Geochim. cosmochim. Acta, *31*, 63 (1967).
Pytkowicz, R. M., Oceanogr. Mar. Biol. Ann. Revs., *6*, 83 (1968).
Sillén, L. G., In: Oceanography, M. Sears, editor, Publ. Am. Assoc. Adv. Sci., *67*, 549 (1961).
Sillén, L. G., Science, *156*, 1189 (1967).

Discussion 4. Carbon Dioxide

Odum

Fourteen Forest Floor Microcosms were studied after 6 months of adaption and the atmospheres of carbon dioxide studied. With daily light and dark cycles, the CO_2 rose and fell several hundred parts per million in the closed systems each one having a different mean depending on the organisms that had developed. The equilibrium levels ranged from 300 ppm in the lowest to 2 000 ppm in the highest. The levels were adequately predicted by the P and R systems model mentioned in my symposium lecture. See model and example of diurnal response in Figs. 1 and 2. Although the time constants were much smaller than

A. Energy

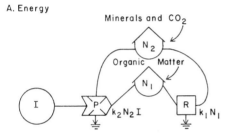

B. Mineral Cycle

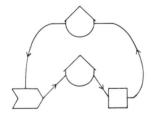

C. Flow of equations in block diagram

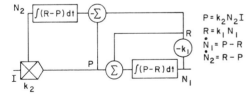

$P = k_2 N_2 I$
$R = k_1 N_1$
$\dot{N}_1 = P - R$
$\dot{N}_2 = R - P$

D. Passive analog

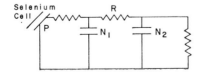

Fig. 1. Microcosm model.

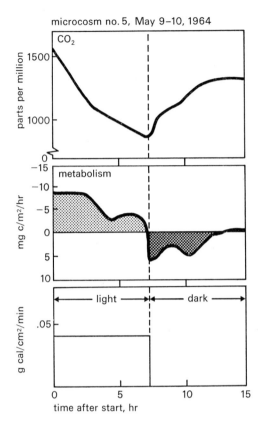

microcosm no. 5, May 9–10, 1964

Fig. 2. Carbon dioxide metabolism of microcosm 5 under square-wave light, May 9 to 10, 1964.

in the biosphere, the experiments suggest that global evolution and ecological successional changes may have contributed to large changes in CO_2 with effects on the climate. This work has just been published including analog simulation: Odum, H. T. & Lugo, A., 1970, "Metabolism of Forest Floor Microcosms" Section I, p. 35–54 in "A Tropical Rainforest" ed. by Odum, H. T. & Pigeon, R. F., Division of Technical Information, TID 24270, Oak Ridge, Tenn. Federal Clearinghouse, Springfield, Virginia 22151.

Machta

The net primary production of about 60×10^{15} grams of carbon per year would deplete the atmospheric carbon dioxide content by 30 ppm per year were it not for compensating decay of older organic material. Thus, very small changes in the world land net primary production, of the order of a few percent, would be sufficient to create changes in the annual growth of atmospheric carbon dioxide of 0.5 to 1.0 ppm per year.

Stewart

I think that we should not be too surprised that the amount of the ocean which must be called into play in order to account for the apparent deficit in atmospheric CO_2 is greater than the volume of the upper mixed layer. Carbon is very biologically active and is subject to other exchange processes such as detritus fall. I understand that strontium-90, which is biologically active, has a significantly deeper distribution than has tritium.

Bowen

Representativeness of C-14 data of Fairhall. — Note that Vogel has found on VTB ARGO stations, no marked difference between C-14 profiles north of Walvis Ridge from those south of Ridge in Cape Basin.

Machta

The C-14 data of Fairhall in the ocean waters are still too scanty to permit a full appreciation of the distribution of C-14 concentrations in the oceans.

Bowen

"Fast-turn over deep-ocean box of Bolin"—most C-14 people have data indicating this, but *all* disregard them because they are so strongly affected by the "one-old-box" model of Broecker or Craig.

Bolin

I am pleased with your remark and indeed agree that the ocean model to be used in this kind of modelling work needs considerable elaboration.

Machta

In predicting the $C^{12}O_2$ concentration for the year 2000, it turns out that character of the exchange between the mixed layer and the deep ocean is not crucial so long as it is measured in terms of hundreds of years. However, if there is an intermediate layer with a shorter response time than a hundred years, this may affect the future predictions of atmospheric CO_2.

Bowen

On some samples taken at same time Roether (H-3) and Bowen (Sr-90, Cs-137) find very strong correlation of these, in respect to vertical distribution; we believe that Rooth-Östlund claim of opposite was based on fact they compared between different places and times.

It should also be noted that many people (ourselves included) have studied materials (such as Ce-144, Pm-147, Zr-95, Pu-239), that are definitely transported vertically because of their attachment to sinking particles. Such nuclides show very characteristic vertical distributions that are very unlike those of Sr-90, Cs-137, H-3 and C-14.

Stewart

This information is important, and more and closer study seems indicated. Regardless of the final conclusions about Sr-90 and H-3, it seems that we must take into account the possibility that different nuclides will have apparently different diffusion properties.

Stewart

Can a biologist give us some idea on to whether increased carbonate levels in the ocean will alter the ratio between, say, organisms with silicon skeletons and organisms with calcareous skeletons?

Bowen

In todays oceans we have three groups of mineral-skeleton formers: $CaCO_3$ (Foraminifera, Coccolithophorids); SiO_2 (Radiolaria, Diatoms, Silicoflagellates); and $SrSO_4$ (Acantharia). Considerable data show that the usual abundance ratio looks like Acantharia 10, Foraminifera 2, Radiolaria 1 and that the three groups cover, in about this ratio, over very large ocean areas. This I take to show that there is no major selection advantage to making a "saturation phase" skeleton ($CaCO_3$) over making "under-saturation phase" skeletons ($SrSO_4$ or SiO_2), and that is unlikely that adding CO_2 to force the equilibrium further toward $CaCO_3$ in surface ocean water would increase production of such skeletons.

Duursma

What is the impact of the increase of CO_2 concentration in the atmosphere on the climate of the earth? In addition will trees and grass grow faster in the same proportion as the CO_2 concentration is increasing?

Bolin

Our knowledge of the climatic consequences of an increasing CO_2 content of the atmosphere is still very incomplete. Manabe and co-workers have, however, shown that, if only considering radiative processes in a vertical air column and permitting convective readjustment, a doubling of the CO_2 content of the atmosphere would cause a temperature increase of about 2.5°C. The same average value is also obtained if using a three-dimensional model of the atmosphere and thus permit the general circulation of the atmosphere to redistribute heat. It then turns out that the temperature increase in polar regions is larger than 2.5°C, but less than this amount in tropical region. It should be stressed that other, compensating or amplifying, effects such as changes of water vapour and clouds in the atmosphere have not yet been included adequately in these computations.

It has generally been accepted that trees may grow faster if the CO_2 content of the atmosphere increases, provided there are not other growth limiting factors that dominate, as for example lack of water. This probable consequence has been included in a rough way in the models presented.

Dyrssen

In my opinion our knowledge about the oceans as reservoirs for CO_2 would be advanced if we would be able to determine the alkalinity and total carbonate, which are approx. 2.4 mmoles/kg sea water, with four figures, pH, pK_1 and pK_2 (acid dissociation constants of $CO_2 + H_2CO_3$) with 3–4 figures, and calcium, which is approx. 10 mmoles/kg with five significant figures.

In a paper by Sillén and myself (Tellus *19* (1967) 113) we tried to show how that the problem of pH, alkalinity and total carbonate would be advanced if one used sea water and not pure water as a standard, i.e. as the concentration of a species in sea water approaches zero, the activity coefficient approaches one (for pH then: $[H^+] \to 0$, $f_H \to 1$). Hansson and Jagner have, however, shown that the treatment of the titration data suggested by Sillén and me will only give approx. 1 % (three figures) accuracy (or precision), but that 0.1 % may be reached with non-linear least-square curve-fitting of the titration data. Within the Geosecs program Bainbridge has modified the Edmond titration vessel (Deep-Sea Research *17*, 737 (1970), which together with a moderate size computer would do the job.

Furthermore, in his thesis (A Computer Treatment of Theoretical and Practical Aspects of Titration Procedures, University of Göteborg 1971) Jagner has been able to show that a computerized photometric titration of calcium + magnesium has a standard deviation of 0.01 %. Using polished magnesium ribbons or ingots as a primary standard an accuracy of the similar order may be achieved. Assuming that the magnesium concentration, which is approx. 53.15 mmoles/kg in sea water, has a fairly constant chlorinity ratio (see remark by

J. Riley on the Mg/Cl ratio), we might have a technique to determine significant shifts in the Ca/Cl ratio.

Finally Hansson has now determined pK_1 and pK_2 with 3–4 figures at 1 atm, 20–40 % salinity, and 5–30°C. He will also produce a standard pH buffer with an ionic composition close to sea water. Such a buffer is essential for the use of a glass electrode in order to avoid ion exchange effects on the glass surface as well as shifts in the liquid junction potential of the reference electrode.

Riley

Deviations in the Mg/Cl ratio as great as 0.25 % from the mean have been observed for some oceanic water masses (Cox and Culkin, 1966; Riley and Tongudai, 1967). The cause of these variations is, as yet, unknown; unlike the variations associated with the Ca/Cl they do not appear to be associated with deep waters.

References
Cox, R. & Culkin, F., Deep-Sea Res. *13*, 789 (1966).
Riley, J. P. & Tongudai, M., Chem. Geol. *2*, 263 (1967).

Waldichuk

The year 2000 has been used as the cut-off point for extrapolation of increase of CO_2. Since combustion of fossil fuels has been designated as the main contributor to this increase in CO_2, might it not have been more logical to consider the end point as the time when fossil fuels are expected to be exhausted? If so, would you care to speculate what the effect of increasing CO_2 to that point would be on climate, if any, and whether there might then be a trend toward restoration to earlier carbon dioxide levels.

Bolin

The computations that have been presented could easily be extended in this way. The consumption of fossil fuel in the future is of course not known accurately and a more precise computation is therefore not very meaningful. It is, however, quite clear that the amounts of fossil fuels are that large and the adjustment time of the oceans that slow, that a doubling of the CO_2 content of the atmosphere is well conceivable towards the middle of next century even if the use of nuclear power increases rapidly. I rather prefer, however, to interpret the computations in the following way. By the year 2000, the change of CO_2 in the atmosphere probably will become large enough to have some climatic effects on a global scale. Other factors will then probably come into play, which have not at all been considered sufficiently well yet. The present model will therefore probably not be very realistic. It may, however, serve to indicate when this will happen and the answer is the one given, i.e. about the year 2000.

Pytkowicz

I am confused by your statement that the rate limiting step for CO_2 exchange is diffusion. Is not the usual explanation for the slow rate of exchange of CO_2, as compared for example with oxygen, that the rate limiting step is the hydration of CO_2?

Bolin

I may not have clarified this point well in my verbal presentation. The slow transfer is due to the fact that the equilibrium of the CO_2 system is shifted towards bicarbonate and carbonate ions. Very little remains in the form of dissolved CO_2, which can exchange directly with the atmosphere. The hydration is then not fast enough to replenish (or vice versa) the CO_2 at the surface, but transfer by molecular diffusion between the surface and the interior of the fluid is the main mechanism. At least a ten fold increase of the reaction rate is necessary for it to have a significant effect.

Bolin

What effects like temperature can effect the rate of sea-air exchange to CO_2?

Odum

There is an effect of pumping CO_2 out of sea waters due to alternating photosynthesis and respiration that operates daily in estuaries and possibly annually and in flows from place to place. Photosynthesis (P) followed by respiration (R) or vice versa moves the pH up and down according to Fig. 3. In the zone of seawater the pH change is fairly symmetrical with P or R. However, the

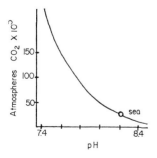

Fig. 3.

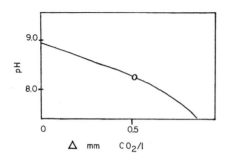

Fig. 4.

effect on CO_2 pressure is asymmetrical. If there is a cycle with photosynthesis and respiration alternating the pH oscillation will drive more CO_2 out than comes in keeping the sea undersaturated (Fig. 4).

References

Fig. 3 is from Beyers, R. J., Larimer, J. L., Odum, H. T., Parker, R. B. & Armstrong, N. E. "Directions for the determination of changes in carbon dioxide concentrations from changes in pH", Publ. Inst. Mar. Sci., Univ. of Texas, 9, 454 (1963).

Fig. 4 is from Harvey, H. W. "The chemistry and fertility of sea waters", Cambridge 1955.

Mercury—A Case Study of Marine Pollution

By Arne Jernelöv

The problems arising from mercury contamination in the aquatic environment were first recognized after the catastrophy in Minamata in Japan. In that case inorganic mercury and methyl mercury were released from the industry, methyl mercury being formed through a chemical alkylation process prior to the discharge. The situation in Niigata might have been similar.

From an ecological point of view, however, the cases in Japan are different from the mercury problem as we know it in Scandinavia. In Sweden it was found "that the fish contained methyl mercury also when all known outlets contained inorganic mercury or phenyl mercury" (Westöö 1966). The explanation for this and the key reaction for the ecological behavior of mercury turned out to be the biological methylation of mercury. (Jensen and Jernelöv 1967 and 1969). In a lake or a closed estuary the mercury balance can be illustrated in the following way (Fig. 1).

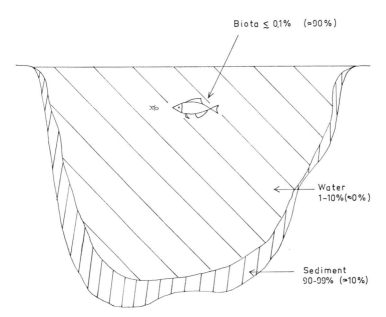

Biota $\leq$ 0.1% ($\approx$90%)

Water 1–10%($\approx$0%)

Sediment 90–99% ($\approx$10%)

Fig. 1. Relative distribution of total and methyl mercury between biota, water and sediment in a typical limnic ecosystem. The first figures refer to total mercury and the one in paranthesis to the proportion of methyl mercury in that phase of the system in relation to the total amount present in the ecosystem.

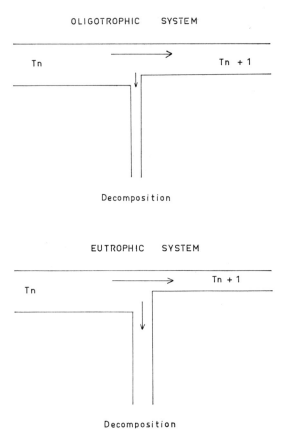

OLIGOTROPHIC   SYSTEM

Tn   Tn + 1

Decomposition

EUTROPHIC   SYSTEM

Tn   Tn + 1

Decomposition

Fig. 2. Transfer of energy and materia from one trophic level in an aquatic ecosystem to the following. In the oligotrophic (more balanced) limnic system a larger proportion is transported to the following trophic level while in the eutrophic system a larger proportion goes to decomposition.

Further investigations have shown that mercury "in water" exists almost entirely bound to suspended particles. (Beijer, Jernelöv, Olson private communication).

Conversion of inorganic mercury to methyl mercury occurs in the surface layer of the sediment or on suspended (organic) particles in the water. A "normal" conversion rate in a Swedish lake is $\approx 0.1\%$ per year of the total mercury present.

The biological formation of methyl mercury occurs in a variety of microorganisms representing aerobic and anaerobic bacteria as well as fungi, and the conversion rate is correlated to general microbiological activity. However, most physical and chemical factors have some effect on the mercury methylation rate. From a human point of view the importance of the biological methylation of mercury arises from the resulting levels in fish and other edible aquatic organisms. The level in the fish is, of course, the result of intake (correlated with methylation rate), dilution through growth and excretion. Many factors which increase the methylation rate and general microbiological activity also increase the growth rate of fish and perhaps even the excretion rate. To illustrate this I would like to try to discuss briefly the effect of an increased nutrient level in the aquatic ecosystem on the mercury concentration in fish.

1. If the nutrient level is increased the microbiological activity goes up and so does the rate of biological methylation of mercury.

2. The growth rate of fish and the amount of organisms increase, which means that the formed and released methyl mercury will be diluted in more tissues.

3. In an oligotrophic system most energy and matter on one trophic level is transferred to the next. In an eutrophic system a larger proportion of the energy and matter on one trophic level goes to decomposition and a smaller proportion is transferred to the next trophic level (Fig. 2). This means that a smaller proportion of the methyl mercury which accumulates in organisms will reach the top-predators with the critical concentrations.

4. If there is a high nutrient level in the aquatic system, the sedimentation rate will be high and thus tend to cover the mercuryrich sediment. This will decrease the formation and release of methylated mercury (Fig. 3) (Jernelöv 1971 a).

As a further complication (one of many) a high nutrient level will increase the probability of oxygen deficit and occurrence of hydrogen sulphide. If that happens mercury will be bound as mercuric sulphide and the availability for methylation will be very low. (Fig. 4). (Fagerström and Jernelöv 1971).

Observation by Olson strongly suggest a clear negative correlation between mercury levels in fish and eutrophy of lakes. Studies on the biochemical pathways for biological methylation of mercury in Neurospora crassa have shown a correlation between resistance towards high concentration of inorganic divalent mercury in the substrate and the ability to methylate mercury (Landner 1971). If this correlation is supposed to be valid for microorganisms in general this might lead to far-reaching ecological consequences (Jernelöv 1971 b).

The principal transport of mercury in a closed aquatic ecosystem can be illustrated in the following way. (Fig. 5).

Mercury entering the ecosystem will end up in the biologically active sediment (or on suspended particles in the water). Most of this mercury will finally be bound in an inorganic form (e.g., to sulphides or iron complexes) and transported to the mineralogenic layers. Part of the mercury will be recirculated through biological conversion to mono- or di-methyl mercury. In due time, this mercury will be returned to the sediment.

The relative rate of these processes determines the mercury concentration in the organogenic sediment. If the concentration of mercury is increased in the organogenic sediment by more or less temporary human activities, the orga-

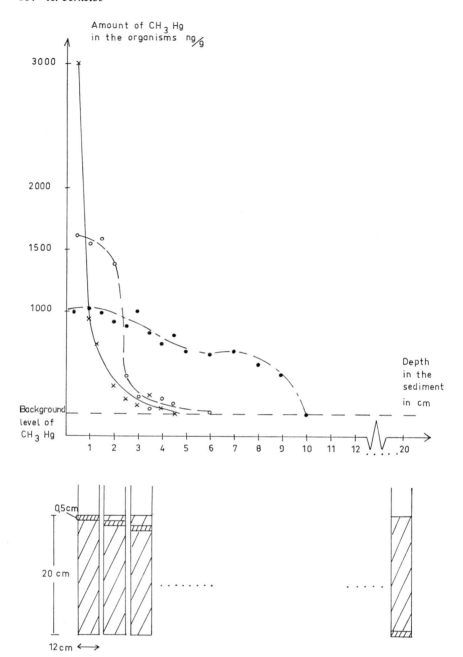

Fig. 3. Amount of methyl mercury found in fish (mean of triplicate determinations) when the layer containing inorganic mercury is situated at different depths. At bottom is a schematic picture of the stratification of the sediment in successive series of tubes. ×—Series with only microorganisms; O—series with Tubificidae; ●—series with *Anodonta*.

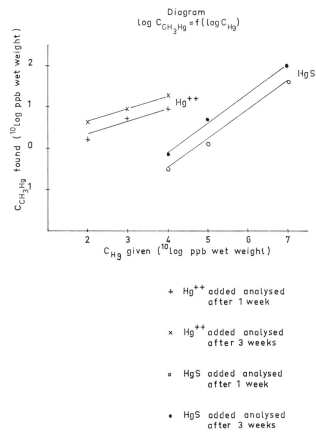

Fig. 4. Formation of methyl mercury from mercury(II) chloride (Hg^{++}) and mercury(II) sulphide) (HgS).

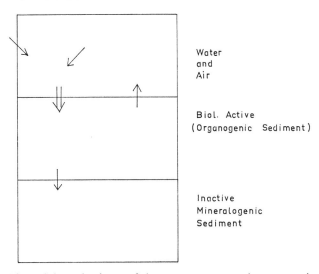

Fig. 5. Schematic picture of the mercury transport in our aquatic ecosystem before addition of "extra" mercury.

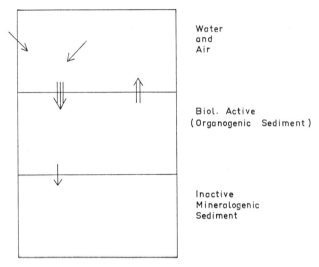

Fig. 6. Schematic picture of the transport of mercury in an aquatic ecosystem after addition of "extra" mercury.

nisms resistant to higher mercury concentrations will be favoured in comparison to others. Within species—as well as between species—competition will result in a selection pressure more in favour of the resistant individuals, which means that the relative number of these will increase. Assuming a correlation between good ability to methylate mercury and resistance towards higher mercury concentrations in the substrate, methylating organisms will therefore be favoured and the temporarily increased mercury concentration in the sediments will result in a higher degree of recirculation. As a consequence, the percentage of mercury bound in the mineralogenic sediment will decrease. The resulting principal transport of mercury in the aquatic ecosystem can thus be illustrated as in Fig. 6.

The lower degree of fixation, the higher degree of recirculation and the larger amount of mercury that is transported to the sediment per unit of time will result a maintenance of higher concentrations of mercury in the organogenic sediment. Thus, the selective advantage of high methylation ability on the part of the microorganisms will be the same. The process can be described as a "negative feedback". Of course, this model is very much simplified, and the argument can be made much more sophisticated by the addition of questions like:

"How does dilution affect the process?" "What does it mean that the mercury returning to the sediment will largely be in the form of methyl mercury bound to dead organisms, while the mercury entering the ecosystem presumably was in an inorganic form?"

Time does not permit me, here and now, to try to go into these complications. The principle, however, will be the same even after quantitative modifications: A temporary increase in mercury concentrations in the sediments might cause (have caused) a change in the selective pressure on the microbiological community leading to a permanently higher recirculation rate for mercury and thus maintaining higher methyl mercury concentrations in water living organisms.

The marine part of the mercury pollution problem offers two recognized, distinctly different, questions: increased mercury concentrations in organisms in estuaries (sometimes as high as 10–20 ppm) and high concentrations of mercury in high-sea predators like swordfish and tuna-fish.

Without suggesting that they represents the whole truth I would like to mention a few circumstances which may help in the understanding of the observed phenomena.

Some of the estuaries where the very high mercury concentrations in organisms have been observed are exposed to strong tidal fluctuations. From experiments and observations on drying dredged sediment from lakes it has been found that in the presence of air and moisture the rate of mercury methylation may be extremely high. (Jernelöv, Lann and Lord 1971). The tide zone seems to be an almost ideal place for a similar process.

As I said earlier, recent studies in fresh water have shown that almost all mercury analyzed as being "in water" is bound to inorganic or organic particles. Generally (although with many exceptions), the complexes between divalent mercury and organic particles are stronger than those with inorganic particles. In equilibrium most of the mercury will thus be found in the organic "phase". This is generally the case in sediments. However, in "the water" the particles are not necessarily in contact with each other and it takes a considerable time before equilibrium is reached.

In salt water the predominant form of mercury ought to be the tetrachloride complex, $HgCl_4^{2-}$ (according to Dyrssen). This means that if the formation of this soluble complex is stronger than the binding of mercury to particles, the chloride ions will tend to extract mercury from particles.

Laboratory experiments with binding of divalent inorganic mercury to kaolin and boiled homogenized egg-white at different salinities have shown that the soluble chloride complex competes successfully with kaolin but not with egg-white (Fig. 7). This means (if kaolin and egg-white are representative for inorganic and organic particles respectively) that when water containing divalent inorganic mercury on suspended particles moves toward increased salinity, mercury will be extracted from the inorganic particles. Thus the state of equilibrium in which the main part of the mercury is bound to organic substances will be reached much more rapidly. As inorganic mercury is methylated on organic substances, this relocalization of mercury will increase the methylation rate.

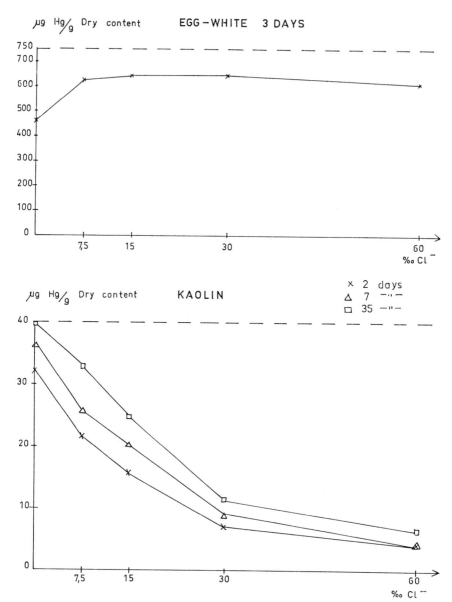

Fig. 7. Binding of inorganic divalent mercury to eggwhite and kaolin at different salinity. The dots represent average of two analysis.

When discussing mercury contamination of sword-fish and tuna-fish in the oceans, one has to remember that this ecosystem (at least from a mercury turn-over point of view) is extremely oligotrophic. Most of the energy and matter will be transported to the next trophic level. Addition of organic matter like oil might increase the microbiological activity and methylation rate consider-ably, without affecting growth rate for standing croup of fish. This means that the mercury levels in the top predators will also be very sensitive to changes in the ecosystem other than a change in the amount of mercury in the system.

To sum this up I would like to stress three ecological hazards arising from mercury contamination of the environment.

1. That "temporary" human discharges of mercury might cause a self-maintained incrase in the methyl mercury concentration in the biota.

2. That tidal areas and estuaries might be favourable for high methylation rates, which could mean that the organisms there also "naturally" contain high concentrations of mercury, but also that they are specially sensitive to further contamination.

3. That due to the extreme oligotrophic characteristics of the high sea and lack of "buffering sediment", marine top predators might increase their mercury levels as an effect of changes in the ecosystem other than an increase in the total mercury concentration.

References

Fagerström, T. & Jernelöv, A., Water Research, Vol. 5, 121–122 (1971).
Jensen, S. & Jernelöv, A., Biocidinformation 10, 3–5, Nordforsk (1967).
Jensen, S. & Jernelöv, A., Nature 223, 753–754 (1969).
Jernelöv, A., Limnology and Oceanography, Vol. 15, No. 6, 958–960 (1971 a).
Jernelöv, A., Zoologisk Revy, in press (1971 b).
Jernelöv, A., Lann, H. & Lord, M., Vatten, No. 2, 234–239 (1971).
Landner, L., Nature, Vol. 220, No. 5294, 452–453 (1971).
Westöö, G., Acta Chem. Scand. 20, 2131 (1966).

A Few Coastal Pollution Problems in Japan

By Jun Ui

Minamata Disease—A Methyl Mercury Pollution in Minamata and Niigata

The name "Minamata Disease" should be noted in the history of marine pollution as the first case of actual danger in human health from industrial activities. A film, which recorded the life and symptoms of Minamata Disease patients (Tsuchimoto, 1970), was shown to the participants during the following comment:

Minamata Disease was discovered by Dr Hosokawa in a small industrial town, Minamata City, in the south-west end of Japan (Hosokawa et al., 1956). The time of its first occurrence is not clear, but similar symptoms could be traced to at least several years before the discovery of the disease. Victims were mostly fishermen in the small fishing villages around the town. About 150 people, at least, showed typical symptoms, and about 40 of them died. The three most typical symptoms were concentric constriction of visual field, ataxy, and loss of sensation, followed by various disturbances in the central nervous systems as well as in the circulatory vascular systems. The damage was mostly irreversible, and there are few cases of recovery. A strange observation was noticed concerning the cats in the same villages; these cats suddenly started running around madly and then died by jumping into the sea. This was noted as "suicide of cats", and the symptoms were generally similar to human symptoms. Such observations, together with the local distribution of patients, led to the conclusion that their main food, fish, was contaminated by some toxic heavy metal in the waste water of the chemical factory, Minamata Factory of Chisso Co., which was the only epidemical special condition in this region. In spite of intensive investigation by the Medical School of the University of Kumamoto, the discovery of the causative agent, mercury (Hg), was delayed till 1959 by various difficulties, including the refusal of information from the factory. A large amount of Hg was discovered in the waste water discharge canal, in toxic fish and in the autopsied bodies of dead patients. In animal experiments with various Hg compounds, however, only methyl Hg gave similar symptoms to Minamata Disease. Minamata Factory was using a large amount of inorganic Hg compounds as catalysts in the synthesis of acetaldehyde from acetylene and in the synthesis of vinyl chloride monomer from acetylene. In 1959–60, the research group supposed that these inorganic Hg compounds were changed into methyl Hg after their discharge into the sea, by an unknown biochemical reaction in the marine environment. In 1962, the direct discharge of methyl Hg was traced to the acetaldehyde synthesis process, and the arguments about the source of methyl Hg were then brought to an end. This methyl Hg accumulated in fish and caused Minamata Disease in fishermen who ate the contaminated fish, so the final cause and effect relation was simpler than expected.

As these discoveries during 1960–62 were, unfortunately, ignored or kept secret in various departments of administration as well as in the factory. The fragmental information available was not sufficient to prevent the second Minamata Disease in Agano River in 1964–65. The second disease was discovered among the river fishermen in the suburb of Niigata City, in the middle of Honshu Island. Some 40 people showed typical symptoms, and 6 had already died. Again, the source of discharge of methyl Hg was traced to the then closed acetaldehyde factory of Showa Denko Co., which was situated at about 65 km up the river from the damaged fishing villages. The estimated concentration factor of methyl Hg from river water into diatoms and fishes was more than 100 000.

Mercury Uses and Levels

Hg compounds have been widely used in various fields of industry in addition to use as catalysts in the synthesis of acetaldehyde and vinyl chloride, and the total consumption in industry has on an average been about 1 000 tons/year, in the last ten years. Besides industry, considerable amounts of phenyl Hg have been applied directly to rice fields as a fungicide, between 1954–67, the average amount being some 200 tons/year, that is 50–70 g/ha rice field/year during this period. Because of the wide-spread application of Hg to rice fields, most rivers and coastal waters have been more or less contaminated by Hg, and it is very difficult to find unpolluted river and coast for comparison. Tokyo Bay receives about 200 kg Hg/day from various sources, and the distribution of Hg among water biomass and sediment is much complicated by the existence of heavy organic pollution in the bay. Generally, the accumulation in the fish in Tokyo Bay is low and reported to be less than 1 ppm. It is an interesting fact that both cases of Minamata Disease occurred in water relatively less polluted by organic matter.

Recently, it was reported that a few species of pelagic fish such as tuna, swordfish and certain shark had relatively high Hg contents, up to 1–2 ppm (McDuffy 1971, Ministry of Welfare of Japan, 1969). It is not, however, clear whether the coastal pollution by Hg in Japan has any relation to this phenomenon. The fact that six samples of tuna from the Indian Ocean showed a

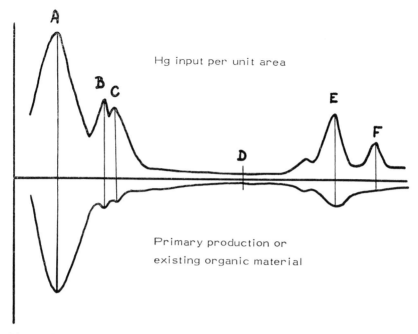

Fig. 1. Simplified model for mercury accumulation into biomass.

rather even distribution between 1.0–1.2 ppm may suggest a relatively high accumulation in pelagic fishes in natural condition. Parallel analysis of man-made pollutants such as DDT and PCB may give some clue as to the source of accumulation and its mechanism.

The following explanation may be possible for the wide difference between the accumulation of Hg into fish and the quantity of Hg in the same district of the sea.

The magnitude of accumulation of Hg in fish and other biomass could be influenced by the ratio of Hg input and the quantity of existing organic material (i.e. biomass in most cases) or the rate of primary production in that region. Further, many factors, such as the form of the Hg compounds, the rate and equilibrium of the methylation reaction of Hg, oxygen and H_2S concentration in the environment etc., could influence the magnitude of accumulation of Hg. In point A in Fig. 1, even if the input of Hg is quite large, the accumulation is small when a large amount of organic matter pollutes the region, and results in the fixation of Hg by H_2S under anaerobic conditions. Tokyo Bay and many other polluted coastal areas represent the case at point A. In point B (Mina-mata) and point C (Agano River), the input was about 30–60 kg/day, but high accumulation occurred in fish because of a rather low concentration of organic matter in the form of biomass in the respective regions. In point D, where the concentration of Hg is quite small, and even smaller for the actual accumulating methyl Hg, considerably high Hg accumulation could occur in biomass if the existing biomass is much smaller. The case of tuna in the Indian Ocean may be the case represented by point D. In Scandinavian countries, the discharge of Hg compounds was much smaller than in Japan, and in most cases it was less than 1 kg/day. Observed high accumulation in fish in spite of this lower input may be the result of oligotrophic conditions in their lakes and coasts. The situation corresponds to points E and F. Similar considerations might be applicable for other highly accumulating toxic materials such as DDT and PCB etc.

Cadmium Accumulation in Coastal Shellfish and Sea Algae in Japan

Since around 1945, a strange disease called "Itai-itai Disease" with pain and fracture in bones had been observed in Toyama District. After a long, difficult investigation, the cause of this diesease was shown, in 1962, to be a long period pollution by cadmium (Cd), which had been discharged from Kamioka copper mine of Mitsui Metal and Mining Co. Since about 1 900 Cd in mining-waste had been deposited in rice fields through river and irrigation systems, and subsequent pollution of food and drinking water by Cd caused this strange disease. Since 1966, considerable Cd contamination has been found in fresh water as well as in coastal sea water, and around 1 ppm Cd has frequently been found in shellfish and edible algae (laver) from various coasts where the discharge of Cd has occurred from mining and industrial waste, such as Ariake Sea and Miyako Bay, etc. (Min. of Welfare, 1970).

Hitherto there is no evidence of a natural reaction to form an organo-metallic compound of Cd, such as we saw for Hg. Again, it is an interesting fact that in the liver of a certain squid from the Indian Ocean, the accumulation of Cd was found to be greater than 100 ppm (Min. of Welfare, 1969), which might suggest the possibility of a natural accumulation of Cd.

PCB as a Potential Health Hazard for Mankind, and Its Accumulation in Fresh and Coastal Fish in Japan

Occasional food contamination by PCB (poly-chlorinated biphenyls) occurred as early as 1968, but little attention was paid to it from the point of view of environmental pollution. The following quotation from Isono (1971) probably provides the best and shortest description of the situation:

"More than 5 000 people suffered from chloracne-like skin eruption, complicated by pigmentation, vomiting, visual disturbance, muscle pain, palsy, fatigue, and so on. They were poisoned by the rice oil made by Kanemi Co., Ltd., which had been widely

	PCB residues (ppm, wet weight)			
	Meat			
	(dorsal)	(abdominal)	Liver	Fatty tissue
Tokyo Bay[a]				
young sea-bass[1]	3.4	1.7	17	120
plaice	0.1	0.3	4.5	nd
goby	—— 0.2		—— 5.6	——
Seto Inland Sea[a]				
grey mullet[2]	1.1	3.9	0.7	18
young yellowtail[3]				
dead	6.6	16	8.4	26
alive	0.1	0.5	0.1	nd
sardine[4] (dead	—— 1.3		—— 3.7	——
Lake Biwa[b]				
several kinds of carps	10–20 (whole body)			
Osaka Bay[c]	(meat)			
a kind of gull[5]	5–36 (m. 15)			
a kind of gull[6]	13–27 (m. 20)			
merganser[7]	7 and 10			

[a] Dr. R. Tatsukawa et al. Dept. of Agricultural Chem., Ehime Univ., Matsuyama, Ehime.
[b] Dr. K. Fujiwara et al. The Public Health Inst. of Kyoto City, Kyoto.
[c] Dr. T. Kashimoto et al. The Public Health Inst. of Osaka Prefecture.
[1] Lateolabrax japonica. [2] Mugil cephalus [3] Seriola quinqueradiata.
[4] Engraulis japonicus. [5] Larus ridibundus. [6] L. crassirostris.
[7] Mergus serrator. nd, not determined.

used for food in that area. Further investigation showed that the disease was caused by PCBs, which had been used as a heat-transfer media in the manufacturing procedure of the rice oil and were accidentally mixed in it. It seemed that the patients had taken at least 0.5–2g PCBs.

During these three years, several people died of this disease, while only a few got better. A large amount of PCBs was found in the dead patient's sternal marrow, heart, trachea and alimentary canal. This disease also gave some serious consequences to pregnant women. They had babies with significant pigmentation on skin. At least two babies were born dead.

In Japan, PCBs are produced in two chemical companies; one is Kanegafuchi Chemical Industry (Trade name, Kanechlor) and the other Mitsubishi-Monsanto Chemical Company (Aroclor and Santhotherm). About 12 000 t of PCBs was produced in 1970, and 60% was used for insulating fluids of capacitators and transformers, 15–20% for the solvent in pressure-sensitive copying paper, 10% for heat-transfer media, and 5–10% for plasticizer of various polymers and for exportation.

Now PCBs have brought another trouble in Japan. This spring, large amounts for PCB residues were detected in fishes and sea birds (See table), just as has been reported in Europe and USA. Besides, the PCB contents of fishes in Japan are generally much larger than those reported from the other area of the world (0.1–1 ppm). It must be pointed out that the yellowtails found dead showed larger PCB contents than those alive, and that fishes from open seas have less PCBs than those taken near the coast of industrial zones. PCB residues have been found also in sludge in harbors near industrial regions, fresh water and sea water.

In the case of Lake Biwa (lying five miles east of Kyoto, 674 km²), PCBs used in many electric factories near the lake seem to pollute the water, resulting the accumulation of the pollutants into fishes directly or through the food chain. The water of Lake Biwa, which is used for drinking in Kyoto City (Population, 1 420 000) and Osaka City (2 980 000) was found to contain 0.1–1 ppb of PCB residues.

As is well known, fish is the main protein source for us. Generally a Japanese eats about 80 g of fish a day. The PCB pollution is offering a new serious problem in Japan. The fishes near the coast of Japan are already contaminated with considerable amounts of pesticides and heavy metals such as mercury, and we are afraid that a synergistic effect will be given by these pollutants including PCBs."

Although most uses of PCB are in various closed systems such as capacitor insulators, transformer coolants, heat-exchangers etc., there is always some chance of spillage and accidental release to the environment. In addition, some uses such as copying papers and plastic plasticizers, may entail disposal by burning, leading to the discharge of a considerable amount of PCB in the form of vapor as well as aerosols, because the temperature in most refuse incinerators is not sufficient to decompose the very stable PCB into HCl and CO_2. Our rough estimation from fragmental information concerning PCB production figures and its demand, is as follows; 20 % of the PCB produced annually escapes into air and 5 % into water, both finding their way into the ocean. Part of the PCB emitted into the air may be carried a long distance by wind, while injection into water may cause rather local pollution.

Recent reports from various places show a rather high PCB/DDT ratio in oceanic biomass, i.e. more than 1, in spite of the low ratio of PCB/DDT which has been discharged into the environment, that is about 0.25 in our estimation (NAS 1971). In this early stage of investigation, it is difficult to explain this large difference. However, it may suggest that PCB has a stronger persistence and a stronger accumulating tendency than DDT. If this is true, a more intensive investigation of the Kanemi Rice Oil Case would be very important, not only from the point of view of public health, but also from that of environmental pollution.

References

Hosokawa, H. et al. Strange new disease in Minimata, report for the meeting of Kumamoto Medical Society, Jan. 1957.

Isono, N., Critical News No. 1, in Jishu Koza, *1*, No. 4, 64 (1971).

McDuffy, B., Private communication at the FAO Conference in Rome, Dec. 1970.

Ministry of Welfare, Japan, Study on mercury contamination of food, annual report for limited circulation, 1969.

Ministry of Welfare, Japan, Study on cadmium contamination of food annual report for limited circulation, 1969.

National Academy of Science (U.S.A.), Report of the working group for Marine Environmental Quality Study, 1971 (in press)

Tsuchimoto, A., The life of Minamata patients (16 mm film), Higashi Production Group, 1970, Tokyo, Japan.

Chlorinated Hydrocarbons in Open-Ocean Atlantic Organisms

*By George R. Harvey, Vaughan T. Bowen,
Richard H. Backus and George D. Grice*

Introduction

Within the past year we have collected a considerable series of open ocean organisms specifically to be analyzed for chlorinated hydrocarbons, for petroleum residues, and for a variety of toxic elements; some sediment cores were also collected. This is part of a multi-institution program, being supported by the U.S. National Science Foundation under its program for the International Decade of Ocean Exploration, to measure the concentrations of a variety of chemical pollutants in organisms of the open ocean, and to assess the significance of these concentrations in terms of possible effects on open ocean ecosystems.

It is our purpose here to present the data so far accumulated showing concentrations of p, p'-DDT (1, 1, 1-trichloro-2, 2-bis (p-chlorophenyl) ethane) and its degradation product p, p'-DDE (1, 1-dichloro-2, 2-bis (p-chlorophenyl) ethylene), and of the class of polychlorinated biphenyls (PCBs); this small body of data appears surprisingly selfconsistent and suggests some reasonably straightforward hypotheses of the biological pathways of the two groups of compounds. We realize that the number of analyses is very small but we are also acutely conscious that there is much thought about the control of open-ocean concentrations of chlorinated hydrocarbons without the support of any data. In view of this, and of the facts both that our data indicate some hypotheses as more immediately preferable than others, and that some open-ocean organisms are shown to have already accumulated pesticide concentrations in the physiologically active range, we decided to present the data now, and to work as hard as could be done at explaining them. It is, of course, our hope that this will stimulate others to examine facets of the problems exposed.

Methods of Collection and Analysis

The figure shows the various sampling transects we have so far made, and indicates the sorts of samples obtained. It was our intention to look for gradients of pollutant concentrations in reference to a few major features, such as the river-borne supplies to the Hudson and Savannah estuaries, the southward

12 – 719717 *Nobel Symposium 20*

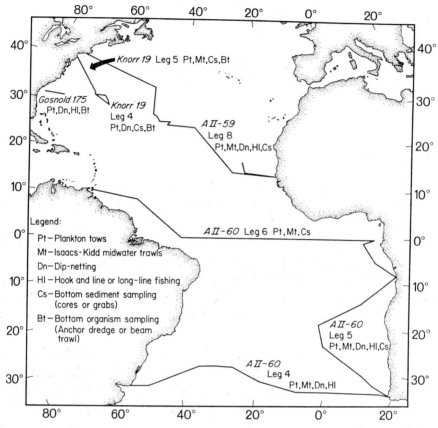

Fig. 1. Cruise Tracks, and kinds of sampling employed in collecting samples to be analyzed for pollutants in the open Atlantic Ocean.

transport, in the Canaries Current, of European petroleum (Horn et al, 1970), trade-wind transport to the North Equatorial Current, the gyral circulation of the Sargasso Sea, and the large currents of the South Atlantic.

Organisms have been collected by dip-netting (Sargassum, flying-fish, trigger-fish, squid, etc.), by hook and line (dolphins, sharks) or by nets (standard plankton nets, or Isaacs-Kidd mid-water trawls). A full description of the precautions we have taken against contamination has been prepared for publication elsewhere (Grice et al., 1972); in essence it has depended on the use of residue-free ethanol (from ethylene hydration) for washing of implements and containers, avoidance of plastics, and preservation by freezing in glass or in washed aluminium foil. We believe the data presented here confirm that on general research cruises such samples can be obtained, substantially free from contamination by chlorinated hydrocarbons; a smaller amount of data appears to show this also in respect to petroleum.

The extraction and cleanup procedure used was essentially as described in

the "Pesticide Analytical Manual", Vol. 1, of the U.S. Federal Drug Administration. The sample was extracted three times with redistilled hexane in a
Virtis homogenizer. The dried extract was concentrated in a Kuderna-Danish
apparatus and was partitioned three times with acetonitrile to separate the
chlorinated hydrocarbons from the fat. The acetonitrile solution was diluted with
brine and extracted twice with hexane. The dried and concentrated extract was
applied to the top of a 10×2.5 cm column of activated Florisil. The chlorinated
hydrocarbons were eluted from the column with 6 % ethyl ether in hexane
(v/v). The eluate was then concentrated to an appropriate volume (0.1 to 5 ml),
chosen, by gas chromatography of intermediate stages in the concentration step,
to give a measurable amount of DDT or DDE. Tests have shown that concentration to as little as 0.1 ml can be done in the Kuderna-Danish apparatus with
no serious loss of total DDT-family compounds; in some cases, however, local
over-heating of the concentrator converts DDTs to DDEs, as has occurred,
we believe, to cause the low ratios observed in the second and eighth samples of
the Table. After concentration an aliquot, not more than 10 microliters, was
injected into a gas chromatograph having a 2-mm by 2-m glass column packed
with 8 % QF-1 and 2 % OV-17 on Gas Chrom Q, and with a nickel-63 electron
capture detector. The presence of the DDT family was confirmed by dehydro-
chlorination with potassium hydroxide in methanol. PCBs were determined by
matching the array of peaks on the chromatogram to the nearest-fitting Aroclor
(usually 1254) and measuring the areas of four corresponding peaks.

Results

In the Table are shown the data now available; in every case the concentration
is shown in reference to drained, fresh weight of organism; in some cases it is
also shown in reference to *lipid*—defined here as all that group of compounds
extractable with n-hexane. The organisms are arranged, in the Table, in two
groups: the surface-living organisms and plankton in order of increasing
trophic level, and the mesopelagic organisms in order of increasing depth of
habitat.

Discussion

The data do not speak strongly to an east-west gradient of concentrations of
chlorinated hydrocarbons in the North Atlantic; there is not even any consistent
indication of a systematic pattern of PCB to DDT ratios. It is well known
(Richardson, et al., 1971) that ratios of PCB to DDT are very much higher in
pollution from mean European sources than in that from North America.
We have seen only two samples (zooplankton K-19-4-28 and flying fish

Chlorinated Hydrocarbons in North Atlantic Organisms

(µg per kg fresh weight - values in brackets are per kg lipid)

Sample #	IDENTIFICATION	Date Collected	Position	Depth Caught(m)	p,p'-DDT	p,p'-DDE	Total DDT	PCB(as Aroclor 1254)
All-59-29	Sargassum	Nov.70	26°N;36°W	Surface	0.4	0.1	0.5	10
All-59-39	Sargassum	Dec.70	35°N;48°W	Surface	<0.01	0.2	0.2	20
All-59-22	Zooplankton (#6 mesh)	Nov.70	23°41'N;34°29'W	0-100	<0.01	<0.01	<0.01	300
All-59-36	Zooplankton (#6 mesh)	Dec.70	30°52'N;47°30'W	0-100	<0.01	<0.01	<0.01	450
K-19-4-10	Zooplankton (#6 mesh)	Mar.71	30°N;60°W	0-200	0.7 (120)	<.01	0.7	110 (19200)
K-19-4-28	Zooplankton (#6 mesh)	April 71	32°N;64°W	0-200	9 (1180)	0.6 (70)	9.5	7 (925)
All-59-1	Flying Fish (Cypselurus exsiliens) (muscle)	Nov.70	14°N; 19°W	Surface	0.4 (115)	0.2 (64)	0.6 (179)	1.4 (410)
All-59-16	Flying Fish (whole)	Nov.70	22°N;33°W	Surface	2 (150)	0.5 (32)	2.5 (185)	6.8 (490)
K-19-4-17	Flying Fish (Prognichthys rondeletii) (muscle)	March 71	30°N;60°W	Surface	<0.01	4 (1480)	4 (1480)	<4
All-59-14	Trigger Fish (Canthidermis maculatus) (muscle)	Nov.70	19°N;30°W	Surface	0.05 (50)	0.07 (70)	0.1 (120)	1.9 (1900)
All-59-11	Dolphin (Coryphaena equiselis) (liver)	Nov.70	17°N;28°W	Surface	60 (1190)	35 (800)	95 (1990)	1056 (21,100)
All-59-27	Dolphin (Coryphaena hippurus) (muscle)	Nov.70	25°N;36°W	Surface	2 (1940)	1 (1350)	3 (3300)	10 (10,000)
All-59-2	Shark (Carcharhinus longimanus) (liver)	Nov.70	14°N;22°W	Surface	38 (79)	62 (127)	100 (206)	300 (620)
All-59-8	Mesopelagic Crustacean (Systellaspis debilis) (37, whole)	Nov.70	15°30'N;26°20'W	90	1.8 (96)	1.3 (72)	3.1 (168)	8.9 (490)
All-59-4	Mesopelagic Fish (Chauliodus sloani) (1, large, whole)	Nov.70	14°50'N; ;25°34'W	660±60	3.3 (432)	1.8 (232)	5.1 (664)	14.5* (1900)
All-59-33	Mesopelagic Fish (Chauliodus danae) (5, whole)	Dec.70	28°N;45°W	800±50	5 (630)	7 (880)	12 (1510)	59 (7300)
All-59-34	" Crustacean (Systellaspis debilis) (17, whole)	Dec.70	28°N;45°W	800±50	3.4 (100)	2.3 (69)	5.7 (169)	35 (1040)
All-59-26	Mesopelagic Fish (Chauliodus danae) (5, whole)	Nov.70	24°55'N;35°53'W	900±10	3.2 (372)	2.2 (318)	5.4 (700)	10* (1460)

*As Aroclor 1260, because of better matching of the chromatographic pattern.

K-19-4-17) that could possibly represent North American pollution unmodified. There are, however, indications that DDT and PCB are transported by the atmosphere in different physical states. Risebrough (1968) found up to 164 mg/kg of DDT in the trade-wind dust at Barbados but has never found PCB in dust samples either from Atlantic or Pacific collections (Risebrough, personal communication). If a large fraction of atmospheric DDT is carried on dust, and delivered (as in nuclear-test fallout) in formed precipitation, whereas most PCBs are moved as gases in the atmosphere, then it would not be surprising to find that the European ratio PCB:DDT preponderates in the region of largely easterly winds. We are arranging to extend our collections into the North Atlantic region of westerlies, to examine this question further. Clearly this ratio difference will be illuminating in considering the South Atlantic samples (see Figure).

The strikingly high DDT (and low PCB) in plankton sample K-19-4-28 we attribute specifically to Bermuda as a source. This sample was collected only about 40 km from the island, and near the area where Chow and Patterson

(1966) observed high (and we believe island-influenced) concentrations of lead in surface water.

On two other points we believe the data support tentative conclusions:

1. While both DDT and PCBs increase in concentration along oceanic food chains, there are significant differences in their pathways.

2. There is a significant downward pathway out of the euphotic zone in the bodies of mesopelagic organisms undertaking daily vertical migrations.

Food-Chain Relationships

The *Sargassum* samples are the only representatives of the primary producer level; open-ocean samples collected with number-6 nets (0.23-mm aperture) rarely contain significant amounts of phytoplankton. Both *Sargassum* samples show appreciable concentrations of DDT-family and of PCB hydrocarbons. At this stage, a reasonable simplifying assumption is that these have been accumulated by surface absorption, but it is not yet possible to confirm whether this has been a direct process of the plant surface or whether uptake has been mediated by the petroleum residues also associated with the *Sargassum* surface (Youngblood and Blumer, Teal and Burns, personal communications). Considering the usual variability of chlorinated hydrocarbon content found among individuals of the same species and habitat (Holden, personal communication), one cannot be sure that the differences shown by these *Sargassum* samples are significant. The DDT-family concentration was higher in the sample collected closer to areas rich in observable petroleum waste, whereas the PCB level trended oppositely. Clearly, in any case, both classes of chlorinated hydrocarbons are entering the *Sargassum* food web at the producer level.

Considering the concentrations observed in *Sargassum*, the three zooplankton samples not influenced by Bermuda are surprising; these collections consisted roughly, less than half of grazers, and half or more of stage-1 predators and detritus feeders, if comparable to Sargasso Sea collections described by Grice and Hart (1962). The extremely low concentrations of DDT-family in two of the samples and the extremely high concentrations of PCBs, in all three, are equally unexpected. The latter are possibly attributable to ship contamination:PCBs are usual constituents of hydraulic fluids, which tend to be widely dispersed on research vessels because of leaks from hydraulically governed winches or other gear. We are assured, however, that on the vessels used in collecting our samples neither hydraulic fluids nor heat exchangers were potential sources of any chlorinated compounds similar to those we measured. The three openocean plankton samples agree closely, and the two fish liver samples (which we believe could not have been contaminated by hydraulic fluid) showed PCB concentrations of the same range as those of the plankton. All this seems to indicate that the high PCB levels in zooplankton are real. Accepting this, it is reasonable to argue that the levels of PCBs in zooplankton and in *Sargassum* are interpretable simply in terms of the surface:volume ratios of the two kinds of samples. This suggests either that some zooplankton surfaces exclude DDT-family hydrocarbons or that these compounds are rapidly absorbed and excreted by some zooplankters. Neither of these hypotheses is very attractive; a third, less obvious, alternative is that the zooplankton samples, each collected at night because of the much greater nighttime density of plankton in the upper 100 meters, may have been heavily weighted with deep-living organisms that had not had time to raise their DDT levels by feeding, but had quickly come into equilibrium, by surface uptake, with the PCB content of the upper layer of the ocean. This last hypothesis has the advantage of being readily testable, by comparing concentrations in daytime versus nighttime plankton tows; we are proceeding to make this comparison. It does appear, to the extent that these plankton are representative, that predators on zooplankton ingest much greater amounts of PCBs than of DDT.

Flying fish are typically predators on zooplankton (Parin, 1970), although with considerable variations in prey-selectivity among the various species. Off Barbados (Hall, 1955; Lewis, Brundnitt and Fish, 1962), larval fish, crustacea and thaliacea are preferred, in that order; more important, perhaps, is that feeding is confined to nighttime; consequently the diet is strongly biased toward zooplankters that are vertical migrators. The levels of PCB in flying fish muscle indicate that these compounds are relatively unavailable to these predators, compared to the DDTs. This, of course, depends now on the assumption that the ratio PCB in muscle to PCB in liver (surely the major depository) in flying fish is like that in dolphin; by analyses of whole flying fish we are now examining this question; the one whole flying fish in the Table gave results in the right direction. The increases in DDT concentration from prey to predator (1 to 3 orders of magnitude) are not unreasonable by comparison with better unravelled food webs.

The trigger fish, as a probable scavenger, was expected to show much higher DDT levels than we observed. A careful examination of stomach contents of this and related species may be illuminating in respect to patterns of DDT avoidance. The pattern shown could, however, reflect simply a very different disposition of fat deposits between trigger fish and flying fish.

Dolphin and white-tip shark represent two more trophic levels: dolphin generally are described (Parin, 1970) as predators chiefly on flying fish, although one of us (RHB) has observed a great variety of surface fishes in dolphin stomach contents; the white-tip shark feeds on squid (which are predators on flying fish, migratory mesopelagic fish, and anything else that moves) and on fish, including predators such as scombrids (Backus, Springer and Arnold,

1956). The increase in DDTs content in dolphin muscle over that of flying fish is less than expected but this is shown, by the values of DDT in lipid, to be largely a reflection of different fat-storage patterns in the dolphin. The shark would have been expected to show higher DDT levels than the dolphin, as occupying a higher trophic level; the considerable difference in DDE :DDT ratio may show that the shark actually metabolizes and excretes DDT more efficiently than do the bony fish. It is also likely, considering the very much greater proportion of liver to body in sharks than in bony fish, that the total DDT concentration per gram body weight was higher, as expected. Calculations supporting this are discussed below.

We cannot explain the very much higher PCB level in dolphin versus shark liver, just as we cannot explain the very low PCB levels in the lower-stage predators. It appears that the DDT data are consistent with a progressively increasing concentration at each higher trophic level, once the step plants-to-grazers has been passed, whereas the PCB data do not show this. The high PCB levels in shark and dolphin are perfectly consistent with the hypothesis that these compounds are not transferred along food chains, but are absorbed directly from the water and show high concentrations either in relation to rapid equilibration (because of high surface-to-volume ratio) or in relation to the long equilibration times available for large (and long-lived) predators. Clearly, examination of age-series of several predator species will illuminate this question; we have begun such an examination.

Vertical Movement by Biota

To assess both the importance of organisms in transferring chlorinated hydrocarbons down from the euphotic zone, and the degree to which mesopelagic and benthic organisms may be protected, by their positions, from exposure to such pollutants, we have begun analyzing a considerable variety of relatively abundant deep-water organisms collected in Isaacs-Kidd midwater trawls. Data are presented in the Table for five collections, of three such species.

a) The mesopelagic fishes, *Chauliodus danae* and *C. sloani*, spend the daytime hours deeper than 400 m, and migrate at night into the upper 100 m (Badcock, 1970); *C. sloani* spends the day slightly deeper than does *C. danae*.

b) The caridean decapod, *Systellaspis debilis*, spends the daytime hours about 700 m (± 100 m), and at night migrates upward but rarely to shallower than 150 m (Foxton, 1970); some of our catches (see Table 1) show *S. debilis* may migrate to a somewhat shallower depth in the open Atlantic than that observed by Foxton near the Canaries.

In neither case is there good information on the trophic level occupied; both are predators, *Systellaspis* certainly on prey of smaller size than that of *Chauliodus*.

The concentrations of DDTs and PCBs in these organisms are surprising both for their high values and for their similarity. *Systellaspis*, living deeper in the water column and (probably) at a lower trophic level, exhibits a range of DDT or PCB concentrations overlapping those of *Chauliodus*. In comparing these data with those of the "surface" organisms one must bear in mind that the deep organisms were analyzed whole. For better comparison we may calculate that the white-tip shark (estimating liver at one-seventh body weight and muscle concentrations like those of dolphins) would have shown a whole-organism level of not less than 17 ppb DDT-family and 47 ppb PCB. A similar computation can be made for the dolphins (assuming that the dolphin liver, as does that of blue-fin tuna, white or blue marlin—Krumholz, 1959—represents only 0.5 to 1 per cent of the body weight); in this case one calculates that the "mean" dolphin would have shown a whole-organism level of not less than 4 ppb DDT-family and 21 ppb PCB. Considering the relatively small percentage of body weight probably represented by viscera other than liver (total viscera ranged from 2.5 to 5.5 % body weight of large marine fish, and from 3 to 7.5 % of fresh water fish—Krumholz, 1959), very much higher than the expected concentrations of chlorinated hydrocarbons would be required in viscera other than liver to raise the "whole organism" concentrations significantly above those estimated.

It is evident that organisms spending most or all of their time below the euphotic zone of the open ocean have been able to accumulate both DDTs and PCBs to concentration levels directly comparable to those in nearsurface high-trophic level organisms. It appears to us also that the existence of these high concentrations in the bodies of organisms undertaking regular extensive vertical migrations in the open ocean confirms a biological mechanism that may be quite active in controlling surface-ocean concentrations of chlorinated hydro-carbons. Analysis of sediment cores, of large diameter and undisturbed surfaces (Burke, 1968), already collected for this purpose will allow us to estimate how effective the biological process is in removing these toxic materials from the whole water column.

The concentrations of chlorinated hydrocarbons reported here are in the ranges known or believed to be of physiological significance for some organisms. For example, eggs of peregrine falcons containing as little as 23 μg DDT per kg, have been reported to have failed to hatch for that reason (Ratcliffe, 1967). At sublethal concentrations of DDT, parr of Atlantic salmon have shown severe disruption both of their learning responses and of their thermal acclimation (Anderson, 1971); application to the sublethal concentrations used in this study, of reasonable (5×10^4 or 10^5) concentration factors for DDT by aquatic organisms leads to the range of whole organism concentrations we have found. Very little is yet known about the metabolism of PCBs or about their sublethal concentration ranges; their persistence in nature is expected (Rise-brough, personal communication) to be much longer than that of DDT, and we believe some of the high concentrations we have found in open ocean organisms to be real causes for concern.

Summary

PCB has been readily demonstrable in all, and DDT in most of a series of organisms collected from the open North Atlantic Ocean. No strong evidence was obtained of an east-west gradient in concentration between the Cape Verde Islands and Bermuda.

The data are compatible with a systematic increase in concentration along food chains, although details of the patterns suggest that the mechanisms of uptake may be different for PCB than for DDT.

A group of fish and crustacea which feed near the sea surface at night but migrate to considerable depths during the day show DDT and PCB concentrations not greatly different from those of predaceous organisms whose lives are spent mostly in the upper layers. We believe this shows that biological removal processes may help to control chlorinated hydrocarbon concentrations in the open ocean.

This work has greatly benefited from the cooperation of the officers and men of R/V Atlantis II and R/V Knorr; many of our colleagues have helped in the collecting, especially D. W. Masch and J. E. Craddock. J. M. Teal helped with identification of invertebrates. H. P. Miklas assisted with the analyses. Financial support has been chiefly from the US National Science Foundation under Grant GX-28334; ship time was supported by NSF under grants GA-1298 and GD-27251, and by the US Atomic Energy Commission under contract AT(30-1)-2174. This is Contribution Number 2786 from the Woods Hole Oceanographic Institution.

References

Anderson, J. M., Proc. Roy. Soc. Lond., B, *177*, 307 (1971).
Backus, R. H., Springer, S. & Arnold, E. L., Jr., Deep Sea Res., *3*, 178 (1956).
Badcock, J., J. mar. Biol. Assn. U. K., *50*, 1001 (1970).
Burke, J. C., Limnol. Oceanogr. *13*, 714 (1968).
Chow, Ts. J. & Patterson, C. C., Earth Planet. Sci. Lett., *1*, 397 (1966).
Foxton, P., J. mar. Biol. Assn. U. K., *50*, 939 (1970).
Grice, G. D. & Hart, A. D., Ecol. Monogr., *32*, 287 (1962).
Grice, G. D., Harvey, G. R., Bowen, V. T. & Backus, R. H., Bull. of Environmental Contamination and Toxicology, in press (1972).
Hall, D. N. F., Colonial Office (Britain), Fishery Publications *7*, 1 (1955).
Horn, M. M., Teal, J. M. & Backus, R. H., Science *168*, 245 (1970).
Krumholz, L. A., Zoologica *44*, 127 (1959).
Lewis, J. B., Brundnitt, J. N. & Fish, A. G., Bull. Mar. Sci., Gulf and Caribbean, *12*, 73 (1962).

Parin, N. V., Ichthyofauna of the epipelagic zone. Translated by M. Raveh; Edited by H. Mills. U. S. Dept. of Commerce, Clearinghouse for Federal Sci. and Tech. Inform., Springfield, Va. (1970).

Ratcliffe, D. A., Bird Study, *14*, 238 (1967).

Richardson, A., Robinson, J., Crabtree, A. N. & Baldwin, M. K., Pesticides Monitoring Journal, *4*, 169 (1971).

Risebrough, R. W., Huggett, R. J., Griffin, J. J. & Goldberg, E. D. Science, *159*, 1233 (1968).

Discussion 5. Mercury. Chlorinated Hydrocarbons

Berner

What explanation can you offer for the enhancement of mercury methylation by increased oxygen concentration in dredged material?

Jernelöv

There are at least two processes that will contribute: The microbiological activity will increase considerably when organic sediments are exposed to air, and, if mercury exists as HgS, methylation takes place through a two-step process involving first oxidation of sulfur and then methylation of mercury. In water with an oxygen pressure of maximum 10 ppm the first step will by far be rate determining. In air with an oxygen pressure of 21 % it will not.

Duursma

Measurements we made for J. K. Miettinen with radioactive mercury (ionic and methylated) tracers showed that fresh water sediments have much higher affinity for both forms than marine sediments. These data support both your data showing that mercury is more strongly bound to organic matter than to inorganic matter, because the fresh water sediments had more organic matter than the marine sediment as well possibly that mercury is desorbed from inorganic sediments by higher chlorinity of the water. Anoxic systems, which contained H_2S in excess, showed a much higher quantity of mercury in solution than was possible on base of the sulfide solubility product.

Jernelöv

Evidently the theoretical solubility product does not apply to the situation in any natural system and, of course, you also have the possibility for formation of soluble HgS_2^{2-}.

Jernelöv

When comparing the different peaks on chromatograms from North and South Atlantic, do you find any significant difference in relative peak heights? If not, it is unlikely that the different vapour pressure accumulation factor and persistence would give the very same result if the distribution occurs through the atmosphere after individual evaporation of the compounds. Does not this rather suggest a spreading of PCB aerosol?

Bowen

So far we have seen in open ocean organisms no measurable changes, in relative peak heights of PCB:s from those that characterize standard commercial PCB mixtures. We certainly agree with your interpretation of this observation.

Chesselet

We have very recent but still very crude indications by filtrations above equatorial Atlantic of large volumes of air ($>5 \times 10^5$ m^3) with controlled collection efficiency, that the fingerprints of PCB collected as particles are the same as standard PCB. This should mean that, at least, a large fraction is associated with the aerosols load, with no phase change.

Microbial Activity as a Biogeochemical Factor in the Ocean

By Yuri I. Sorokin

Introduction

The metabolism of the microbial population was long ago accepted as a basic agent in the biogeochemical turnover of the aquatic environment (Issachenko, 1951, Butkevich, 1958, Kuznetzov, 1959). The biogeochemical activity of the microbial population displays itself mainly through the processes of aerobic and anaerobic decomposition, thereby also supplying the microbial cells with energy. During the process of microbial decomposition, most of the organic matter entering the water basin or having been produced in it is oxidised. The decomposing activity of the chemoautotrophic bacteria is responsible for the turnover of sulphur, nitrogen and iron. The anaerobic decomposition promotes the oxidative transformation of the organic molecules, and the decrease in their molecular weight. It is also responsible for the formation of reduced sulphur and nitrogen compounds. A considerable part of the energy evolved during the microbial decomposition (20–40 %) is used by the microbial cells for the bio-synthesis of their biomass. The process of microbial biosynthesis is often igno-red but it is usually no less important as a biogeochemical factor than microbial decomposition. It results in the transformation of different kinds of dead organic matter and CO_2 to microbial cell protein (Parsons & Strickland, 1962, Sorokin, 1965). This process is also accompanied by the inclusion in the cell synthesis, and thus in the food chains of an appreciable amount of inorganic elements such as N, P, S, Fe, Mn, Co and some trace metals.

Methods

The development of methods for the evaluation of microbial biomass and its production, and for the determination of the rate of microbial decomposition and of the activity of the different physiological groups of microflora have now made the quantitative description of the *in situ* rates of the important biogeo-chemical processes proceeding through the mirobial activity possible. The microbial biomass is measured for these purposes by a direct microscopical count and sizing of stained microbial cells in slide or filter preparations (Rasumov, 1947, Sorokin, 1971) or by biochemical estimation of ATP (Holm-Hansen, 1966). The rate of microbial production and decomposition can be measured, using the radiocarbon method, by estimating the uptake of labelled CO_2 in the dark in bottle experiments (Romanenko, 1964, 1965, Sorokin, 1965, 1971). The methods are based upon the existence of definite relationships between the decomposition, the biosynthesis and the rate of utilisation of the external CO_2 in the natural microbial population. To study the microbial assimilation or turnover of the inorganic substances N, S, P or of some of the metals, isotopes of the corresponding elements are usually used (Dugdale & Goering, 1964, Pomeroy, 1960, Sorokin, 1964, 1971). Measurements are made using short-time bottle experiments with fresh samples of water or of bottom sediments.

In biogeochemical studies of water basins it is very important to obtain the characteristics of the real localisations of the active microbial population promoting the specific processes, such as the organic decomposition, sulphide oxidation, sulphide formation, nitrification, etc. Enumeration of specific bacteria cannot usually give reliable information, since the maxima of the number of specific bacteria and of the biochemical activity of the microbial population rarely coincide. To solve this problem a series of radiocarbon methods for the registration of the rate of microbial biosynthesis in samples in the presence of

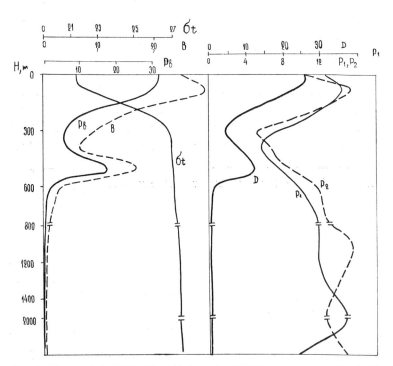

Fig. 1. The vertical distribution of the microbial biomass in mg C/m^3 (*B*), the *in situ* production in mg wet biomass/m^3/day (*Pb*), the potential bacterial production in mg C/m^3 in natural (P_1) and in previously filtered water (P_2), the destruction in mg O_2/m^3 (*D*), and of the water density (σ_t) in the Central Pacific (5°S, 168° E).

specific substrata have been developed. For example, to evaluate the localisation of the active population of Thiobacilli, the $C^{14}O_2$—assimilation was measured in samples of water in the presence of thiosulphate and oxygen (Sorokin, 1964, 1970*b*).

Microbial Activity in the Tropical Pacific

Below are given some of the results obtained by the use of the above methods for solving some problems concerning biogeochemical activity and trophical importance of the microbial population in the tropical parts of the Pacific Ocean and in the Black Sea. Typical pictures of the vertical distribution of the microbial population and of its metabolic characteristics are given in Figs. 1–4. These figures together with Table 1, in which the values are given for a surface area of one m², demonstrate several important regularities of the structure and functioning of the community of planktonic microflora. One of these is the layer structure of the population (Sorokin, 1971). Four main layers of increased microbial activity were found. One of them is the surface film, where the bacterial biomass and production is several times that in the underlying water. The second and the third layers, 25–35 m and 60–80 m, respectively, are the

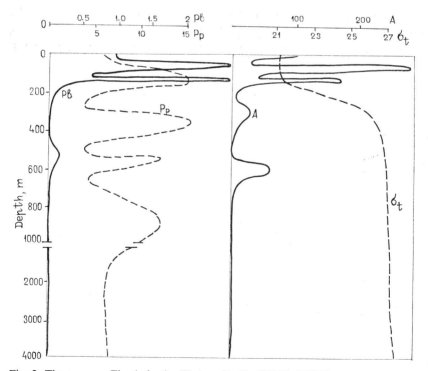

Fig. 2. The same as Fig. 1, in the Western Pacific (13° N, 140° E).

Table 1. *Rate of bacterial production as compared with primary production and destruction*

Position of stations	Depth, m Total	Depth, m Taken for calculations under/m²	Bacterioplankton Biomass (B) g C/m²	Bacterioplankton Production (P₍ₜ₂₎) g C/m²/d	$\frac{P_t}{B}$	Photosynthesis production (P₍ₚ₂₎) g C/m²/d	Destruction (D) D g C/m²/d	Destruction (D) $\frac{D}{P_p}$
Lagoon of Butaritari atoll	24	22	1.49	0.41	0.28	0.15	1.15	7.7
Slope of the same atoll	670	300	1.38	0.93	0.67	0.24	2.60	11.0
Shelf off the Great Barrier reef	70	70	1.20	0.81	0.67	0.62	2.27	3.7
Neritic zone east coast of Australia	2 900	300	0.53	0.58	1.10	0.12	1.63	13.6
North trade wind current	5 200	5 000	0.73	0.71	0.97	0.28	1.98	7.0
Equatorial zone	5 000	5 000	0.91	0.59	0.65	0.56	2.0	3.5
South trade wind current	4 500	1 000	0.39	0.48	1.2	0.29	1.34	4.6

layers of most active photosynthesis, corresponding to the optimum of under water illumination and to the upper limit of nutrients inside the euphotic zone. The thickest and most stable layer is the third layer, the position of which is

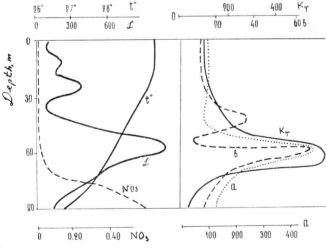

Fig. 3. The results of analyses of water samples taken by using a bioluminiscent indicator: *t°*—temperature; *L*—relative bioluminiscence; NO₃—nitrate nitrogen, mg N/l; *K*ᵣ—relative distribution of living phytoplankton %; *b*—wet biomass of planktonic bacteria, mg/m³, *a*—relative activity of heterotrophic bacteria. Western Pacific (9° S, 164° E).

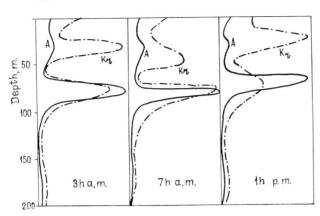

Fig. 4. The daily fluctuations of the vertical distribution of the activity of heterotropic bacteria (*A*), and of the active phytoplankton (*K*ᵣ). Western Pacific (4° N, 135° E).

regulated by the light and nutrient limitations. It is situated at the upper part of the thermocline. The stable position of this layer provides the formation of a kind of planktonic biocoenosis. The accumulation of animals migrating during the night to feed in this layer can be registered with a bioluminescent indicator (Fig. 3). The structure of the microbial population is found to be stable during the day (Fig. 4).

The fourth layer of increased bacterial activity is usually situated at a depth of 500–600 m, corresponding to the boundary between the surface and the intermedial water, where the temperature is 7–8°C. Several data, e.g. the position of the sound scattering layers (Kinzer, 1966), indicate the accumulation here of planktonic animals. Besides the layers of maximum microbial activity, there can also be found layers with very deep minima even inside the euphotic zone. The cause of the formation of these minima is far more difficult to explain. Their formation is probably connected with some peculiarities of the processes of vertical turbulence inside the thermocline layers.

Bacterial Production and Decomposition

The existence of layers of increased bacterial production and biomass is one of the most important conditions for the participation of planktonic bacteria in the trophical chain. The average size of microflora is too small to be filtered out by the filter feeders with a gain of energy. Another condition is therefore the aggregation of natural bacterioplankton. About one third of its cells are present in the aggregates larger than 4 μm which can be filtered out and consumed even by the coarse filtrators prevailing in the pelagic tropical waters (Sorokin, 1971). In the deep water layers below 800 m, the rates of bacterial production and decomposition decrease 100–200 times and the biomass of bacteria 20–30 times compared with the surface layers (Fig. 1). The *in situ* experiments show that bacterial metabolism is inhibited in deep water by the low temperature. Labelled organic matter (protein hydrolysate) was kept for a week at 4 000 m in a water bottle, closed at the same depth. During the exposure only about 0.3 % of the initial hydrolysate present at the concentration 0.1 mg/l was utilised by the natural microbial population (Fig. 5). When, afterwards, the same sample was kept at 30°C the organic matter had, however, been completely used up by the microflora after one day. This experiment provides evidence for the absence of a prevailing specific psychrophylic microflora in deep waters. The rate of the *in situ* destruction was equal to 0.1–0.3 mg O_2/m³/day. The stock of oxygen in them ought therefore to be sufficient for about 50 years.

The calculations on the rate of total microbial decomposition of organic matter in the Pacific Ocean were made on the basis of the curve of its vertical rate as measured in the tropical Pacific, taking the temperature scale in different regions (Table 2) into account. The value for the annual decomposition, recalculated for all oceans, was found to be about 8×10^{10} tons of carbon per year. This is 3 times more than the primary global oceanic production measured with the aid of the C^{14} method. This divergence can be accepted as a consequence of a serious underestimation of the primary production in the ocean,

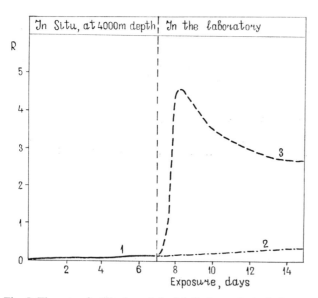

Fig. 5. The rate of utilisation of the labelled protein hydrolysate by bacterial population in a sample of sea water taken at 4 000 m depth in the Western Pacific Ocean and exposed with the C^{14}—hydrolysate in situ for 1 week (1), and subsequently in the laboratory at 2°C (2) and at 30°C (3). The initial concentration of the hydrolysate was 0.3 mg C/l and its initial radioactivity was 1.2×10^6 cpm/l; R denotes the radioactivity in the bacterioplankton expressed in 100 cpm/ml.

Table 2. *The calculation of annual destruction in the Pacific Ocean*

Latitude range	The average surface temperature	Daily destruction[a] in the sur-face layer mg O_2/m^3	Daily destruction in the layer 0–4 000 m g O_2/m^2	Daily destruction in the district 10^6 tons of O_2	The annual destrcution[b] 10^9 tons of C
60°–70° S	− 1.3	1.1	0.37	4.4	—
50°–60° S	5	2.2	0.66	7.3	—
40°–50° S	11.1	4.0	0.89	10.8	—
20°–40° S	20	9.5	1.88	50.1	—
20° S–20° N	26	16	3.05	194.0	—
20°–40° N	21	10	1.97	43.2	—
40°–60° N	7	3	0.71	12.1	—
Sum for the whole ocean	—	—	—	322	43

[a] Calculated taking $Q_{100} = 2.6$ (Sorokin, 1969). The daily destruction at $t° = 28°$ accepted 18 mg O_2/m^3/day.
[b] The average annual destruction will be about 0.18 mg O_2/l/year.

as measured with the C^{14} method. The calculations of the possible feeding rations for the total animal population prove this point, since these give values close to $8–10 \times 10^{10}$ tons of carbon per year (Sorokin, 1971).

The determinations made in different regions of the tropical Pacific show that the bacterial production and, moreover, the bacterial decomposition in the water column, exceeds the primary production as measured with C^{14} several times (Table 1). These data initiate the question about the sources of the excess of organic matter to cover this discrepancy. A hypothesis was developed according to which the thin surface layer of warm tropical waters occupying only about 1 % of the total volume of the ocean water serves as a pool, where the main part of the total stock of dissolved organic matter of the Ocean is destroyed by the microflora (Sorokin, 1970). About 95 % of this stock is preserved in the cold deep waters by the action of the low temperature strongly suppressing the destruction. This material is transported to the surface of the tropical regions during the upwelling of the deep waters. The stock of dissolved organic matter in the deep and intermedial waters is replenished by their formation in the regions of subpolar convergences, where the primary production is high, but the rate of destruction, being suppressed by low temperature, is low. This hypothesis explains the data on the relatively high content of labile organic matter in the deep waters as indicated by the estimations of the potential bacterial production and BOD, as well as by the direct estimations of the content of low molecular weight organic matter in deep waters (Menzel & Goering, 1966). The time of the advection of deep water from the Antarctic convergence to the tropical divergences including their upwelling to the surface, according to some new data (Chekotillo, 1965) could take around 5–10 years. So the global circulation of the vast masses of the oceanic waters have to be accompanied by the transport of the large masses of the dissolved organic matter, which on arriving at the layer of warm surface tropical waters is decomposed by microflora, utilising its energy for the biosynthesis. This concept of separate places for the creation of organic matter and its decomposition by microflora should, no doubt, help to understand different biogeochemical phenomena observed in the ocean.

Microbial Transport of Cobalt

A consequence of the predominance of microbial population in the processes of biosynthesis taking place in the tropical waters is the wide scale participation of bacterioplankton in the consumption of some of the elements from sea water and in their vertical transport to the bottom. This transport proceeds mostly in a state of faecal pellets excreted by zooplankton feeding on the bacterioplankton. For example, during the study of the biogeochemical mechanism of the formation of manganese nodules on the ocean floor, it was very difficult to explain the mechanism of the sedimentation of cobalt which is present in the nodules in considerable amounts. This metal does not form hydroxides. It is present in sea water in a stable ionic form and is scarcely adsorbed on the surface of particulated matter. But it was, however, found to sedimentate easily in biological systems containing bacteria and a filtering animal. It has been found that cobalt-57 is consumed by microflora in the synthesis of vitamin B12 whereupon these bacterial cells are filtered out and eaten

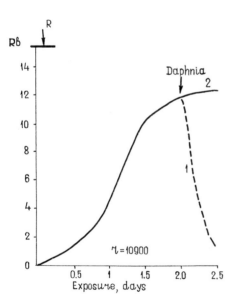

Fig. 6. Biological sedimentation of cobalt in water by inclusion in the food chain: bacteria–daphnia. A solution of $Co^{57}Cl_2$ and 30 mg/l glucose was added to the lake water. After two days of exposure this water was poured into two 0.5 l bottles. In one of them 100 species of Daphnia pulex were placed (1). The second bottle was left as a control (2). Rb is the radioactivity of cobalt-57 in bacterial cells in cpm/ml. R is the initial radioactivity of $Co^{57}Cl_2$ added in cpm/ml. r is the radioactivity of cobalt-57 in cpm in the bodies of Daphnia after the end of the experiment.

Table 3. *The calculation of the time of the complete utilisation of iron, manganese and cobalt in the ocean by their assimilation by phytoplankton and bacteria. P is the annual production of dry organic matter*

Element	Assimilation of the element (A) g/year				A (sum)	The supply of element in the Ocean[a] g	Time of complete utilisation years
	by phytoplankton ($P = 8 \times 10^{16}$ g)		by microbial population ($P = 1.6 \times 10^{16}$ g)				
	% of assimilation of element during biosynthesis	A	% of assimilation during biosynthesis	A			
Fe	0.44	3.52×10^{14}	0.025	4×10^{12}	3.56×10^{14}	1.4×10^{16}	40
Mn	0.044	3.52×10^{13}	0.0025	4×10^{11}	3.56×10^{13}	1.4×10^{15}	40
Co	0	0	0.02	3.2×10^{12}	3.2×10^{12}	7×10^{14}	220

[a] After Goldberg, 1961.

by the daphnia. The major part of the isotopic cobalt initially present in ionic form in the experimental vessel sedimented after 24 hours to the bottom with faecal pellets of the daphnia (Fig. 6). The same phenomenon was easily observed in an analogous experiment with oysters instead of daphnia (Sorokin, 1971). As was stated by Sokolova (1970), the bottom fauna in the oligotrophic regions of the Ocean, where the nodules are formed, consist mainly of filtering animals, most of them being attached to the surface of the nodules. Thus their pellets enriched with directly filtered out iron and manganese, and containing cobalt of bacterial origin, is excreted directly on the surface of the nodules, in this way promoting their growth. Using cobalt labelled with Co^{57} for the estimation of its consumption by bacterioplankton, and estimating the bacterial biosynthesis in the same sample with the aid of C^{14}, it was possible to measure the amount of cobalt per mg of bacterial organic matter produced. It was found to be about 0.005 %. The time for complete assimilation of cobalt in sea water through bacterial biosynthesis was estimated to be 200 years (Table 3).

Microbial Consumption of Phosphorus

The second example of relatively high activity of microflora in tropical waters concerns the phosphorus consumption by the planktonic community. When measuring the rate of consumption of labelled inorganic phosphate in light and dark bottles we usually found that the consumption in the dark bottles is equal to or greater than that in the light bottles. A higher consumption in light bottles was found only in those containing water from the depth of phytoplank-

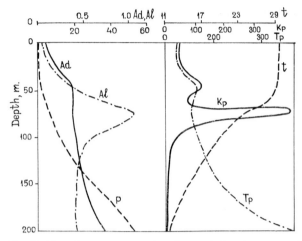

Fig. 7. Phosphorus consumption in a planktonic community of the euphotic zone in tropical waters (4° N, 135° E). *P* is the content of phosphate in water in μg P/l; *Al* and *Ad* are the consumption of phosphorus by organisms in the light and in the dark bottles, respectively, in μg P/l/day; T_p is the time for complete turnover of phosphate in hours; K_p is the relative distribution of phytoplankton in %; *t* is the temperature of the water.

ton accumulation (Fig. 7). These data indicate that the main amount of inorganic phosphate is consumed and kept by the bacterioplankton rather than by the phytoplankton. It is therefore probable that the time of turnover of phosphate in tropical waters even in the euphotic zone at a high temperature is very low, of the order of 100–200 hours. This competition of bacteria with phyto-

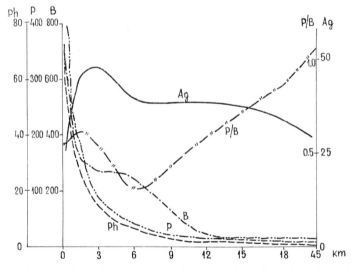

Fig. 8. The scale of changes of the wet biomass of bacterioplankton (*B*, mg/m³), its production (*P*, mg C/m³/day), primary production (*Ph*, mg C/m³/day) and the percent of aggregated bacteria (*Ag* %) in the NE direction from the lagoon of the inner reef close to Heron Island (Great Barrier Reef, Australia) to the open sea.

Table 4. *Characteristics of the total number (N), biomass (B), and production (P) of bacterial population in the upper layer of the bottom sediments of different types in the Pacific ocean. The data are given per cm³ wet silt*

Positions of stations and types of sediments	Depth m	N 10^6/cm³	B μg C/cm³	P μg C/cm³/d
Fanning atoll, coral sand	25	2 030	91.0	22.6
Slope opposite Tokyo bay, Japan, fine alevritic. gray silt.	2 725	196	9.4	1.3
Slope opposite Tahiti, aleuritic sandic. grey silt.	1 100	105	5.1	0.33
Equatorial region, 160° W, diatomic radiolaric. silt.	5 020	37	1.7	0.14
North Pacific 23° N, 170° E, deep sea red clay.	5 810	14	0.66	0.06
South Pacific, 20° S, 160° N, deep sea red clay.	5 330	7.1	0.34	0.003

plankton for the nutrients can be accepted as being one of the possible significant causes of the scarcity of tropical phytoplankton. Thus in tropical waters the planktonic microflora plays rather the role of consumers of nutrients than of producers through organic mineralisation (Johannes, 1964). The reproduction of mineral forms of the nutrients is more likely to be due to zooplankton.

Near-Shore Effects

The bacterial biomass and its metabolic activity decreases 10–20 times from the eutrophic shore waters of bays and lagoons to the surface oligotrophic pelagic tropical waters (Fig. 8). The biomass decreases from 60 to 2 mg C/m³, the rate of production from 40 to 2 mg C/m³/day and the rate of the microbial destruction from 0.3 to 0.02 mg O_2/1/day. The bacterial population of the bottom sediments of the ocean changes even more (Table 4): the biomass decreases 300 times and the production 1 000 times from the coral sediments of a shallow lagoon to the deep water red clays (Sorokin 1970a).

Vertical Distribution in Sediments

The analyses of the vertical distribution of microbial activity in the bottom sediments have shown that living microflora is present only in the upper 10–15 cm layer. Below this layer the sediment was found to be sterile. This was shown by several indicators of microbial activity as well as by plate counting (Fig. 9). It can therefore be concluded that the diagenesis of organic matter in the bottom sediments 20 cm below the bottom surface proceeds without the participation of bacteria. The same was shown to be true in the sediments of the Black Sea

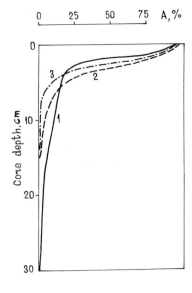

Fig. 9. The relative activity, *A*, of heterotrophic microflora, as estimated with the aid of labelled hydrolysate, in sediment columns in the Central Pacific: 1—slope of the Tutuila Island; 2—equatorial region (160° W); 3—Trade Wind zone (18° S, 164° W).

(Sorokin, 1964). The cause of the absence of living microorganisms in the deep layers of bottom sediments cannot be due to lack of utilisable organic matter. Special analyses of the potential bacterial production and BOD in the samples of sediments from a core depth of 2–3 m showed definitely that they contain utilisable organic matter in a quantity not much less than in the surface layers of the sediments (Sorokin, 1970 *a*). It can be supposed that inhibition of bacterial activity in columns of pelagic sediments can be related not only to the low temperature, stopping the utilisation of stable organic matter, but also to the absence of free oxygen. The latter situation can take place even at the high redox potential provided by the presence of metal hydroxides. In the columns of sediments enriched with labile organic matter the microbial metabolism can proceed through anaerobic oxidation-reduction, but in the poor sediments of the oligotrophic regions of the Ocean, the labile organic matter is scarce, and anaerobic metabolism based on stable organic matter is at low temperature energetically nonprofitable and therefore impossible.

Formation of Manganese Nodules

A definite enrichment of bottom microflora has been observed on the surface of manganese nodules. However, the microflora usually consisted of heterotrophic bacteria (Fig. 10). All attempts to find specific bacteria that oxidize manganese (Metallogenium) or iron (Galionella) were unsuccessful (Sokokin, 1971 *a*). Nevertheless, the presence of heterotrophic microflora only should perhaps accelerate the growth of the nodules. Bacteria oxidize the organic component of the organic-mineral complexes accumulating at the surface of the

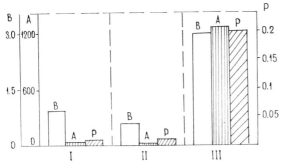

Fig. 10. The biomass (*B*, mg C/1), the production (*P*, mg C/l/day), and the activity (*A*, cpm/ cm³) of microflora in the surrounding silt (I), in scraped material from the bottom surface of a manganese nodule (II) and from the upper side of the nodule (III). Pacific Ocean (20° S, 162° E), depth 5 020 m.

nodules and thus promoting the formation and purification of metal oxides (Erlich, 1963). The oceanic manganese nodules are formed under conditions of extremely high redox potential ($+550$ mV), of extreme oligotrophy, and at very low concentrations of Mn^{2+} and Fe^{2+}. The rate of their growth can be measured in geological time-scale (1 cm per 10^5–10^6 years). All these conditions are quite different from those for the formation of lake manganese ore and nodules, which proceed by the participation of specific manganese and iron bacteria. Thus, the formation of oceanic nodules occurs most probably without the participation of specific bacteria. It proceeds through physical-chemical and biological processes of sedimentation such as adsorption, assimilation, co-sedimentation and oxidation of the ionic forms and hydroxides of the ore-forming metals at the solid surfaces of the nodule nuclei, and subsequently at the surface of the growing nodules. It is not a purely geological process (Gold-berg, 1961), and not a purely biological process (Kalinenko et al., 1962), but it is a good example of a biogeochemical process. Neither is it quite correct to say, on the basis of the participation of specific microflora, that the process of lake ore formation is purely biological. Indeed, during its formation an ap-preciable (if not major) part of the iron and manganese is oxidized by a purely chemical process through autocatalysis.

Chemical and Microbial Oxidation of Sulphide

In general we have to evaluate very carefully the role of microflora in the oxidation of those mineral compounds which are easily oxidized chemically. The oxidation of sulphides in the Black Sea can be taken as one example. For about 70 years microbiologists and hydrochemists have discussed the mechanism of hydrogen sulphide oxidation in this basin—is it chemical or microbiological? Studies of this process with the aid of labelled sulphide

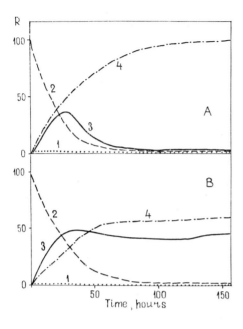

Fig. 11. The dynamics of the ratio of the values of radioactivity of sulphur compounds (R) during oxidation of labelled sulphide in a water sample from the upper part of the hydrogen sulphide zone of the Black Sea (depth 220 m). A—water + bubble of air; B—same + antiseptic (chloroform). $1-S°$, $2-S^{2-}$, $3-S_2O_3^{2-}$, $4-SO_4^{2-}$.

(See Fig. 11) have shown, however, that this process proceeds through two stages. The first stage is purely a chemical oxidation of the sulphide to sulphate and thiosulphate. The second stage is the oxidation of thiosulphate by Thiobacilli (Sorokin, 1971*b*). The first stage of sulphide oxidation proceeds chemically even in cultures of Thiobacilli (Sorokin, 1970*b*). Obviously they can not compete with the first order chemical reaction of sulphide oxidation. So we have here a complex biogeochemical process. It is very important to take this mechanism of sulphide oxidation into account when evaluating in the basin the energy efficiency of chemosynthesis of sulphide oxidation and the absolute rate of sulphide oxidation (Table 5). By the oxidation a considerable part of sulphide sulphur is converted into thiosulphate. Since this is difficult to analyse it has usually been ignored. We have hydrolysed the thiosulphate with silver ions for the determination of the absolute rate of sulphide oxidation in the Black Sea (Sorokin, 1971*b*). We found the rate to be 500 mg $S^{2-}/m^2/day$. The corresponding value for chemosynthesis was found to be 100 mg C/m^3 and its energy efficiency to be 15 %. The value of chemosynthesis in the open sea was often approximately the same as the production of phytoplankton. Here, as in the tropical ocean, it is necessary to accept the existence of a side—inflow of energy—in this case in the state of sulphides. These can be transported from the slope regions of intensive sulphate reduction (Sorokin, 1964). Thus the transport of energy proceeds in the state of sulphide from the place of its generation by sulphate reduction to the place of its oxidation by Thiobacilli. We have here

Table 5. *The rate of H_2S oxidation and the efficiency of chemosynthesis in the water column at the deep sea station N 1. Exposure time 27 h. at 5–7°C*

Depth m	H_2S mg S^{2-}/l	O_2 mg/l	Eh mV	R (total sulphur)	r^a (SO_4+ $\frac{1}{2}S_2O_3$)	$\dfrac{r}{R}$ %	Rate of oxidation of S^{2-} to S^{6+} μg S/l per day	Chemo-syn-thesis μg C/l per day	Effici-ency of chemo-syn-thesis %
135	0.01	0.17	0	4 870	1 755	36.0	3.2	0.2	12
145	0.05	0.12	− 10	5 020	1 310	26.3	10.3	2.1	36
155	0.15	0.08	− 15	3 220	695	21.6	25.4	4.4	33
170	0.32	0.03	− 32	5 070	318	6.3	10.2	2.1	38
210	0.86	0	− 100	5 120	158	3.1	2.3	0.3	25
240	1.36	0	− 120	3 100	110	2.8	0	0.02	—
350	2.30	0	− 148	5 740	161	2.8	0	0	—
Begin-ning of experi-ment	—	—	—	3 170	88	2.8	0	—	—

^{a} $\frac{1}{2}$ S_2O_3 is the sulphate part of thiosulphate molecule.

another example of the important role that microflora play in the energy inter-connection between regions of generation and regions of utilisation of chemi-cally bound energy.

References

Butkevich, W. S. (in Russian) Selected works, Ac. Su. USSR, Moscow 1958.

Chekotillo, K. A. (in Russian). The time of the vertical transport of water masses in the ocean. "Oceanologial Studies", Moscow *13*, 37 (1965).

Dugdale, R. C. & Goering, J. J., High nitrogen fixation rates in the Sargasso and Arabian seas. Limnol. Oceanogr. *9*, 504 (1964).

Erlich, H. C., Bacteriology of manganese nodules. Appl. Microbiol., *11*, 15 (1963).

Goldberg, E. D., Marine Geochemistry, J. Geol. *62*, 249 (1961).

Holm-Hansen, C. & Booth, C. R., The measurement of adenosine triphosphate in the oceans and its ecological importance. Limnol. Oceanogr. *11*, 548 (1966).

Issatchenko, B. L. (in Russian). Selected works. Ac. Aci. USSR, Moscow 1951.

Johannes, R. E., Uptake and release of dissolved organic phosphorus by representa-tives of a coastal marine ecosystem. Limnol. Oceanogr. *9*, 224 (1964).

Kalinenko, V. O., Belocopytora, O. V. & Nikolaeva, G. G. (in Russian). Formation of iron-manganese nodules. Oceanologia, *2*, 1050 (1962).

Kinzer, H., The organisms from the sound-scattering layers in the waters with the high oxygen deficit. Abstr. II. Intern. Oceanogr. Congr., Moscow 1966.

Kuznetsov, S. I., Die Rolle der Microorganismen in Stoffkreislauf der Seen. Berlin 1959.

Menzel, D. & Goering, J. J., The distribution of organic detritus in the ocean. Limnol. Oceanogr. *11*, 333 (1966).

Parsons, T. R. & Strickland, J., On the production of particulate organic carbon by heterotrophic processes in sea water. Deep-Sea Res. *8*, 211 (1962).

Pomeroy, L. R., Residence time of dissolved phosphate in natural waters. Nature *131*, No. 3115 (1960).

Rasumov, A. S. (in Russian). Methods of microbiological studies of water. Ed. by the Inst. WODGEO, Moscow 1947.

Romanenko, W. I. (in Russian). Heterotrophic CO_2 assimilation by aquatic microflora. Microbiologia *33*, 379 (1964).

Romanenko, W. I. (in Russian). The ratio between the oxygen consumption and CO_2 uptake by the heterotrophic bacteria during their growth in the peptone media. Microbiologia, *34*, 397 (1965).

Sokolova, M. N. (in Russian). The weight Characteristics of meiobenthos from different deep sea trophical regions of the Pacific Ocean. Oceanologia *10*, 348 (1970).

Sorokin, Yu. I. Primary production and bacterial activity in the Black Sea. J. du Conseil. Expl. Mer *29*, 41 (1964).

Sorokin, Yu. I. On the trophic role of chemosynthesis and bacterial biosynthesis in water bodies. Mem. Ital. Ist. Idrobiol. *18* (suppl.), 187 (1965).

Sorokin Yu. I. (in Russian). On quantitative evaluation of the role of bacterioplankton in carbon cycle in tropical oceanic waters. Doklady Acad. Nauk SSSr, *193*, 923 (1970).

Sorokin, Yu. I. (in Russian). Characteristics of the number, activity and production of bacteria in bottom sediments of the central Pacific. Oceanologia, *10*, 1055 (1970a).

Sorokin Yu. I. Interrelation between sulphur and carbon turnover in meromictic lakes. Arch. hydrobiol. *66*, 391 (1970b).

Sorokin, Yu. I. On the role of bacteria in the productivity of trophical oceanic waters Int. Rev. Gesamten Hydrobiol. *56*, 1 (1971).

Sorokin, Yu. I. (in Russian). On the microflora of manganese nodules from the ocean floor. Microbiologia *40*, 563 (1971a).

Sorokin, Yu. I. (in Russian). Experimental data on the oxidation rate of hydrogen sulphide in the Black Sea. Oceanologia *11*, 423 (1971b).

On the Age of Stable Organic Matter—
Aquatic Humus in Oceanic Waters

By Boris Skopintsev

Institute of Fresh Water Biology of the USSR Academy of Sciences, Borok, Yaroslavl, USSR (communicated by Yuri Sorokin)

According to the radio carbon dating of dissolved organic matter from the deep (1 900 m) waters of the North-East Pacific Ocean, its mean age is 3 400 years (Williams, 1969, 1970), whereas the carbon in the inorganic matter is not as old—2 194 and 1 480 years.

On the basis of this value and assuming the total content of dissolved organic carbon in the bulk of the oceans at a depth of 300–3 800 m to be 6.3×10^{17} g C (mean concentration 0.5 mg C/l), the amount of organic carbon entering the ocean can be calculated.

Under the steady state conditions $6.3 \times 10^{17}/3\,400 = 1.85 \times 10^{14}$ g C of organic matter arrive annually in the deep oceanic waters. Expressed as a percentage of the organic carbon produced biologically by plankton in the ocean each year $[100 \text{ g C/m}^2 \times 3.6 \times 10^{14} \text{ m}^2 = 3.6 \times 10^{16} \text{ g C/y}]$ this is $\dfrac{1.85 \times 10^{14} \text{ g C}}{3.6 \times 10^{16} \text{ g C}} \times 100 = 0.5\,\%$.

According to my calculations (Skopintsev 1964a, 1966a, 1967), the residence time or the age of the organic carbon in the oceanic waters coincides with the value given by Williams. The results of experiments on the decomposition of mixed dead plankton (Skopintsev 1947, 1964b) served as a basis for this calculation. From the decrease in the amounts of organic C, N and P and from the increase in the amounts of mineral compounds of N and P, the mineralization of the organic matter after a period of 60 days in darkness, at an average temperature of 14°C, under aerobic and anaerobic conditions, was shown to be about 70 and 60 %, respectively, of the initial concentration. After five years the mineralization had reached 80 %.

Thus, one can assume that about 80 % of the dead residues of plankton and bacteria consists of easily assimilated organic compounds and the remainder, 20 %, of newly formed organic matter in the form of very complex compounds, characterized by a relatively high biological stability. This is the aquatic humus, about 1/4 existing in dissolved form, and 3/4 in suspended form (Skopintsev 1948, 1950, 1960). In natural conditions where zooplankton is present in the water, the assimilation of the organic matter produced biologically by phytoplankton is higher.

Khailov (1971), referring to the work of Odum & De La Cruz (1965) and of Sorokin (1965), points out that "according to some publications, 95 % of the organic matter are utilized by the secondary producents in form of detritus from a link of the primary organic production".

The amount of organic carbon reaching the bottom of the Oceans yearly in the form of suspended particles as a percentage of the annual production of phytoplankton is according to Trask (1939) 5 %, to Datsko (1959) 4 %, to Bogdanov et al. (1971) from 1 to 12 %. On an average, it will be about 5 %.

I assume that the mean production of phytoplankton in the ocean (not taking the metabolites excreted by phytoplankton into account) is 120 g C/m^2 per year. For the whole ocean it should be around 3.8×10^{16} g C/year.

If we accept that the annual income of the aquatic humus of planktonic origin is 3 % of the annual production, then for the whole volume of the ocean it will be 11.5×10^{14} g C/year. The annual income of the aquatic humus of terrigenic origin is 5 g C/m$^3 \times (3.6 \times 10^{13}) = 1.8 \times 10^{14}$ g C/year. The income of organic matter to the ocean from atmospheric waters is small. The total annual income of aquatic humus to the ocean is thus 13.3×10^{14} g C/year.

Assuming an average concentration of organic carbon in the oceanic waters of 1.5 g C/m^3 (alt. 1.0 g C/m^3) (Skopintsev et al., 1966b) the total content (in a volume of 1.3×10^{18} m^3) is 2×10^{18} g (alt. 1.3×10^{18} g). The residence time will then be:

$$\frac{2 \times 10^{18}\,g}{1.33 \times 10^{15}\,g/yr.} \approx 1\,500\,yr. \left(alt.\ \frac{1.33 \times 10^{15}\,g/yr.}{1.3 \times 10^{18}\,g/yr.} \approx 1\,000\,yr.\right)$$

As can be seen, the results obtained by these calculations of the residence time of the aquatic humus in the ocean are relatively close to those of Williams (1969, 1970). This would suggest that the assumptions made here are acceptable.

References

Bogdanov, J. A., Lisitzin, A. P. & Romankevitch, E. A., Organic Matter of Suspended Particles and Bottom Sediments of the Seas and Oceans. In "Organic Matter of Recent and Fossil Sediments". Publishing House "Nauka", Moscow (1971).

Datsko, V. G., The Organic Matter in the Water of the Southern Seas of the USSR. Publishing House, Akad. Nauk, USSR, Moscow (1959).

Khailov, K. M., Ecological Metabolism in the Sea. Publishing House "Naukova Dumka", Kiev (1971).

Odum, E. P. & De La Cruz, A. A., AJBS Bulletin No. 13, 3 (1965).

Skopintsev, B. A., Akad. Nauk, USSR, Doklady, *58*, No. 8 (1947).

Skopintsev, B. A., Trudy of the State Oceanographic Institute, No. 10 (1948).

Skopintsev, B. A., Trudy of the State Oceanographic Institute No. 17 (1950).

Skopintsev, B. A., Trudy of the Marine Hydrophysical Inst. Academy of Sciences of USSR, *19* (1960).

Skopintsev, B. A., Results of the Investigations under the Program of the International Geophysical Year. The Oceanological Investigations, No. 13 (1964a).

Skopintsev, B. A., Ljubimova, E. M. & Timofeeva, S. N., Scientific Papers from Institute of Chemical Technology, Prague, Technology of Water *8*, 1 (1964b).

Skopintsev, B. A., Oceanologia *6*, No. 3 (1966a).

Skopintsev, B. A., Timofeeva, S. N. & Vershinina, O. A., Oceanologia *6*, No. 2 (1966b).

Skopintsev, B. A., Akad. Nauk, USSR, Doklady *174*, No. 6 (1967).

Sorokin, Yu. I., In Proceed. J. B. P. Symp. on Primary Production in Aquat. Environ., Pallanza Mem. Inst., Ital. Idrobiol. *18* (suppl.), p. 187 (1965).

Trask, P., Sympos. Recent Marine Sediments USA, p. 428 (1939).

Williams, P. M., Oeschger, H. & Kinnery P., Nature *224*, No. 5216 (1969)

Williams, P. M., Research of the Marine Food Chain. Inst. of Marine Resources La Jolla, USA (1970).

Factors Controlling Marine Ecosystems

By John H. Steele

The differences between terrestrial and marine food chains are striking and are well documented in terms of biomass and energy flow. One major feature is that usually less than 10 % of plant material on land is eaten while living and nearly all enters the decomposer cycle. For this reason vegetation normally dominates the biomass. In the sea probably 90 %, or more, of the plant production is eaten by herbivorous zooplankton and the fall-out of organic matter to the sea below the euphotic zone is largely faecal material. In consequence the phytoplankton biomass is of the same order of magnitude as the herbivores. These very different patterns of energy flow have obvious consequences for the passage of possible pollutants through the food chains, particularly the accumulation of persistent toxins at higher trophic levels in the marine system. These factors can affect us directly through food taken from the sea, or may be visible to us through their consequences for predatory birds. On the other hand, effects of toxins within food chains may be less apparent and less easy to separate from natural fluctuations. Significant changes are most likely to arise when the organisms affected have a major role in controlling other groups or trophic levels. Thus as well as measuring levels of toxin concentrations in organisms, we need to assess the likely consequences for the whole system of metabolic or behavioural alterations at a particular trophic level.

Although we do not know how extensively the generalisation holds, for terrestrial systems we usually assume that a significant part of the limitation on direct grazing of vegetation is the result of predatory control of the herbivores. Defoliation is the result of a breakdown of this control and, again, there is the assumption that the herbivores have no pattern of behaviour which, as a group, will prevent them grazing the plant populations beyond the limits of recovery. These effects on vegetation can result from the introduction of exotic species, from inappropriate conservation measures, or from the use of pesticides which can thereby become "addictive" (MIT, 1970). Thus our concern with the reduction in numbers, or the complete disappearance, of species of predators arises not merely from their loss *per se* but also from the probability that this will upset the rest of the system.

In looking at the open sea, the question I wish to consider is whether we can assume that the same general pattern operates. One major difference is that the phytoplankton are eaten almost as soon as they are produced, so that the level of plant matter is always very low. In fact, a main technical problem is to demonstrate experimentally that the herbivorous zooplankton can feed at a high enough rate to satisfy their needs for metabolism, growth and reproduction. If the numbers of zooplankton are kept under control predominantly by their predators then this control, operating close to the margin of starvation for the herbivores and extinction of the plants, would need to be very much more sensitive than its terrestrial counterpart. It seems difficult to accept this and thus I think we are forced to consider the possibility that much of this control is exercised by the zooplankton themselves. This suggestion is neither very acceptable, nor very helpful, unless it can be supported by evidence of the functional responses of individual organisms which could produce the required distributions at different trophic levels. Such responses which could have an effect at the population level are likely to arise from feeding behaviour, either directly through growth or less directly through the effect of food intake on reproductive potential or survival of very young stages.

For terrestrial animals Holling (1965) has proposed two general patterns of feeding response which he terms "invertebrate" and "vertebrate", Fig. 1. The experiments on which these conclusions were based had one significant difference; for the invertebrate there was no choice of food species whereas for the vertebrate a choice was available and the "vertebrate response" was that to the preferred food. There is evidence from populations of insectivorous birds (Tinbergen, 1960; Gibb, 1966) that this latter response occurs under natural conditions. As Holling, Tinbergen and Lack (1966) have pointed out this response will tend to induce stability in the prey population, as well as in the predator. The simple "invertebrate" response of Fig. 1 is basically unstable since, for example, without some density-dependent control the predator can graze the prey to extinction. The assumptions underlying the concept of carnivore control on land are, thus, that carnivores show the type of threshold response of Fig. 1 but herbivores as a group have the simple type of response.

In aquatic systems where small crustacea are the dominant herbivores, the most likely assumption based on terrestrial experience, is that such organisms would have a very simple response to changes in concentration of their food supply. Holling quotes experiments with *Artemia* (Reeve, 1963) in support of this conclusion. Reeve's experiments, however, and others which have given similar results, used a single species of phytoplankton as food. Evidence for a different conclusion has been provided by experiments on the feeding of marine copepods with natural, mixed species, food (Adams & Steele, 1966; Parsons et al., 1969). The results of Parsons et al., in particular, gave conclusive proof of a food threshold below which the copepods did not feed. Recently, laboratory experiments with two sizes of food showed that copepods could display the same type of response to a preferred size of food as that proposed by Holling

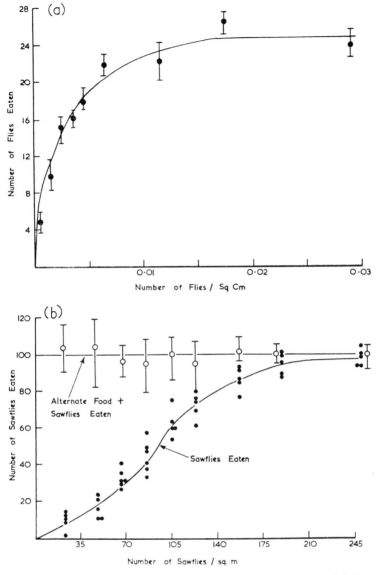

Fig. 1. (*a*) Functional response of individual mantids to density of adult female houseflies. (*b*) Effect of prey density on number of prey eaten by a deermouse (from Holling, 1965).

for a carnivorous vertebrate (Richman & Rogers, 1969). The copepods, *Calanus* sp., were fed on a culture of a diatom which tended to divide synchronously so that just before division the number of paired cells was much higher than at other times. The feeding rate of the copepod on the paired cells was very much higher than the rate on the smaller single cells (Fig. 2). These results taken together suggest that, to a first approximation, a threshold effect is the natural response of zooplankton to variations in food concentration but that, in detail,

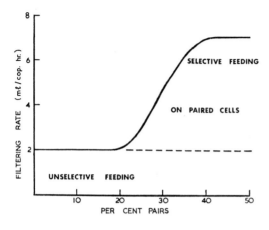

Fig. 2. Filtering rates of *Calanus* at varying percentages of paired *Ditylum* cells (from Richman & Rogers, 1969).

this response depends on the existence of some choice of food organisms among the phytoplankton.

To study the consequences of this response, a computer simulation model has been developed which includes the effect of nutrient concentration on plant

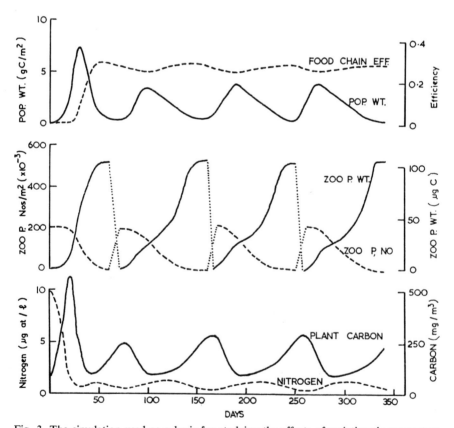

Fig. 3. The simulation used as a basis for studying the effects of variations in parameters.

growth rate, a grazing rate by the zooplankton dependent on a threshold, and arbitrarily defined predation patterns on the zooplankton. This model will be described in detail elsewhere but a brief summary is given as an Appendix. Some of the conclusions relevant to this discussion will be mentioned here. The model gives realistic average levels of the various parameters so long as the zooplankton feeding threshold is not zero. It has been used to simulate conditions after the start of the spring phytoplankton outburst in the northern North Sea. The cycling of the parameters, Fig. 3, is the result of time-lag effects when the model is run with only one cohort at any time. When the threshold is set at zero the model is very sensitive to variations in other parameters, unless the predation on the zooplankton is at such a high level that the herbivore population is extremely low and the phytoplankton unrealistically high. This is illustrated by the difference between a high and a very high predation rate, where the former is still insufficient to prevent a collapse of both plant and herbivore populations, Fig. 4. In other words, for stability with no herbivore feeding threshold, the model has to resemble a terrestrial ecosystem.

Three other deductions from the model need to be mentioned here. (1) Very large changes in the relation of plant growth rate to nutrient concentration have relatively little effect on the steady state levels of the plant or animal populations. (2) With the control exerted on the system by the threshold herbivore response, predation on the herbivores does not need to be severe. In fact the most realistic picture emerges when predation is mainly on the older copepodite stages, that is just before and during the adult phase. This has some justification from data on natural populations (Cushing & Tungate, 1963; Parsons et al., 1969) and underlines the difference between marine and terrestrial systems (3) However, one major weakness of the model is that, to accommodate the very large fluctuations that could occur in the physical environment, some restriction to prevent overproduction of copepod nauplii is required since this can still depress plant population growth rate excessively. This problem is not nearly so great as with fish populations but it is difficult to provide satisfactory evidence to account for such a density dependent response. This, however, merely accentuates the sensitivity of marine ecosystems to details of zooplankton behaviour.

In summary I am suggesting that if we wish to examine the structure of ecosystems as a guide to the possible ways in which we may alter them by our activities, then the picture of reality which we use for the open seas must be different from that we use on land. As an extreme simplification, on land the critical control appears to lie within the carnivore-herbivore web, whereas in the sea it appears to operate at the herbivore-plant level. The main problem is to show how such differences depend on behaviour patterns of individual organisms and I have proposed that there are results to support these hypotheses.

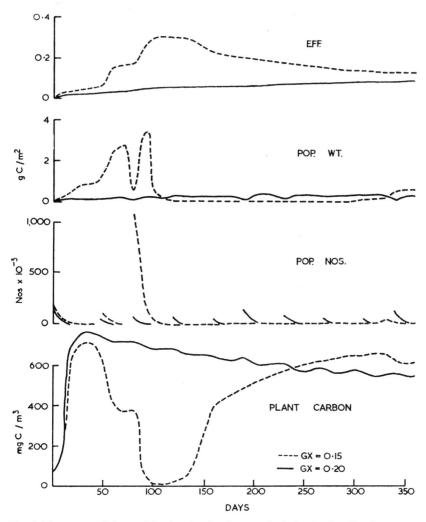

Fig. 4. The output of the model using the simple type of relation to describe the response of each trophic level, showing the need for a very high predation rate (GX) to prevent extinction of the herbivores.

How would such hypotheses affect our attitudes to man's intervention in marine food chains?

We are able to interfere directly with the plant, herbivore or carnivore communities on land. We have learnt to understand some, but not all, of the consequences of such intervention. In particular, when we remove other carnivores to leave ourselves as the sole predators on certain herbivores then we must manage these grazing stocks very carefully. Often we appear unable to be as successful as a natural system and this is a reflection of the subtlety of control which predator populations are presumed to excercise. In the sea, until recently, the only significant intervention has been at the predator level, by commercial

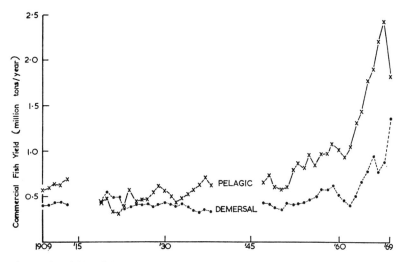

Fig. 5. The yields of fish which feed mainly in the water (pelagic) and those which feed on the bottom (demersal) of the North Sea.

fishing. The idea that certain regions are overfished is commonplace. The main evidence has been provided for certain demersal species in the North Sea (Beverton & Holt, 1957). Yet the total yield of demersal fish from the North Sea remained remarkably constant until 1960 and has increased significantly since then, Fig. 5. Since the demersal fish rely predominantly on the benthic fauna for their food and these, in turn, depend on the fall-out of organic debris, they do not affect the production cycle directly. The alterations in fish population structure by increasingly heavy fishing do not appear to have altered the total energy flow within this benthic part of the food web. The ultimate limitation is the fall-out of debris but a major ecological problem in the energy regime within the benthic system concerns the role of bacteria. In the North Sea the relatively large yield of demersal fish implies that, if bacteria play a relatively major role in transforming the organic debris that falls to the bottom, then they must do this very efficiently. Until this aspect is clarified the mechanisms of transport of toxins into this part of the food chain cannot really be described.

For pelagic fish species the evidence for overfishing is less adequate. The disappearance of the Pacific sardine has been attributed to overfishing but could be due to natural changes in the community structure. For a similar change in the English Channel where herring were replaced by pilchards (Cushing, 1961) there is no evidence that the change can be attributed to the effects of fishing. In both cases, although there were other changes in the plankton, there is no suggestion that the cycles of energy flow at the plant-herbivore levels were significantly altered by the changes in the fish populations. In the Antarctic the virtual elimination of the whales which feed on the herbivorous krill, do not appear to have caused any massive imbalance in the system. The most recent event has been the very marked increase in pelagic yield from the North Sea, Fig. 5. This has reached a level where there are doubts if it can be sustained, and fears that the recruitment to the herring stocks could be affected. International legislation to decrease the fishing effort on the North Sea herring stocks has been introduced (ICES, 1970). Yet there are no very obvious effects on the plankton. Over the years 1949–69 the results of the Plankton Recorder Survey have shown a decline in certain plankton species but similar decreases were also noted in the North Atlantic (Glover et al., 1970). There are other predators besides commercially fished species and changes in their abundance will influence the effects of heavy fishing.

It is difficult to assess the role of fishing quantitatively in terms of alteration in predation on plankton or on detritus feeding benthos but this relatively uncontrolled activity by man appears to have had little effect on the rest of the system. This would tend to confirm the concept that a significant part of the control of the system depends on the feeding and reproductive responses of the herbivores. Obviously there are limits to the intensity of fishing effort but these limits probably depend on the consequences of a decrease in the reproductive potential of a fish stock. Further, although there are problems about the large flow of energy to the fish populations, the relatively poor relation between growth rate of fish and their stock size that has been found for a fairly large range in stock size may be because the energy flow is controlled more by the herbivores than by their predators.

If fishing appears to have relatively little effect on the rest of the marine food web, one more recent consequence of human activity, eutrophication, has caused considerable alteration in aquatic systems. This has been most obvious in large freshwater lakes, especially Lake Erie, where the system is altered at all trophic levels (Beeton, 1969). In the Baltic the consequences are now becoming increasingly apparent (Fonselius, 1970). Other evidence for the effects of changes in nutrients are more tenous. Cushing (1961) and others noted a change in phosphate concentration in the English Channel at the time when the switch from herring to pilchard occurred. It has also been suggested that recent dinoflagellate blooms which may have caused paralytic shellfish poisoning along the British coast could be due to nutrient enrichment. Red tides in other areas are nautral occurrences but they illustrate the types of disturbance that may occur. A comparison has been made between upwelling and artificial eutrophication (Saunders, 1969) in terms of the existence of anaerobic water near the bottom. However the high yields of specialised herbivores such as anchovy suggest that a large part of the plant production is utilised (Ryther, 1970). In the model described here, if the rate of nutrient input to the euphotic zone is increased then there is an increasing productivity at all levels but no drastic alteration in balance. However, the implicit assumption in the model is that the increased plant production will be of species, or groups of species, which will still stimulate the type of feeding behaviour used in the model. One of the usual consequences of experimental nutrient enrichment is to promote growth of species which were almost undetectable beforehand. Further, the dominant species are usually fewer in number and, often, one species forms nearly all the biomass. It is quite possible that these sort of changes could upset zooplankton feeding behaviour and in the extreme case where there is only one plant species, feeding behaviour could follow the simple pattern where there is no threshold. If this happened then, as the model suggests, the system might tend to a very rich flora without a comparable herbivore population. This is often found in eutrophic water masses. The conclusion would be that this is not solely because of the nutrient enrichment but partly because of a breakdown in feeding patterns.

This hypothesis proposes that the alteration in species composition is responsible for the imbalance. This alteration is towards a lower "diversity" and so, superficially, would support the idea that the low diversity often associated with "polluted" conditions is the explanation for the alteration in structure of such systems. This connexion is only possible, however, if one predicates the changes in behaviour of the type outlined above.

This discussion of the effects of fishing and of eutrophication is intended as a background to a more general consideration of the ways we may alter the food webs in a manner deleterious to ourselves. We are concerned with two quite different types of results; those where the breakdown of a significantly large part of the marine structure decreases the advantage we can get from the sea; and those which affect us, either through our food supply or our amenity, without really altering the marine environment itself. Eutrophication is a potential example of the former; at present overfishing is still the most obvious way by which we alter our marine resources.

The question that is raised is whether those contaminants of marine systems which show "biological amplification", such as DDT and organic mercury, will cause any danger to the system itself or only to the top predators such as sea birds, marine mammals or man. Since there is considerable pressure to ensure that these organisms do not suffer ill effects, the first, simplest and most extreme hypothesis is to assume that the rest of the system will be relatively unaffected. In certain cases, such as the sea bird kill on the west of Britain in 1969 (Anon, 1971), it is possible that the effects of toxins may act as an extra factor in addition to natural stresses imposed by unusual environmental conditions and so tip the scale between life and death.

For fish at a lower trophic level, the effects of such contaminants are, *a priori*, likely to be less, unless the fish are more vulnerable to them. However, the synergistic effect of such toxins combined with heavy and sustained exploitation of the commercial species might have more serious effects on recruitment than the consequences of the occasional natural catastrophe. Even so, if one accepts the hypothesis that the most critical component is the phyto-zooplankton link, large changes in the fisheries do not necessarily upset the basic structure of marine ecosystems. On the other hand, this assumption requires that plants and herbivores are not very much more sensitive to low body burdens of these toxins than predators at higher trophic levels. This appears to be borne out for phytoplankton (Menzel et al., 1970) where significant effects of DDT on oceanic species occur only at concentrations above saturation, approx. 1 ppb. For zooplankton, however, Menzel et al. (reported in MIT, 1970) has given evidence that the offspring of copepods exposed to concentrations of .01 ppb DDT do not reach maturity. Although this concentration may still be well above that in the open sea it suggests that general effects at the zooplankton level cannot be ignored.

It is curious, since it is a reversal of the situation on land, that an increase in primary production should be the main method of altering aquatic systems. In Lake Erie this has apparently produced an alteration in the species composition at all trophic levels. It is more difficult to think of growth promoting effects which could act directly on the phytoplankton in the open sea. Even eutrophication is likely to be a problem only in coastal or semi-enclosed areas near large industrial and populated centres. If other substances caused a moderate decrease in rate of plant production for a given rate of nutrient supply, the model described here suggests that this could be accommodated by relatively small shifts to a new balance of nutrient concentration, plant growth rate and herbivore grazing. Again, this depends on the continued existence of appropriate herbivore feeding patterns acting as a control on the plants but, *a priori*, these patterns are less likely to be affected by a decrease in abundance of one or two plant species than by a marked increase in previously minor components which is the usual consequence of enrichment. In either case it is the response of the herbivores which is most important.

In summary, the general views on control of terrestrial ecosystems do not appear adequate as a basis for considering effects on marine systems. Under normal conditions in the sea nearly all the energy produced by phytoplankton passes through the zooplankton before it enters higher trophic levels either by grazing on the zooplankton or by transferring the organic matter to the bottom, or deeper water, as faeces. The feeding patterns of copepods are probably a critical factor in maintaining this close control. The rate of predation by carnivores may be determined more by efficiency in energy conversion than as a general controlling factor and so, although large changes would obviously alter the system, smaller disturbances are more likely to affect us through our commercial harvest of certain of these predators.

Obviously it is desirable to investigate all possible effects at all trophic levels. However, there is often a need to restrict work, or even to speculate on possible consequences with only limited information. In terms of effects on man, the heavily exploited fish species are of most concern not merely because of direct toxic intake by us, but because our exploitation already imposes a considerable stress on the fish populations. In terms of effects within the system itself, the herbivorous copepods seem most likely to be the critical component. A further problem is the fate of their faecal material. Approximately 30 % of the plant material produced reaches the bottom mainly as faecal material in shelf areas, or deeper water in the open ocean. We do not know the exact way in which this is "processed", including the quantitative role of bacteria, before it turns up in macro-fauna. Yet these transformations are crucial for our understanding of the fall-out of toxins in coastal areas before they reach open seas, for the retention times in the bottom of these areas, and for their eventual appearance in demersal fish which are one of the main products we consume directly.

References

Adams, J. A. & Steele, J. H., Shipboard experiments on the feeding of Calanus finmarchicus (Gunnerus), in Some contemporary studies in marine science (ed. H. Barnes) George Allen & Unwin Ltd., London 1966.

Anon., The sea bird wreck in the Irish Sea, Autumn 1969. The Nat. Env. Res., Council Pub. Ser. C., No. 4, 1971.

Beeton, A. M., Eutrophication, Nat. Acad. Sci., Washington, 150 (1969).

Beverton, R. J. H. & Holt, S. J., Fish. Invest. Lond. Ser. 2, *19*, 1957.

Cushing, D. H., J. mar. biol. Ass. U.K., *41*, 799 (1961).

Cushing, D. H. & Tungate, D. S., J. mar. biol. Ass. U.K., *43*, 327 (1963).

Fonselius, S. H., Tellus, *22*, 533 (1970).

Gibb, J. A., J. Anim. Ecol., *35*, 43 (1966).

Glover, R. S., Robinson, G. A. & Colebrook, J. M., FAO Tech. Conf. on Mar. Poll., FIR, MP/70/E-55 (1970).

Holling, C. S., Mem. ent. Soc. Can., *45*, 5 (1965).

ICES, Liaison Committee Report, Int. Council Explor. Mer Coop. Res. Rept. Ser. B, 1970, 54 p (1970).

Lack, D., Population studies of birds. Oxford Univ. Press, London 1966.

M. I. T., Man's impact on the global environment. M. I. T. Press, Cambridge Mass 1970.

Menzel, D. W., Anderson, J. & Randtke, A., Science, *167*, 1724 (1970).

Parsons, T. R., Le Brasseur, R. J., Fulton, J. D. & Kennedy, O. D., J. exp. mar. Biol. Ecol., *3*, 39 (1969).

Reeve, M. R., J. exp. Biol., *40*, 195 (1963).

Richman, S. & Rogers, J. N., Limnol. Oceanogr., *14*, 701 (1969).

Ryther, J. H., Science, *166*, 72 (1970).

Saunders, H. L., Brookhaven Symp. in Biol. *22*, 71 (1969).

Tinbergen, L., Archs. Neerl. Zool., *13*, 265 (1960).

Appendix

The simulation is supposed to start at the onset of the thermocline in an area like the northern North Sea. There is a rate of exchange, V, between the upper, euphotic, layer with a nutrient concentration, R, and the deep water where the concentration is RO. At the same time plants are lost by mixing downwards, assuming that the deep water plant concentration is negligible. The limiting nutrient is taken to be nitrogen and all organic matter is assumed to have the same composition so that nutrient uptake by plants and excretion by animals can be considered in terms of a carbon equivalent and then carbon is used throughout as the unit of measurement. A Michaelis-Menten type of relation is used to describe rate of nutrient uptake by plants as a function of nutrient concentration, i.e. as

$$ARP/(B+R) \tag{1}$$

where P=plant carbon; A & B define the shape of the curve. In practice A & B can be varied considerably without altering the general conclusions.

Zooplankton grazing is assumed to depend on plant concentration, i.e. as

$$C(P-P1)/(D+P) \tag{2}$$

where C and D define the curve and $P1$ is the threshold at which feeding ceases. 70% of food eaten is assumed to be assimilated. The feeding rate of an individual copepod is taken to be proportional to $W^{0.7}$ where W is the carbon content. One component of respiration, F, is also assumed to be proportional to $W^{0.7}$ but a further component E is taken to depend on feeding rate as well. It has been found that more realistic results are obtained with $F=0$ and E chosen to give a gross conversion efficiency of about 40%. This assumption is in general agreement with experimental work. The respiration rate is used to derive an excretion rate of nutrients into the upper layer by assuming a proportion U of time is spent by copepods in the upper layer.

The initial and final weights of an individual copepod are taken as 0.2 and 100 μgC corresponding roughly to the weights of naupliar and adult *Calanus* sp. Once 100 μgC is reached the copepods are assumed to be adult and food intake for the following 20 days is used for egg production with the same efficiency as for growth. 10 to 30% of the carbon content of the eggs is assumed to form the weight of the nauplii population which start the next generation.

The predation on numbers, Z, of the herbivore can follow two possible patterns, a fixed percentage mortality, GX, at any weight and population number; or a mortality dependent on the biomass ZW in the form

$$-G(Z-Z1)\ (W-W1)/(H+ZW) \tag{3}$$

where $Z1$ and $W1$ are thresholds below which predation ceases. $Z1$ is a very low value corresponding to the concentration of the overwintering stock; $W1$ is used to test variations in predation but is here set at 5.0 μgC. The general equations for daily change in the parameters are thus—

$$DR/DT = -ARP/(B+R) + V(RO-R) + U(E(P-P1)/(D+P) + F)ZW^{0.7} \qquad (4)$$

$$DP/DT = ARP/(B+R) - VP - CZW^{0.7}(P-P1)/(D+P) \qquad (5)$$

$$DW/DT = ((0.7 \; C - E) \; (P-P1)/(D+P) - F) \, W^{0.7} \qquad (6)$$

$$DZ/DT = -G(Z-Z1) \; (W-W1)/(H+ZW) - GXZ \qquad (7)$$

except that terms containing $P-P1$, $Z-Z1$, $W-W1$ become zero for $P \leqslant P1$, $Z \leqslant Z1$, $W \leqslant W1$ respectively. Also for $W \geqslant W2$, the adult carbon content, DW/DT represents the material added for egg production.

Chemical Cycles with Energy Circuit Models

By Howard T. Odum

Introduction. Modelling Symbols

In the expanding quest to understand the large and complex systems of cycles of the earth, the seas, and man, comprehension requires the simplification that comes with making models. Each type of model may bring new concepts into existence in men's minds, condensing complexity of the real world within the capacity of the simpler human comprehension. Among the modelling and modular languages being developed for synthesis of macrosystems is an energy language that we have used to study and simulate some contrasting systems of ecology, anthropology, and other sciences. In this essay this energy circuit language is used to consider the chemical cycles that sustain the sea.

The modelling of material fluxes and budgets is now a standard part of any consideration of chemistry of the lands, seas, and atmospheres. What we now need is modelling of the total system of all the total energies including those of man's system including information and cultural programs of control. The energy language is a way of visualizing and synthesizing all types of components.

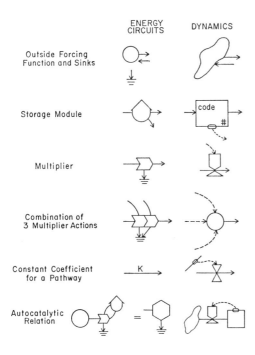

Fig. 1. Comparison of symbols of the energy circuit language (left) with "Dynamics" symbols of Forrester (1963).

The energy circuit language has been described in several previous papers (Odum, 1967, 1968; Odum and Pigeon, 1970; Odum, Nixon, and DiSalvo, 1971) and applied to a wide variety of systems in a book (Odum, 1971 a). Some of the main symbols are given in Fig. 1. The language is a formalization of concepts of energy flow in which pathways represent either the energy flow driven by single forces or those driven by populations of forces. Each driven flow has opposing forces of frictional, inertial, or static nature, the latter derived from downstream storages of potential energy. Details about the language in relation to concepts of physics and chemistry were given previously (Odum, 1971 a). As defined, the language is supposed to use the constraints from basic laws of physics and chemistry and the principles of larger systems at the same time. Since the pathways represent all energy flows, and since theorems of the language allow all flows of matter and information to have their energy values at their points of action in the system, a common denominator is provided for all parts of all kinds of systems.

Comparison of Energy Language with Forrester's Language

One of the characteristics of the energy language is its simple representation of network phenomena that are often represented as a system of differential equations, a more difficult language but one familiar to scientists and engineers. Whereas the energy language was developed first from consideration of energy laws, ecological data on food chains and some physical and chemical laws about forces, fluxes, and reactions, it was discovered later that it was also a form of visual mathematics, each modular symbol having an algebraic term for the system of differential or difference equations used in translations for computer simulation.

This year Larry Peterson and I (Odum and Peterson, 1971) found that an older language of symbols first developed by Forrester (1963, 1970) to summarize digital programs based on empirical coefficients had symbols that seem to match the ones derived from energy considerations. Notice the comparison in Fig. 1. We would judge that Forrester was modelling energies and true forces without knowing it just as we were writing a symbolic language that automatically translates into his Dynamo digital program without our knowing it. Forrester calls his language and its simulation "Dynamics". Among biologists who have used it for ecological systems are King (Paulik, 1967) and McRoy (1971). That two entirely different processes of thinking should develop similar languages suggests that basic concepts are involved. In the dynamics language, the use of a different kind of line for each class of matter, energy, or information is quite unnecessary since there is an energy value for all flows, not just for flows of fuels and sunlight. Both languages are being used in parallel efforts to consider large scale world processes. The translation in Fig. 1 may be helpful to readers used to a single language. Both languages serve similar roles in giving the human mind concepts which can be easily held and readily translated into other languages for other purposes such as simulation.

There is an intellectual's tendency to seek an explanation in that special language that is familiar to him before he accepts a phenomenon. If a new language turns out to be simpler in expression of the particular phenomenon than older ways of thinking about the same relationship, the custodian of the old may only accept it as a teaching device or popularization because he cannot easily accept a loss of status of the more difficult ways of expression for which he takes pride in mastery. It is an instinctive reaction to regard the simpler way of doing something as less valuable. One's language carries one's thoughts. If one has complex mental procedures, they are not necessarily more useful than simpler ones even if they did take more training to learn. These symbolic languages by uniting concepts may have the simplicity to displace some more cumbersome mathematics for general modelling, at least for some kinds of minds.

Notes on the Use of the Energy Language with Chemical Systems

The following points about the energy language are offered to clarify its use in chemical systems as illustrated by the diagrams in Fig. 2.

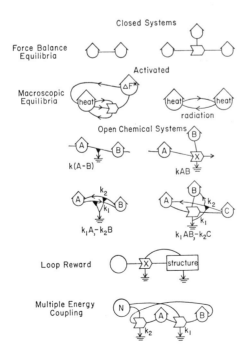

Fig. 2. Some configurations of force balance and energy flow common in chemical systems expressed in energy circuit language.

Equilibrium. At the top are two systems at equilibria in the sense of simple physical balance of static forces from energy storages. The pathway lines are lines of force action. There are no heat sinks and no energy flow. The exact relationship between the energy stored and the force delivered depends on the type of energy stored (tank symbols).

Chemical equilibria. Illustrated in the two systems of the second row in Fig. 2 are chemical equilibria which are microscopically and locally not in true force balance. Accumulations of energy at random produce some momentary storages of higher potential energy that are subsequently dispersed back into the base level of average molecular momentum that we call heat.

Open chemical systems. Shown next are four familiar, open, chemical systems with heat sinks representing heat dispersion and entropy increase. On the left the flow between energy storage A and B is in proportion to the difference in the forward and backforce on the single pathway as in flow in an electrical field. The other three systems have no backforce but have separate pathways for return flows. These can establish steady states; two have multiplier actions in one direction. In a multiplier action, one of the two converging flows may be a tiny but required item such as a trace element or even a unit of information. Its energy value becomes that of the reaction as much as that from the apparently larger flow.

Selection for structural feedback facilitation. Inherent in the language is the provision that any energy flow generates randomness and choices from which natural selection continually selects according to the principle of maximum power toward maintaining the flow. Even at constant temperature, the thermal randomness that generates local energy concentrations gives natural selection the means for developing feedbacks that facilitate flow in the pathway. These feedbacks constitute pathway structure that may take the form of storages, eddies, gradients, membranes, catalysts, or more complex means for using energy storages for maximizing energy flows. Such feedbacks are illustrated in the loop reward diagram in Fig. 2. Because of these mechanisms, flows do become a function of the potential energies available as soon as choice, selection, and loop rewards develop. Natural selection is nature's Maxwell demon and the main basis for introducing new information.

Force-flux conventions. A chemical audience may be used to the problem in steady-state thermodynamics of flux not being proportional to thermodynamic force when the force is chosen as the chemical potential. Rather than make this selection for force and the necessary accompanying assumptions about small distance from reversibility, we define a second force-flux law that includes mass action concepts. A pathway may represent a flow of energy under impetus of a population of similar forces acting so that the flux is proportional to the number of unit forces. The number of forces (n) is related to population force (N) to which flux (J) is proportional. The energy circuit networks may have some pathways which have single driving forces and others which are the action of population force. We, thus, combine chemical kinetics and steady-state thermodynamics in the one more general language in which every pathway without acceleration fits one of the two linear laws ($J = LX$ or $J = LN$). For more discussion of these definitions see Odum (1971).

Energy coupling to a cycle. Illustrated in the last diagram of Fig. 2 is the outside energy source coupled to a circular chemical cycle with each step the result of a multiplier action of an outside and a cyclic storage developed force. There is no upstream or downstream in the circular loop although there is an upstream-downstream sense in the flow of outside potential energies into dispersed heat (sinks).

Energy value of a reactant. A storage may have as many energy values as it has reaction pathways. If the reactant from a storage is a tiny quantity with a large energy release of another power flow, it serves as an amplifier. When energies are fed from downstream back upstream, the flux may leave its storage with one value as related to its storage input process but after upstream coupling, it may develop the new value of the power flow facilitated there. For example, a cycling chemical substance develops new values of potential energy in each reaction step coupled to outside components.

Storage distribution as a facilitating structure. Illustrated by the last diagram in Fig. 2 is Lotka's principle that in a closed steady-state cycle, the storages develop in inverse magnitude to the pathway conductivities that follow. In such cases greatest energy storage develops in a different part of the cycle from the site of maximum outside energy application. The lesser outside energy has the lesser multiplier action. The distribution of energy storage within the cycle becomes self adjusted to maximize the flow and, thus, is another case of feedback of information and structure towards power maximization, competition, and system survival. For example, if energy of (N) with k_1 is smaller than with k_2, storage A becomeslarger than B.

The physical systems of the sea such as eddies and gyres are also examples of the distribution of energy storages in non-random pattern. Such maximization is the basic explanation for development of turbulent eddies with the energy storage that is feasible depending on the size of the outside energies available for maximization (Odum, 1968); in the discussion one participant indicated that similar applications have been made by J. Malkus). The energy diagrams such as those in Fig. 2 help us generalize about organic evolution, chemical reaction development, social change, and geophysical systems as variants on one basic plan. Consider next overall geochemical processes with energy language

Compartmental Models in Geology

In a recent book, Harbaugh and Bonham-Carter (1970) review the use of compartmental and other models in geology including applications to sedimentary depositions, deltas, salt domes, reef developments, and many others. Much of the book concerns the simulation of a field of unit models each feeding its shared inputs and outputs into each other, thus, producing the geographical mapping of variables characteristic of much geological data. One may simulate a whole system by such joining together of unit models or make a unit model apply to the whole of the system. In this paper the latter class of models is considered.

Harbaugh and Bonham-Carter include an overall two-compartment model for the earth sedimentary and igneous cycle citing a manuscript by Garrels and Mackenzie. They simulated the model considering the shape of growth curves with a case of steady input and one with constant mass constraint. These models are drawn in energy language (which automatically expresses the differential equations of the model) in Fig. 3. Note that the energy sources and pumping actions are dashed since they were not explicitly covered by these

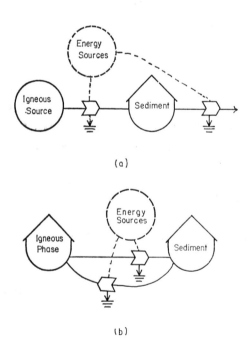

(a)

(b)

Fig. 3. Energy circuit diagram of earth model simulated by Harbaugh and Bonham-Carter (1970): (a) with constant addition of new mass from igneous source; (b) with constant mass constraint.

authors who, in effect, assumed them constant by using constant transfer coefficients.

The Harbaugh and Bonham-Carter book helps express an optimism also felt by this author in an emerging subject of systems geology and geochemistry, as its hydrological and mass models are generalized to include all of the energies and forces of a system. Hopefully, the energy language may be helpful in these kinds of synthesis. The discussion of unsettled issues and two analog simulations that follow show the methodology.

Those not used to the approaches of compartmentalizing for conceptual and simulating simplicity may be disturbed when known processes are lumped or seem to be omitted. A process that one is holding constant as in a controlled experiment becomes a constant coefficient and a property of the pathway, and thus, seems to disappear in these models. Where these methods have been much used in ecology, experience has gradually given empirical guidance on which processes are important and dominant in these systems. At present, we have less experience with whole earth models, but we must get on with efforts of these cycles and check them by comparison of the simulations with the real data which are still very approximate in these fields.

World Geochemical Processes Simplified with Energy Circuit Language

As a unit of the world's geochemical cycles, the ocean's processes and man's effect on constitution of the sea can be understood only in perspective of the main cycles of the lithopshere, atmosphere, and hydrosphere. The energy circuit language may be helpful in organizing our understanding and hypotheses about which flows are linear, which are multiplicative actions, which are important, and which receive outside forcing energies. By diagramming subsystems and subcycles, it is possible next to focus on various ideas about the origin, stability, and changes in the sea as related to man and other changing patterns.

Goldschmidt Reaction

To illustrate energy diagramming of geochemical models, consider the reaction in Fig. 4a that may be called conveniently the Goldschmidt reaction after the originator of the calculations of the stoichiometry of the overall process (Goldschmidt, 1933; Goldberg and Arrhenius, 1958). In an overall way, the reaction of acid volatiles on igneous rock can produce a medium like sea water plus residual soils and sediments. According to some ideas, this class of reactions describes early events in our world starting with initial igneous conditions. In our current world, the reaction may be only a smaller part of the system of cycles now operating. In Fig. 4*b* more of the details of the input and output flows are shown. Note that a source of energy directly or indirectly from the sun is involved for the stirring and mixing of the reactants. As drawn, such a model implies much simpler kinetics than the millions of tiny component processes that we know to be involved in such a world-dimensioned process. Yet, considering accuracy of our data and the crudeness of our questions, simple models may be an adequate summarization, but one has to check performance against the real world, a difficult kind of test to make with huge world systems.

Goldschmidt Microcosms

In Fig. 4*c* is an apparatus in which we refluxed acids on rock with four replications in 1957 to simulate the Goldschmidt reaction. Data are given in Table 1.

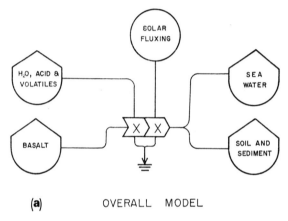

(a)   OVERALL   MODEL

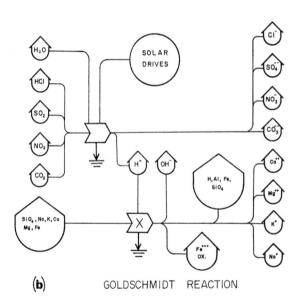

(b)   GOLDSCHMIDT   REACTION

Fig. 4. Goldschmidt Reaktion: (*a*) overall process; (*b*) separate elemental flows shown; (*c*) Goldschmidt microcosm.

Table 1. *Ionic concentrations after refluxing 10 g of Basalt in Goldschmidt Micro-cosms[1]. See Fig. 4c*

Trial	Initial Conditions, %		Volume ml	Months refluxed	pH	Final Concentrations, ppm				
	HCl	H_2SO_4				Na	K	Ca	Mg	Fe
1	1.9	0.50	150	6	3.5	177	15 000	180	101	0.0055
2	1.1	0.04	100	2	1.0	69	31	14	2	0.0035
3	0.3	0.10	400	2	0.4	36	6	1	0.4	0.0011
4	0.3	0.10	50	2	2.5	53	150	2888	123	0.0059
sea					8.2	10 561	400	400	1272	

[1] Work by Walter Abbott and H. T. Odum supported by National Science Foundation grant in 1957 on ecological microcosms.

In the period of 2 to 6 months that these systems were cooking, it was clear that something like sea water was evolving. The pH was rising and it became doubtful that the earth should need millions of years for neutralizing any accumulation of acid volatiles to form sea water if this was the history. The appearance of substantial iron which would precipitate as the pH neutralized suggested some precambrian iron deposits of the sedimentary and metamorphosed rock record. Whether operating on an igneous earth or on a small scale, the reaction may be relatively fast whenever there are igneous rock surfaces. This part of the igneous cycle may have a relatively fast reaction rate.

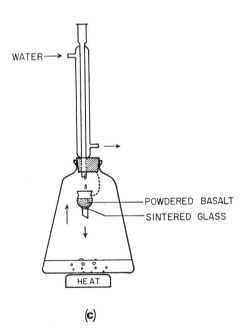

WATER→

POWDERED BASALT
SINTERED GLASS

HEAT

(c)

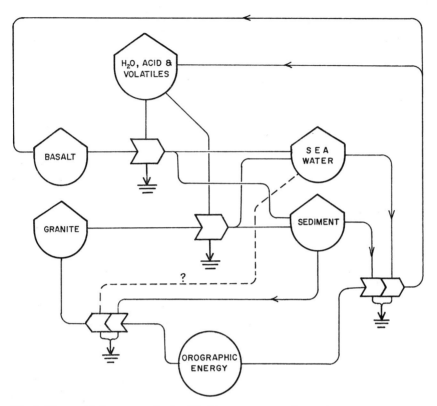

Fig. 5. The earth's igneous cycle simplified into two competing pathways, the volcanic and plutonic-granitization flows.

The Igneous Cycle

The Goldschmidt reaction (Fig. 3) is only a part of the main igneous cycles since volcanoes and plutonic uplifts continue drawing their input materials and end energies from some recycled materials. Other processes only somewhat known transform sediments into igneous rock with uplift. Compartmentalizing for simplicity the overall igneous cycle is given in Fig. 5. Like some ecological systems this network has two competing multiplicative pathways with shared common reactants which are regenerated by common recycle reactions. Although the substances are different, the energy circuit language helps us recognize a system similar to the photosynthesis and respiration model of world biosphere that cycles nutrient elements with competing production pathways.

The Equilibrium Model

The Goldschmidt reaction has sometimes been visualized as producing an ocean by a running down process from initial potential energies with elements distributed ultimately according to stable equilibria without requiring any roles for recycling. The equilibrium model for the ocean developed by Sillén (1961) seemed to resemble the modern ocean as if the world were dead without incoming energies, without new volcanoes, without cycling, without spreading sea floors, or without a sedimentary cycle. It was an astonishing fact requiring explanation that the real steady-state ocean should have some similarity with an equilibrium model. Consider the nature of cycles and their self-regulated storage structures under selection for survival by maximizing power.

Adaptive Value of Pseudo-Equilibrium States in an Open System

Consider the open cyclic steady state given in Fig. 6, which has outside energy drive in two parts of the cycle, but derives potential energy from its own storages in the other two pathways. Suppose the storages are self adjusting to maximize power flow by means of natural selection from among random variations generated in any power flow. Which distribution of storages so maximizes incorporation of inflow energies? With the help of the energy circuit diagram we see that energy incorporation is a multiplicative action at the intersection of the outside source and the flow from an inside storage just upstream. Energy is maximized when the upstream storage is maximized. In this instance, the cycling matter is a reactant and, thus, a part of the energy reaction by which outside energy sources are incorporated. In Fig. 6 if outside energy sources were stopped, the system would run downhill with storages ending up in the compartments (E) that were interacting with outside energies. Regular equilibrium would result. Calculations such as those by Sillén of an equilibrium model for the sea are computations of the final concentrations in the run down compartments. Thus, the distribution of mass that is self regulated to maximize power is only slightly different from the distribution at equilibrium. Some storage is required in non-equilibrium compartments to maintain steady recycle.

There is a second feature of storage in systems that favors near-equilibrium mass distributions. Maintaining storages is expensive in energy either because of the losses in adventitious lateral pathways or in the energy costs that the system must spend to prevent that loss if they are so organized. In either case, the losses are proportional to the surface to volume ratio as described in the

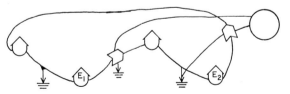

Fig. 6. Energy circuit diagram of a geochemical cycle with 4 compartments driven by external energy coupling through two of the pathways. Power is maximized by a pseudo-equilibrium mass distribution.

theory of population force discussed elsewhere (Odum, 1971*a*, 1971*b*). However, storage of matter in run-down equilibrium states has no energy costs or losses and, thus, is economical. Systems that distribute their cyclic masses in near equilibrium distributions minimize losses and maximize capture of input energy pumping, thus, competing with alternative pathways for these energies.

Another way of thinking of the equilibrium state storage distributions is one of high energy relative to outside energy sources. Having a low energy state relative to the cycle maximizes high energy relative to the source. As described in relation to the development of information in human affairs, the expenditure of potential energy into heat actually increases the energy multiplier value of the cycling system.

Steady State Ocean

In 1950 and 1951 along with details on the strontium cycle, I presented calculations for time constants of main elements in a steady-state lithosphere, ocean, and atmosphere driving the cycles of the common elements. The overall mass movements suggested were those in Fig. 7 (Odum, 1950). Probably improved were the calculations made later by Barth (1952), Goldberg (1961) and others.

The steady-state ocean may be conceptualized into four main component cycles. The first was the igneous cycle subsystem, already sketched in Fig. 5. Sedimentary matter incorporated into igneous and granitization-like processes constituted the upward returning part of the simplified cartoon in Fig. 7.

Another subsystem is the salt and water cycles by which materials move from the sea through the atmosphere to the land as diagrammed in Fig. 8 and discussed in this symposium by Chatellet. The sun clearly drives these pathways directly and indirectly through the atmospheric engines. Potential energy

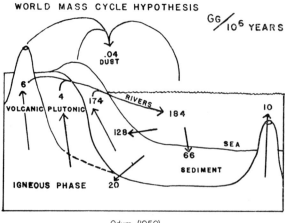

WORLD MASS CYCLE HYPOTHESIS

$GG/10^6$ YEARS

Odum (1950)

Fig. 7. Summary diagram of the hypothesis of a steady state earth surface from Odum (1950).

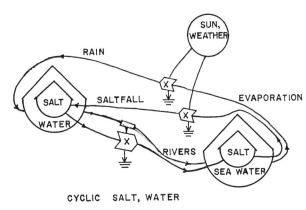

Fig. 8. Overall subsystem for hydrologic cycle and its coupling drives to the cyclic salt system.

of the water drives the return flow of water and also does the work of moving the salts.

A third subsystem is the cycling of solids into marine sediments with elevation again by orographic uplift shown in Fig. 9. This system involves the carbon-dioxide cycle, solution of the alkaline earth elements and others and reprecipitation in biogenic pathways. Parts of this system seem identical with the system presented at our symposium by Pytkowicz. An overall abbreviation of the main features is given in Fig. 9*b*.

The fourth subsystem contributing to the steady-state ocean is the oxidation and reduction system of the living biosphere, which is given in a simple 3-compartment form in Fig. 10 and more complex form in Fig. 25. Fig. 10 includes explicitly the algebraic terms for the pathways as implied by the conventions of the energy circuit language. Scientists and engineers usually recognize concepts of the energy language when we add the algebraic terms with which they are familiar. Simulation of models of this class has been done. For example, John Day did an analog simulation of Fig. 10 finding its charge-up and discharge curves like the ones published for the simpler 2-compartment P–R model (Odum, Beyers and Armstrong, 1963; Odum, Lugo and Burns, 1970).

One of the features of the energy language is its utility for presenting the functions by which one energy flow is coupled to pump another. In the model the return of sediments by uplift is derived in part from the sun-driven hydrological transfers of mass from continent to the sea with isostatic adjustments and deep return flows matter to denuded areas. More controversial are the energy sources for the conversions of sediment into igneous phases and their relation to the observed sea floor spreading. If the continents are still spreading and, thus, not in some kind of overall steady state, then the ocean might not be either. However, perhaps the sea floor spreading is being misinterpreted as a transient rather than a part of a steady recycling steady state.

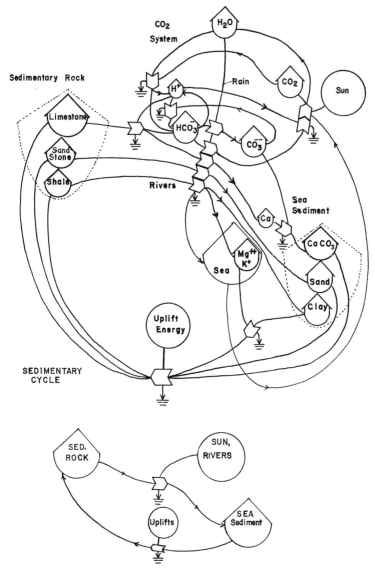

Fig. 9. Overall subsystem of the sedimentary cycle: (*a*) with details of limestone, sandstone, and shale circuits separated; (*b*) overall summary.

Continental Drift or Convection Spacing?

When there are convection vortices in a fluid, these are self-spacing forces, separating their centers of upcurrent while sharing downcurrents. What real evidence is there that mid-ocean ridges do not adjust similarly so as to maintain themselves halfway between the continental sedimentary cycles with asymmetries for oceans where thrusts from the sea are different. Examination of a recent

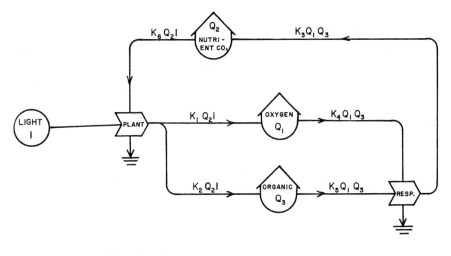

$$Q_1 = K_1 Q_2 I - K_4 Q_1 Q_3$$
$$Q_2 = K_3 Q_1 Q_3 - K_6 Q_2 I$$
$$Q_3 = K_2 Q_2 I - K_5 Q_1 Q_3$$

Fig. 10. A three compartment model for the main oxidation and reduction system of the biosphere, the photosynthetic production, and recycling respiratory consumption.

review written by Dickinson (1971) does not show facts which distinguish these interpretations.

Whereas continents may have been shifting some from time to time, they may have been kept spaced by near steady-state cycles. Continents may have congruent marginal shapes because the two counter-turning rotations are formed similarly by their mid-ocean sea floor circulations and vice versa. Is

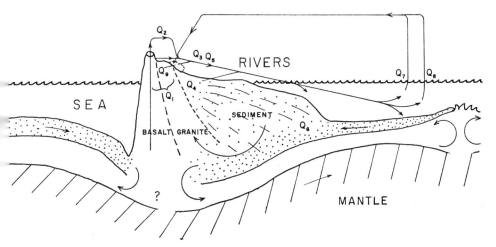

Fig. 11. Phases of earth cycles with compartmental designations used in the simulations in Fig. 14.

there need to postulate that the continents were part of one larger mass? Can we return to uniformitarianism, which was really an older way of describing faith in the steady states? It can be said that all transients are parts of a longer steady state and all steady states are made up of successional transients. For example, the Pacific with less sedimentation may require more area but develop more direct lateral thrust on North and South America equal to the under thrust of the sedimentary Atlantic. Such reasoning relates some of the lateral thrusts to the action of the weight of sedimentation.

Fig. 11 illustrates the familiar difference between the west coast of North America without much sedimentary cycle and the east coast in which the sedimentary cycle in its turning presses plate thrusts down and under the continental masses. The lateral thrust may be, thus, diverted more on the side with more sedimentation. As is well known, the relative role of the sedimentary cycle subsystem and the volcanic cycle subsystem vary, the former being large in the Atlantic and the latter in the Pacific. The higher concentrations of some photosynthetic nutrients, the size of the Pacific, and the atoll depositions are among the oceanic differences that the subsystem ratios may explain.

Where are the Input Energies?

In the world's cycles, one is not certain what the run-down state is or where the main energy inputs are in the cycles. As discussed in relation to Figs. 2 and 6 the coupling of energy input may be at the low energy states relative to the cycle. However, it is not clear whether elevated parts of the continents and the mid-Atlantic ridges are the high or the low energy parts of the cycles. The delivery of input energies to the cycle may be far removed from the orographic and volcanic regions. There may be heat release in crystallization and chemical reactions of transported "fuels" far removed from the energy sources. Or perhaps the motions draw on forces developed from energies elsewhere.

Possible Solar Chemical Drive to Earth Cycles

The energy for the sedimentary and volcanic cycles is often said to be from residual heat gradients, from heat released by radioactivity, and from the lateral weight transport by the atmosphere and oceans under solar drive. Another energy source of possible importance in sediments is the chemical potential energy in the combination of oxidized and reduced substances laid down together which can interact releasing heat when they are transported to sites of higher temperature and pressure. The overall sun's action in photosynthesis is neither oxidative nor reducing but a separation of the two that starts when photons separate electrons from plus charge sites in chloroplast semiconductor elements. As shown in the model in Fig. 10, the production system develops the oxidative and reducing materials that are then recombined in the work of life with a small part of both deposited in the sediments with particles of oxidized and reduced materials together. What is the chemical potential energy in bulk sediment?

Evidence that the deposition of organic and other chemical potential energies in sediments may be of adequate magnitude comes from the rates of heat diffusion from the lithosphere and the sea floor.

A heat diffusion of about 0.4 kcal/m²/day would require a photosynthetic net deposition of about 0.05 g c/m²/day, a figure of the right order of magnitude as compared with estimates of world photosynthetic production.

Even if it is not the sole energy source, the living system may be feeding back control action on the earth systems. Similarly, the carbon-dioxide content of the earth depends on the relative transfer coefficients of the consumer and producer parts of the "P and R" system as we sometimes call the model in Fig. 10.

We showed earlier in terrestrial microcosm measurements that the steady-state carbon-dioxide content in such systems could vary from 300 to 2 000 ppm depending on the ratios of producers to consumers (Odum, Lugo and Burns, 1970). In effect evolution controls the atmosphere and climate.

The Nonliving Feedback of Geochemical Structure to Pumping

Discussed at length in a recent book is the basic model for any surviving system by which there is a feedback from downstream rewarding the upstream pathway with some flow, augmenting service and giving the system competitive advantage over alternative circuits. The models already given in Figs. 5, 6, 8, 9, and 10 have this property. The means for this feedback is the processing of special energy from downstream into structure, storages, and high quality information that serve high degrees of amplification in their effect back upstream. This property may be most complex in living and economic systems, but it occurs in simple non-living systems as well. Weather systems build cumulonimbus clouds and cyclones as the structural means for feeding back services to augment further input energy flow. Turbulent eddies develop when the energy cost of eddies serves to accelerate energy flow over non-turbulent flow competition. The older geochemical systems developed a structure of storage distributions that was in inverse proportion to unit outflow rate as described by Lotka, thus, maintaining maximum flow. In earlier times before man, some of our concentrated types of mineral deposits developed until their outflows equalled their inflow rates. Pockets of free energy were maintained because they were necessary to the self-adjusting survival of the whole cyclic system in competition with alternatives competing for the same energies. These concentrations were the system's self developed structure.

In addition to the mineral concentrations, there were the continents which also served as flow augmenting feedback structures. By emerging above the water, continents harness the solar driven atmospheric systems more effectively, thus, promoting the lateral thrust plate and other processes developing and maintaining the continents. The distribution of the sedimentary cycle between continental circuits and the circuit under the ocean (including sea floor spreading) may keep the continents organized and serve as an energy separation division capable of sensitive self-correcting regulation, a boundary something like biological territories, tribal war systems, or ecological edges. When continents contain too much of the energies, the sedimentary cycle may run faster towards the sea; when the seas contain too much of the energy, landward pressures may increase.

One may regard other geological structural development as contributing to maximizing the earth's energy flow systems in similar reward loop mechanisms. There are the volcanic structures, the reef systems, the beach, the geosyncline sequences and other self developing means for storage of energy and information.

Competition from Life

In an overall sense, the evolution of life with a production and respiration system gradually becoming more and more efficient and detailed, stored the information and structure and began to drain flows of the earth's geochemistry away from purely inorganic cycles. Illustrated in Fig. 12 is the similarity of the role of life and the igneous cycle both taking in oxidized and reduced mixtures, putting out water, carbon-dioxide, and mineral substances important to the

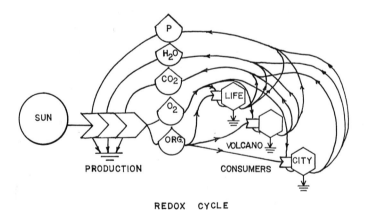

Fig. 12. A diagram of the cycle of production and regeneration compartmentalized to suggest the parallel and competing roles of the biosphere, the volcanic system and the urban system of man.

recycle. Culminating this evolution is the emergence of man, his culture, and finally his machines, some kind of ultimate in the pumping of these cycles.

Man's System as a Volcanic Preemptor

The history of man's increasing capture of energies of the earth show him first a minor consumer, next the main consumer, then the main photosynthetic net producer, and then the main geochemical mining diverter, going deeper and deeper into diversion of the energies of the earth's system. Bertine and Goldberg (1971) and Goldberg in this symposium stress and measure the geochemical alterations by man's total system. Let us make the comparison that man is a fine tuned volcano just as life is a fine tuned fuel fire. Man's main consumptions of fossil fuels, mined raw materials, and water cause the smoke stacks and exhausts to put out acid volatiles such as hydrogen chloride, nitric and sulfuric acid, precursors just like the volcanoes leaving the alkaline elements in ash, solid wastes, and ground wastes. The overall model is given in Fig. 12. How much of the energy of future earth processes are, thus, diverted?

The Temporary Surge in Circuit Substitution

To understand the temporary surge of man's take-over of the geochemical cycle, refer to Fig. 13 where an old pathway below with large storages is replaced with a miniaturized system of man that does not keep large storages. As man begins to divert the fossil fuels, the concentrations of other chemical substances which served as free energy for control of the sedimentary, cycle serve as a surge when diverted to man's noösphere from the geochemical cycle. In principle, at least, the present accelerating civilization of man may be running on energies stolen from the mountain building cycle. Whether the magnitudes are or will become major is an open question. Even some of the nuclear energy that contributes heat to the earth system is being withdrawn now by man with his mining of nuclear fuels. As the diagram shows, the system that ultimately develops with the new pathway will not have the subsidy of using up the old system and will settle into a different steady state. When agricultural man

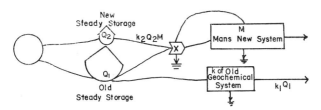

Fig. 13. A new system of man supplies miniaturized means for pumping flux in a geochemical pathway replacing an older system which used a large storage as means for facilitating flux. The old capital storage is available to accelerate the new system until it is exhausted.

displaced hunting man, something like this occurred in depleting the capital base of the hunting economy which was the great game animals and the forest soil. The capital of a discarded system helps to establish the new systems in its early stages, which survive only to the extent that they can stabilize when the subsidy is gone.

These aspects may be described by some generalizations from ecology that concern succession. When the starting state for succession has some large storages initially, the early development of a new system accelerates due to these energy sources, but later settles into a less energetic pattern because the costs of cycling utilize energies whereas in the initial condition the concentrations were already available as a resource. In other words, starting energies were higher than those inflowing at steady state. Thus, fertilized fish ponds return to a lesser metabolism when the inputs of fertilizer are stopped.

Simulation of a Simplified Model of the World Earth Geochemical System

The four intercoupled cycles that were drawn separately in Figs. 5, 8, 9, and 12 can be combined into one large model and simulated for various coefficients

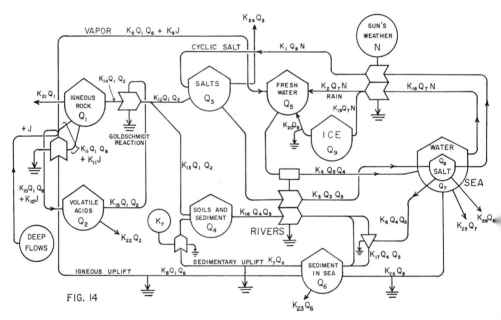

FIG. 14

Fig. 14. A simplified model for the early development of the ocean and its controlling cycles: igneous uplift and water release is an autocatalytic process like that of living units in feeding back structure as a pumping multiplier. Salts and soils develop from the Gold-schmidt reaction. Sun drives the water cycle to which is coupled the movement of sediments and salts to the sea. The outside energy for uplift in this model is not specified and is held constant on both sedimentary and igneous uplift processes. There is a small flow from the deep earth and some return flow when there are high storage levels.

and initial conditions, a fairly tedious task with one coefficient to the pathway even for these simplified models. An international team with a lot of computer resources may be required for a larger model of many elements and subsystems. In the meantime, simpler ones can be considered. In Fig. 14 is a simplified model for a world cycle that has some of the sedimentary cycle, the igneous cycles, and hydrologic-cyclic salt flows that help us with ideas about the origin of the ocean. For aid to the reader, the algebraic terms of the system of differential equations are given on the diagram although the energy circuit language already means these. The analog computer diagram was drawn using this system of terms.

For estimating coefficients values of flux and stock that may have the correct order of magnitude were estimated and entered in the energy network diagram (Fig. 15). Given these at one time, one may calculate the transfer coefficient as the unknown. For example, if a multiplicative junction has known output flux (J) when input storages (A and B) originating the forces are known, then the output is calculated by solving for k.

$$J = kAB$$

The units used become those of the coefficient so that one may work with heterogeneous units.

After scaling the differential equations with the coefficients, the final analog computer diagram was generated as given in Fig. 16. The system was then

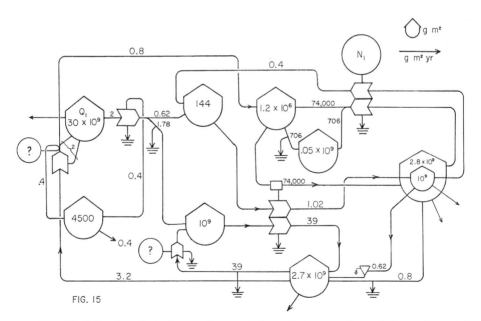

FIG. 15

Fig. 15. Estimates of stock and flux used in preliminary scaling of the earth model diagrammed in Fig. 14.

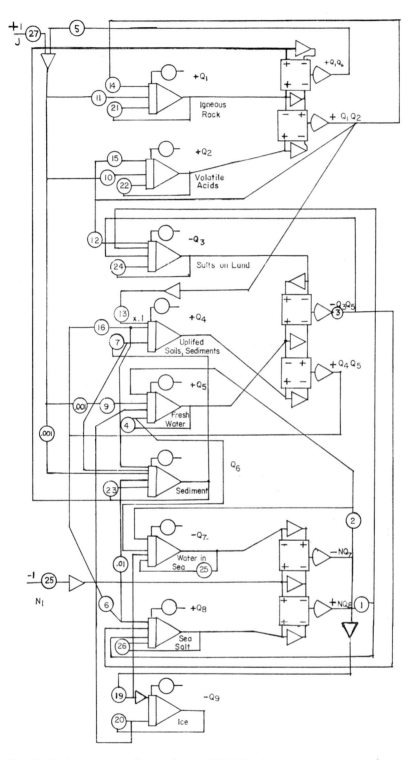

Fig. 16. Analog computer diagram for model in Fig. 4.

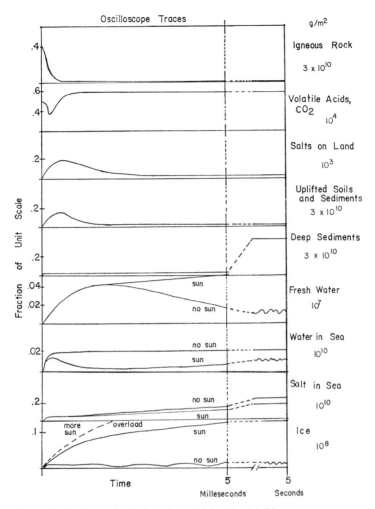

Fig. 17. Preliminary simulation of model in Fig. 14–16.

studied with oscilloscope output traces for various settings of initial conditions and coefficients. There are a very large number of possible combinations even with this simple system and it was useful to have the facility with which an analog computer allows one to vary coefficients at fingertip, turn pathways on and off, vary time scales, and study the system continuously on repeat operation mode. The temporal graphs of the storages are given for one particular setting in Fig. 17 with and without the solar drive forcing function on. The graphs in Fig. 17 represent 50 000 years to one million years. With the sun's action, the model builds a higher level of fresh water and the ice in the glaciers tends to overload beyond the scaling that we provide from our present ideas about possible extents of ice. This model has the property of Simpson's theory of increasing ice ages with the sun pumping more weather. Temperature and heat balance were held constant in this model. Only the water system develops oscillations and noise. For the starting condition of extensive igneous rock, the early part of the system shows a fast reaction with volatile acids, development of an ocean and a cycling salt system. In this model, the initial conditions regarding the amount of igneous rock and volatile acid was not important to the steady state that developed.

In the Harbaugh and Bonham-Carter simulation of sedimentary growth (Fig. 3), steady state was not reached although the model is of the exponential asymptotic first order type whereas the graphs in Fig. 17 did develop a steady-state ocean in a relatively short time. The ultimate differences depend on the rate of reincorporation of sediments into magma and the unknown rate of exchange with the deep phases of the earth.

How real such models are remains to be seen, but the ability of the simple system to produce some of the events of geologic history suggests the possibilities of this approach as it is refined.

Eutrophication of the Sea

One aspect of man's increasing role in the geochemistry of the sea is eutrophication, the acceleration of chemical inputs favoring photosynthesis. Much of the sea is oligotrophic, with dilute life, dilute organic matter concentrations, low concentrations of photosynthetic reactants, and an ecosystem that has developed very complex structure per unit energy available in the form of highly adapted animals such as the larger fishes that carry much of the critical storages and perform important programs of ecosystem management including chemical cycling. Oligotrophic systems can exist in steady state with organisms that cycle matter, process energies, and maintain similar patterns on the average year after year without any net storage gains and without any actions that progressively change structure. With energies scarce there may be evolution but at a slow rate since the energies in alternative choices are less than in more fertile systems. Parenthetically, it should be emphasized that steady state (the ecologist's climax) is possible in either eutrophic or oligotrophic states depending on the inputs as high or low. Also, it should be stated parenthetically that the oligotrophic sea may be processing sunlight with a much greater efficiency of gross photosynthesis than can be determined from metabolic exchange measures if one defines energy flows for only the first step, since the small nanoplankton may be cycling internally rapidly many times faster in the oligotrophic system.

A characteristic of low energy systems is the lack of energies of development of interactions and organization on larger scale. The oligotrophic open sea systems are tied together mainly through a few fish migrations and the physical

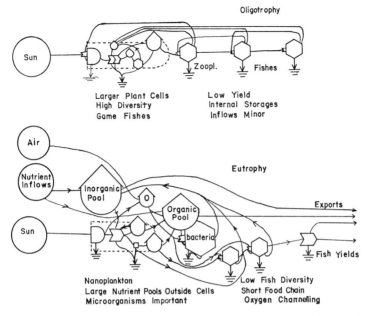

Fig. 18. Energy circuit diagrams comparing principal features of oligotrophic and eutrophic seas where the latter are induced by nutrient inflow.

current systems. Fig. 18*a* summarizes the essence of oligotrophy compared with eutrophy in Fig. 18*b*.

Now the pattern changes as fossil fuel usages by man accelerate the geochemical cycles many of which bypass the older cycles. As long as there are high and accelerating energies of the urban system, the cyclic injections of the raw materials of photosynthesis into the sea increase the eutrophic zones, replacing the oligotrophic, internally-closed cycling system with one which is complete only as part of the larger cycle of land and water. The eutrophic waters do deposit organic chemical potential energy, shortcut many of the larger animals that are neither needed nor competitive with their programs for covering large areas with organizing functions. The rising organic matter concentrations permit foodchain pathways without so large a proportion of the systems work for concentrating actions. The role of direct micro-organism consumers increases, less work of microbial management by the animals being required. In shallow waters, plankton may replace bottom plant systems such as marine meadows, kelps, or coral reefs, the latter being natural eutrophic systems that derive auxiliary energies from current and wave energy pumping but require clear oligotrophic water.

Our land experience with agriculture suggests that the systems which can give high yields to other systems and to man are the ones that are eutrophic and also coupled to channeling mechanisms that remove yields and storages before they develop structure for their own consumption. The contrasting nature of such systems is given in Fig. 18.

Recent efforts to discuss the potential fish yields from the sea have been more realistic than some claims for feeding the world offered in an earlier decade. Present estimates, however, concern the fish yields possible with the present distribution of primary photosynthetic production (Ricker, 1969). Theoretically, as the runoffs of nutrients of the land accelerate with continuing urbanization, intensive agriculture, and increased energy budgets, the resulting eutrophication may be harnessed with much higher yields than now unless accompanying toxic wastes are offsetting.

Channeling the food of eutrophic systems is customary in agriculture and occurs naturally in some marine systems that have sharp pulses or in those with a separation of production and consumption that occurs in the streaming of upwelling zones. More general harnessing of eutrophic production into yield seems possible as coastal eutrophication increases.

Pond Microcosms for the New Coastal Eutrophic Systems

Something of the behavior of an oligotrophic marine system under eutrophication from the treated sewage wastes of man can be seen from our pond microcosms at Morehead City, N.C., where a U.S. Sea Grant Progam has completed a 3-year study of the ecosystems that develop by self design where seeding of species has been added similarly to ponds receiving waste and control ponds (Fig. 19). General summaries are given in project reports (Odum and Chestnut, 1970; Kuenzler and Chestnut, 1971).

Small in size and averaging 0.5 m in depth, these ponds were readily monitored for their total photosynthetic production and respiratory consumption of oxygen. Because diffusion exchange rates with the atmosphere in this situation are small compared to the large changes in concentration due to metabolism, it was possible to use the oxygen change from dawn minimum to late afternoon maximum as a measure of the days production and the change from afternoon to the next dawn as a measure of the nighttime consumption. Representative data from control and waste ponds are available from thesis work by Martha Smith and others included in Fig. 20–23. Figure 20 shows the rise and fall of the oxygen during August 1970 in one of the control ponds (C-3) compared with one of the P ponds. Figure 21 shows the calculated P (production) and R (respiration) values that resulted. Monthly means for a year are given in Fig. 22 and 23 for two of the same ponds.

Clearly the waste receiving microcosms have much higher basic production and respiration and the two are closely correlated as shown in the mirror image pattern in Fig. 21 as well as in other graphs of M. Smith's thesis. As long ago

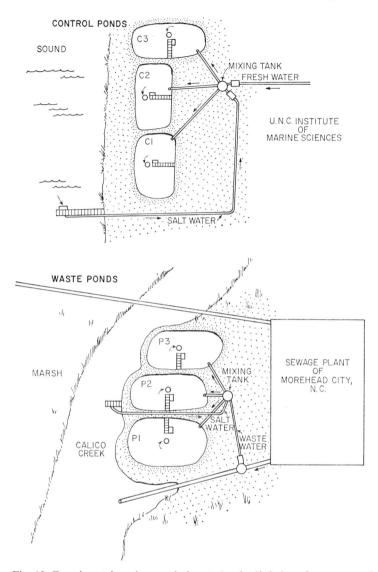

Fig. 19. Experimental marine ponds for study of self design of ecosystems developing with treated sewage: (*a*) control ponds receiving tap water and marine water; (*b*) experiment ponds receiving treated sewage mixed with sea water. Ponds are operated by Institute of Marine Sciences, University of North Carolina at Morehead City, North Carolina.

shown in freshwater fish pond studies, such increases are only partly transmitted to edible products.

The waste ponds by maintaining intense blooms in winter and summer shaded out the bottom plants (*Ruppia*) that were covering two of the control ponds in the third year. The storage of nutrients and chlorophyll in algal blooms was heaviest in the winter although metabolism was much less then. The plankton was dominated by copepod *Oithona* and the bottoms by the

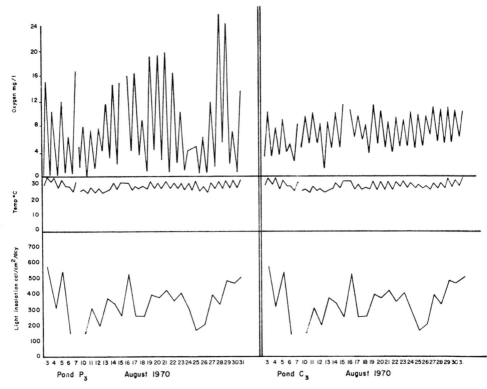

Fig. 20. Records of oxygen temperature and insolation for Waste Pond P-3 and Control Pond C-3 during August, 1070 from Smith (1971). Oxygen and temperature were measured at dawn and at 1630.

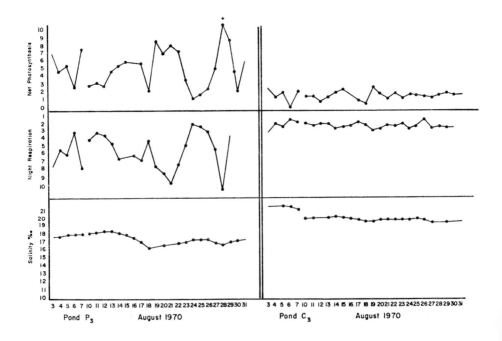

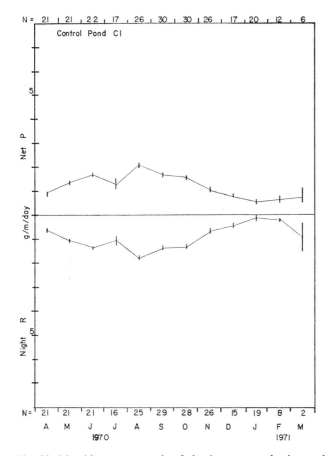

N = 21 | 21 | 22 | 17 | 26 | 30 | 30 | 26 | 17 | 20 | 12 | 6

Control Pond C1

Net P

g/m/day

Night R

N = 21 | 21 | 21 | 16 | 25 | 29 | 28 | 26 | 15 | 19 | 8 | 2

A   M   J   J   A   S   O   N   D   J   F   M

1970   1971

Fig. 22. Monthly mean records of daytime net production and nighttime respiration for Control Pond C-1.

annelid *Capitella*. Larger moving consumers were dominated by grass shrimp, *Paleomonetes*; small air breathing fishes, *Cyprinodon, Fundulus, Gambusia*; and blue crabs, (*Callinectes*). The ponds were apparently exporting substantial protein yields to water fowl also. Many properties found in the third year were like those in the second year; the ponds were beginning to approach steady state in some aspects.

Diurnal Simulation Models

The rise and fall of the oxygen in these ponds like that in many others studied in our previous work in shallow estuaries has established the shape of the daily curves as that predicted by simulations of the P and R model in Fig. 10 (Odum,

Fig. 21. Daytime net production and night respiration calculated for Waste Pond P-3 and Control Pond C-3 based on oxygen data in Fig. 20 from Smith (1971).

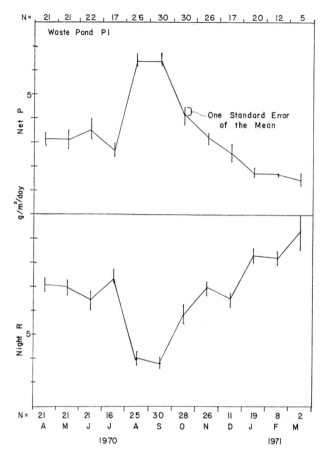

Fig. 23. Monthly mean records of net daytime oxygen production and nighttime respiration for Sewage Waste Pond P-1.

Armstrong and Beyers, 1963; see general discussion, Odum, 1971). The correlation of diurnal day production and night respiration of the simple model is like that of the real world systems.

Among other studies done in our group project was a study of the carbon cycle in these ponds including analog simulation of the diurnal pattern in doctoral dissertation by John Day (1971) with C. Weiss and the phosphorus cycle by H. McKellar (1971) with E. J. Kuenzler including an analog computer simulation for diurnal phosphorus movements. These chemical cycle studies follow the same general methodology of six steps as follows: (1) draw a materials or an energy circuit diagram, (2) write the differential equations, (3) diagram the equations in analog computer language, (4) do the simulation, (5) compare the simulation graphs with observed curves, and (6) readjust the model to improve fit.

Seasonal Simulations of an Estuarine Model with Recycling

One of the first seasonal simulations of a marine ecosystem was done by G. Riley for north Atlantic Waters in 1945, doing the calculations by hand in the pre-computer period. If we take his models given in differential equation form (Riley, 1945, 1946) and translate into the energy circuit language, we obtain the diagram in Fig. 24 which has multiplicative limiting factor actions for nutrients and phytoplankton stock and logistic structure for herbivores (H) and carnivores (C), Riley's model appropriately has turbulent dilution action (Z) and a non-linear temperature action on respiratory drains on the plants. However, there is no feature of recycled nutrients included of the type already given in Fig. 10. Later models such as one by J. Steele at this symposium do have the recycling feature. Recent models for the Peru current by Walsh and Dugdale (1970) simulate the nutrient actions in upwelling stream with similar features.

In Fig. 25 is a simplified model for our sewage waste ponds prepared by W. Smith, J. Day and H. T. Odum which includes inflow and outflows, and recycling of nutrients by consumers, storages for organic and inorganic nutrients, a parallel competing subsystem of bottom plants favored by current but sensitive to shading out by phytoplankton when nutrients are high. Values for storage and flux of the order of magnitude measured in the ponds were used to estimate coefficients. As in the previously discussed example in Fig. 14–16, the energy circuit diagram is a way of writing the differential equations and is a computer program when the coefficients are added. To help the reader not used to the language, the algebraic terms were added although this is unnecessary re-

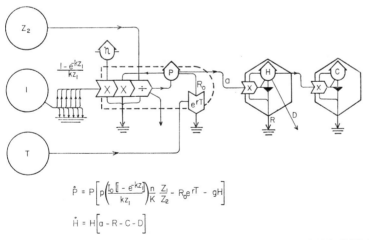

$$\dot{P} = P\left[p\left(\frac{I_0(1 - e^{-kz_1})}{kz_1}\right)\frac{n}{K}\frac{z_1}{z_2} - R_0 e^{rT} - gH \right]$$

$$\dot{H} = H\left[a - R - C - D \right]$$

Fig. 24. Energy circuit translation of models simulated by Riley (1946, 1947). Light, I; temperature, T; turbulence, Z; depth, z; herbivores, H; carnivores, C; D, mortality losses; n, nutrient concentration.

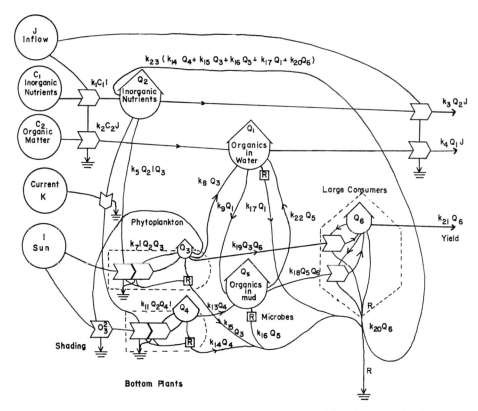

Fig. 25. Simplified model of waste pond estuarine microcosms used for simulation in Fig. 26 (H. T. Odum, J. Day, and W. Smith).

dundancy. This model was patched on analog computer with the usual steps of translating into a diagram of hardware like that in Fig. 16. Then the model was simulated (Fig. 26) with an annual sine wave as input forcing function for light like that with season in the real world. Fig. 16 is the simulation with one setting. The input forcing curve is at the top representing light. Short term oscillations were observed in the phytoplankton as in blooms in nature, and the maximum phytoplankton was in the winter as in the real ponds. Apparently, even this simple one cycle model accounted for some of the main features of these ecosystems.

Maximization of Power by Self Adjusting Storages that Pulse Recycling Pathways

Many of the simulations of ecological systems have involved linear pathways transferring energy downstream from solar sources without multiplicative feedback pathways. However, the property of a multiplicative feedback which rewards the upstream system for its contribution to the downstream unit may be associated with survival and, thus, with all real ecological and geochemical

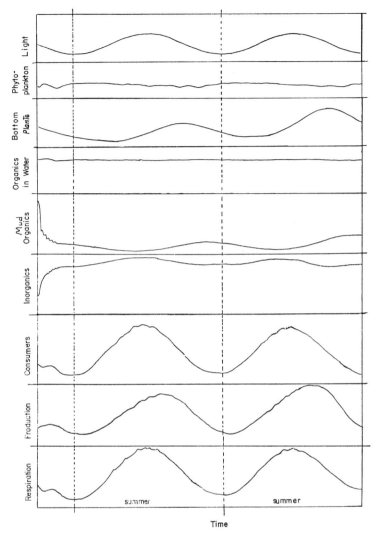

Fig. 26. A simulation of stabilization (succession) and seasonal pattern of the model in Fig. 25 with an input sine wave for light intensity.

systems. Loop reward pathways allows the downstream unit to develop timing relationships that maximize the systems effectiveness in gaining input energy.

For example, Williams (1971) in simulating Lindeman's system of food webs for Cedar Bog Lake, Minnesota, without such multiplicative feedback finds the seasonal pulse of production preceding that of the next level of consumers (the herbivores) and this preceding the pulse of the higher consumers. Yet, as we found in Texas bays (Odum, 1967), the real systems have inherent in their structure of pathways the means for adjusting the pulse of consumption to be simultaneous or earlier than the photosynthesis, thus, providing nutrient

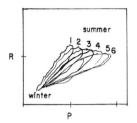

Fig. 27. X – Y recording of P and R in the model of Fig. 25 during the 6 sine wave undulations (years) required to achieve steady state. During succession input production was increased. This simulation started with an initial condition of high organic content in Q_5 because ponds were built with organic mud.

recycling and other work services such as reproduction necessary for maximizing the ability of the system to use the increasing sunlight in the annual cycle. The sewage waste ponds also show P and R processes staying together seasonally as well as diurnally (Fig. 22–23). Is this a property of models of the type which we used to discuss the nature of eutrophication in Fig. 18?

When the model in Fig. 25 was simulated to learn its behavior in succession and in response to a sinusoidal annual variation of light, the model developed adjustments of its nutrients and organic matter storages so that consumption was pulsed in advance of production during the annual cycle, in effect, insuring high concentrations of those recycled items needed for maximization. The model was self-maximizing in respect to the adjustment of storage quantities available to it. Fig. 27 shows the graph of P and R during one simulation of the first 12 cycles, steady state being developed in the 6th year.

Interface Regulation and Yield Possibilities

The microcosms for eutrophication done in this project and the models that help us understand them suggest that increasing eutrophication of the coastal seas may see self stabilizing adjustments in which the chemical cycles are principle control mechanisms. The chemical cycles quite apart from more complex biological succession and evolution may have relatively short-time periods for chemical cycle stabilization. With P and R similar, the eutrophic systems without management may be neither waste disposing nor waste generating, but rather systems for self regulating, power rich interface between man and his more dilute open seas.

Our ponds were inventoried by the group in 1971 after 3 years of self design processes that followed much seeding of miscellaneous organisms. Under the conditions of oxygen extremes, the fertile waste ponds were found with fewer species of higher edible animals than in the control ponds which had a rather normal estuarine composition. Mainly animals capable of air breathing were left in the waste ponds. Because of low oxygen conditions on many predawn mornings, the fishes and crabs surviving were often observed at dawn in the shore shallows washing their gills with surface film waters, making them prime targets for waterfowl that were much attracted to these ponds.

It was a fascinating realization that the oxygen extremes were channeling the food flows into relatively few species with oxygen adaptations. The channeling service was not free since special energies were diverted in the work of adaptation by these species, but the system was much like terrestrial agricultural systems where channeling is done with weeding agents. If such areas can be provided oxygen refuges into which fishes and crabs can move during low oxygen periods, a means is provided for aquaculture harvest, for culling, and for use of species that need more oxygen.

Summary. Value

The systems of chemical cycle pathways are being captured by man's accelerating control of the earth's energy sources with such symptoms as coastal eutrophication and the substitution of his pathways for many of those of the volcano and sedimentary cycle. The energy circuit language helps us recognize principles of energy of chemical cycles that apply to man's new cycles as well as to the simpler old ones. These abstractions may help us attain the simplicity and synthesis for whole earth simulations and perceptions.

In previous discussion (Odum, 1971) we found the state of competitive survival at maximum power attainable by a system of man and nature when it uses both its solar based resources and its energy flows from fossil fuels, not allowing one to interfere with the other. If value is also identifiable with maximum power flows, then maximum value also follows the dual uses of the geochemical cycle inputs and those of the sun directly. Ultimately, there may develop the possibility of man directing too much away from geochemical cycles so that the optimum utilization of sun and sea diminishes. Is man a better volcano and better at aiding the sedimentary cycle than the older geochemical systems in the sense of developing stable steady states which maximize power and, thus, value towards useful purposes related to total system survival?

This work was supported by the Division of Biology and Medicine, US Atomic Energy Commission, Contract No. AT-(40-1)-4150.

References

Barth, T. F. W., Abundance of the Elements, Areal Averages, and Geochemical Cycles, in Geochim. Cosmochim. Acta, *23*, 1 (1952).

Bertine, K. K. & Goldberg, E., Fossil fuel combustion and the major sedimentary cycle. Science, *173*, 233 (1971).

Day, J., Carbon metabolism of estuarine ponds receiving treated sewage. Ph. D. Thesis, Marine curriculum, University of North Carolina, 128 pp. 1971.

Dickinson, W. R., Plate Tectonics in Geologic History. Science, *174*, 107 (1971).

Forrester, J, Industrial Dynamics. M. I. T. Press 1963.

Forrester, J., Urban Dynamics. M. I. T. Press 1970.

Goldberg, E. D., Chemistry in the Oceans, pp. 583–597, in Oceanography ed., Mary Sears, publ. no. 67, Amer. Assoc. for the Advancement Society, Washington, D. C. pp. 3–654 1961.

Goldberg, E. D. & Arrhenius, G. O. S., Chemistry of Pacific Pelogic Sediments. Geochim. Cosmochim. Acta, *13*, 153 (1958).

Goldschmidt, V. M. Grundlagen der Quantitativen Geochemie. Fortsch. Mineral. Krist. Petrog., *17*, 112 (1933).

Harbaugh, J. W. & Bonham-Carter, G., Computer Simulation in Geology. Wiley-Interscience, N. Y. 1970.

Kuenzler, E. J. & Chestnut, A. F., Structure and Functioning of Estuarine Ecosystems Exposed to Treated Sewage Wastes. Annual Report for 1970–1971 to National Oceanographic and Atmospheric Agency, Grant GH 103, Project UNC-10, 345 pp. 1971.

Lotka, A. J., 1925. Elements of Mathematical Biology. Reprinted by Dover, N. Y. 1956.

McKellar, H., 1971. Phosphorous in marine Pond Receiving Treated Sewage, Master's Thesis, "Marine Curriculum", univ. of North Carolina, Chapel Hill.

McRoy, C. P. & Merritt, L., Simulation Model of an Eelgrass Population. Unpublished report, For Foundation Workshop on Modelling, Quantitative Sciences Center, University of Washington, Seattle. 1970.

Odum, H. T., The Biogeochemistry of Strontium. Ph.D. Thesis, Zoology Department, Yale University. 371 pp. 1950.

Odum, H. T., The Stability of the World Strontium Cycle. Science, *114*, No. 2964, 407 (1951).

Odum, H. T., Biological circuits and the marine systems of Texas, pp. 99–157 in Pollution and Marine Ecology, John Wiley and Sons. 1967.

Odum, H. T., Environment, Power, and Society, Wiley-Interscience, N. Y. 336 1971 a.

Odum, H. T., An energy circuit language for ecological and social systems, its physical basis. In press, in Systems Ecology, Vol. 2, ed. by B. Patten, Academic Press. 1971 b.

Odum, H. T., Energetics of World Food Production, pp. 55–94 in President's Science Advisory Committee Report of Problems of World Food Supply, Vol. 3, Whitehouse, Washington. 1967 b.

Odum, H. T., Work circuits and system stress, pp. 81–138, in Symposium on Primary Productivity and Mineral Cycling in Natural Ecosystems. ed. by H. E. Young, U. of Maine Press. 1968 b.

Odum, H. T. & Chestnut, A. F., ed. Studies of Marine Estuarine Ecosystems Developing with Treated Sewage Wastes. Annual Report for 1969–1970, 364 pp. NSF, Sea Grant Project GH-18. 1970.

Odum, H. T. & Peterson, L., Ecological Models for a City. Sympos. Soc. Applied Anthropology. (manuscript). 1971.

Odum, H. T. & Pigeon, R. F., ed. A Tropical Rain Forest. Division of Technical Information, TID-24270. Atomic Energy Commission, 1660 pp., Clearinghouse for Federal Scientific and Technical Information, Springfield, Virginia. 1970.

Odum, H. T., Beyers R. J. & Armstrong, N. E. Consequences of small storage capacity in Nannoplankton pertinent to measurement of primary production in tropical waters. J. Marine Research, *21*, 191 (1963).

Odum, H. T. & Lugo A., with Appendix by L. Burns. Metabolism of Forest Floor Microcosms. Chapter I-3 in A Tropical Rain Forest. U. S. Atomic Energy Commission, Div. of Tech. Information, TID-24270, Clearinghouse for Federal Scientific and Technical Information, Springfield, Virginia. 1970.

Odum, H. T., Nixon, S. & DiSalvo, L., Adaptions for Photoregenerative Cycling. Symp. Amer. Micro. Soc. (pp. 1–29 in The Structure and Function of Freshwater Microbial Communities, ed. by J. Cairns, Research Division Monograph 3, Virginia Polytechnic Institute.) (1971 a).

Paulik, G. J., Digital simulation of natural animal communities. pp. 67–88 in Pollution and Marine Ecology. ed. by T. A. Olson and F. J. Burgess. Interscience, 364 pp. 1967.

Ricker, W. E., Food from the Sea. pp. 87–108 in Resources and Man, National Academy of Sciences, Committee on Resources and Man, W. H. Freeman, San Francisco. 1969.

Riley, G. A., Factors controlling phytoplankton populations on Georges Bank. J. Mar. Res., *6*, 54 (1946).

Riley, G. A., A theoretical analysis of the zooplankton population of Georges Bank. J. Mar. Res., *6*, 104 (1947).

Smith, Martha, Annual cycle of oxygen metabolism in marine ponds receiving treated sewage. Master's Thesis, Department of Zoology, University of North Carolina. (pending). 1971.

Sillén, L. G., The physical chemistry of sea water. pp. 549–581 in Oceanography, ed. by M. Sears. Amer. Assoc. for the Advancement of Science, Publ. No. 67. 654 pp. 1961.

Walsh, J. J. & Dugdale, R. G., A simulation model of the nitrogen flow in the Peruvian upwelling system. Inv. Pesq., *35* 1 (1970).

Williams, R. B., Computer simulation of energy flow in Cedar Bog Lake, Minnesota, based on the classical studies of Lindeman, pp. 543–582 in Systems Analysis and Simulation in Ecology, ed. by B. C. Patten, Academic Press. 582 pp. 1971.

Discussion 6. Microbial Activity. Ecosystem Modelling

Stewart

There is no conflict between the notion that the deep sea water may have a characteristic age of the order of 1 000 years and Sorokin's suggestion that the tropical water may receive additions from high latitude sources within only a few years. As was discussed in Veronis' paper, the flow of deep water follows continental (or ridge) barriers towards the equator and then spreads out into the ocean basin. The boundary flow may have speeds of thousands of kilometers per year, and the equatorial regions are also characterized by high speed zonal flow, so a young age in these regions is quite reasonable. It is the time to spread into the high latitude eastern basins which may be very long.

Duursma

Do you have data on organic matter concentrations which support the production figures for bacteria?

Sorokin

The stock of dissolved organic matter in a water column can support bacterial production under 1 m² during 10–15 years even in tropical waters where the decomposition is most intensive.

Føyn

Do you find variations in the oxygen content of the water which correlates with the variations in the bacterial activity?

Sorokin

Yes. The second maximum of bacterial activity at 500–600 m depth corresponds to the upper boundary of the oxygen minimum.

Grasshoff

I wonder if the production measurements are not influenced of wall effects, replacing e.g. the natural substrate in filtered water. The idea of this independence of bacterial production rate is quite new.

Sorokin

The wall effect is negligible in the short-term experiments on production measurements. This can be demonstrated. Controversary measurements are most certainly connected by the application of plate counting techniques. The bacteria do not need a particulate substrate to take up organic material.

Dyrssen

What is the mean life time of bacteria?

Sorokin

The average life time of the microbial population can be evaluated via the estimation of the time of generation. This can be done by the method of direct count as well as by the radiocarbon method. In oceanic water at 20–30°C it varies in the range of 10–40 hours.

Steele

The fish production in the North Sea is about 0.8 % of the primary production. The steps in the food web formed by plankton and benthos lead to high transfer efficiencies. If bacterial activity in the web is considered to be a significant intermediate step transforming organic matter into food for larger organisms, then the transfer efficiency of bacteria would need to be higher than the value quoted by you.

Sorokin

Having no information about the stock and rate of production of microbial biomass it is difficult to decide something about its possible role in the energy flow in this ecosystem.

Hempel

Steele assumes that the bacteria compete with higher elements of the food chain at the sea bed of the North Sea, making the known ratio between primary production and fish catch even more difficult to interpret. I myself, however, assume that bacteria transferring excretian products of plankton etc. into bacterial biomass re-cycle some additional food to filter feeders. Therefore the presence of bacteria provides fish food indirectly rather than competing.

Hallberg

Since many major diagenetic processes occur in the uppermost 10 cm of a sediment, can you really neglect the impact of bacterial processes on diagenesis in this zone?

Sorokin

In this zone no, but as the matter of fact in the oligotrophic areas of the Pacific Ocean below 10 cm the microbial life was found absent. Therefore we can accept the statement that below this layer the diagenetic processes are proceeding without participation of biological agents.

Dyrssen

I should wish to point out that measurements with the calorimeters developed by Sunner and Wadsö at the Thermochemical Laboratory, University of Lund, show that bacteria cultures feed in steps starting with a large "epicurean" step and a rest. Light attenuation measurements show only a continuous growth and cannot distingusih between dead and living bacteria.

Odum

The direct measurement of total energy flows in whole microcosms (determining the heat sinks of our diagrams) is very exciting and reminds one of the earlier progress in muscle research. We need to do this on even larger microcosms. This seems to be the correct approach rather than using bomb calorimetry to calculate energies that might be flowing in ratio to metabolism, where in fact the reactions are many and involving amplifiers pathways as well as gross fuel flow. Most bomb calorimetry in ecology has been used incorrectly. For example, the caloric value of protein is much greater when used as growth requirements and thus as work gate rather than as a base fuel by organisms. It may be closer to 100 kcal/g than 5 kcal/g.

Chesselet

How do your models describe the genetic evolution at the "right" time scale? Where do you put evolution in the "geo" model?

Odum

Genetic mechanisms in evolution are like the randomness in the fluid systems generating choice from which selection gives structural development either in life, earth structure, or human information. As given in my book "Environment, Power and Society" the power cost of evolution is the energy dispersion in developing both the choices and the choosing mechanism—these are the reward mechanisms feedback loop.

Rickard

Is the definition of all routes, reservoirs and reactions a greater problem in your energy models than in the usual square box, mass balance system approach?

Odum

It should be easier since you have the additional tools and constraints of balancing energies and identifying forcing functions. Each energy model may include in it the mass balance models, but it may include several elements at a time. Mass balance is an additional constraint on an energy model that must be added with an additional equation or an auxiliary diagram.

Johnson

Real world systems have long time constants and large capacities while microcosms do not. So should not negative feedback stabilizers be put in to prevent the large excursions in pH, temp., O_2 etc. from occurring in the microcosm experiments?

Odum

All storages with density dependant outflows are already negative feedback stabilized since they are first order equations. Time constants are a function of resistance and capacitance which together constitute the reciprocal of the transfer coefficient. Microcosms should be scaled similarly. Ponds are similar to shallow estuaries in the parameters used, or as in analog time scaling they tend to have all processes differ by the same time factor.
You are correct that attention should be given to making the time constants similar or in multiple.

Bolin

As you know, I have used some of your concepts implicity in studying the carbon dioxide cycle and I think that the concepts and language you introduce may be very useful for an overall description of complicated physical-chemical-biological systems. It is, however, important to derive the relationships to be used from the basic physical, chemical and biological concepts that are valid, which sometimes may be very difficult or impossible. Let us consider the atmosphere-ocean system and the carbon cycle as an example. We know the equations of motion that govern this system and may in principle formulate the set of differential equations that describes this system including the chemical reactions involved. These equations have time and the three dimensions of physical space as independant variables. To arrive a ta simplified system of equations as given in your presentation, we must integrate those equations over the reservoirs considered and reduce the description of the processes inside each "reservoir" to a simple expression involving a very limited number of variables. This certainly may be possible in simple cases, when only approximate results are being looked for. But the final, simple system we arrive at never is more applicable than our way of including those physical-chemical processes adequately. Thus the oceans is a reservoir, the characteristics of which may be much dependant on the *distributions* of currents and chemicals in the interior, which cannot easily be caught by such simplified models. We then shall have to resort to the solution of the more complete physical-chemical equations analytically or numerically. In the latter case the computations are reduced to the solution of finite differential equations using three-dimensional grids equivalent to a set of non-linear ordinary differential equations with a large number of unknowns (10 000 to 100 000 are being used in the most advanced models). Formally there are of course similarities between such a set and the ones arrived at in ecological systems analysis. One important difference is, however, that the interdependance of the variables have been derived directly from the basic partial-differential equations valid for the system, applying numerical techniques the accuracy of which can be ascertained quite well. As was shown by Veronis we may then use for example the distribution of chemical elements in the ocean to gain an insight into how the physical process interact since the latter have been included into the computations in an internally consistent way. By further pursuing ideas of this kind it might be possible to get closer connections between the systems equations that have been presented and the basic physical-chemical-biological processes they are to describe.

Odum

The models of one level of integration and size have their individual laws that follow as much from their own design of pathways as from the component physics and chemistry of which they are constituted. This is because the natural selection and feedbacks that are generated put constraints on the microscopic processes to perform with kinetic responses almost independent of the details of their mechanisms. For example, limiting factor kinetics are similar regardless of what is being limited or by what mechanisms. Michaelis-Menton modules can be strung together in ever widening circuits of loops within loops without changing the general form of the transfer function.

Parts must perform to system requirements of them or be eliminated. At a larger scale of examples, culture and behavior of man is reprogrammed to provide system performance so that the immense detail we see in them are not so necessary to models for predicting the system as a knowledge of the design of the system that overall energies will demand of the system during selection and reprogramming processes. One branch of systems ecologists think this way because they are used to seeing ecosystems with certain performance properties in common after the selection and survival process.

In regard to comparison of your linear compartment models to these which have more of the multiplier actions and feedback controls, your suggestion might be interpreted as "we should use only linear trivial models because it is hopeless to try to include more of the known accurate kinetics". I would counter that the very area being neglected is that of meso-models that break any system into about 40 units and pathways with slide rule (human) accuracy. To be more detailed is to enter the next lower level of organization of worthwhile procedure in understanding that field but unsatisfactory procedure for prediction on the larger scale as you well indicate.

Man's Role in the Major Sedimentary Cycle

By Edward D. Goldberg

Introduction

The activities of human society are measurably changing the chemical makeup of the earth's waters and airs. The rates of such alterations will increase with the expanding world population and with the growing per capita consumption of materials and energy. During the aquisition and in the utilization of matter and fuels, there are losses and disposals in places other than those from where the materials were originally obtained. When a domain undergoes compositional changes that result in losses or restricted uses of its resources, a state of pollution has come into being. Such contaminated zones will persist until the supply of the pollutant is exhausted or curtailed or until its leakage to the environment is regulated.

Disasters can and have occurred before the pollutant supply becomes limited; the concerns of this presentation will be with the problems of leakages. The ability to predict future levels of pollutants in the atmosphere and in natural waters, coupled with an ability to define tolerance levels for the environment, can form the basis of effective environmental management. Clearly no part of our surroundings will be free of man's wastes. The maximization of waste accommodations with minimum disturbance to natural resources and to living systems should be one of the guiding concepts for environmental managers.

A rewarding entry to understanding the fates of man-introduced materials to the environment is a consideration of the behavior of substances during weathering cycles where there are movements of materials between and within the lithosphere, hydrosphere and atmosphere, transfers often mediated by organisms other than man. For synthetic substances that have little resemblances to naturally occurring species predictions of their flows through geospheres often can be made on the basis of their chemical and physical properties.

A comparison of the fluxes of materials in the sedimentary cycle with those of substances introduced by man to his surrounding will yield a quantitative appreciation of society's role as a geological agent. Mobilization rates of materials as a result of agricultural, industrial or social usages now compete with those that occur during weathering. These impingements have taken place primarily over the last several hundred years.

The Major Sedimentary Cycle

Rock and soil particles are transported from the continents to the marine environment by three agencies: rivers, winds and glaciers. Man has added two others: sewer outfalls and ships.

The river movements of rock and soil materials exceed by at least an order of magnitude their transport through the atmosphere (Table 1). While river discharges predominate in the Atlantic Ocean and its adjacent seas, the solids carried by the principle wind systems, the trades, mid-latitude westerlies (the jets) and the polar easterlies, are transported within latitudinal belts.

Man's injections into the environment also display a latitudinal zonation. The principle utilization of energy and materials takes place in the mid-latitudes of the northern hemisphere. The flow of this energy and matter through a society, and consequently the leakage to the surroundings, can be measured by the Gross National Product (GNP) of a country (Goldberg and Bertine, 1971). The nine countries with the highest GNPs, USA, USSR, Japan, Federal Republic of Germany, France, Great Britain, Canada, China and Italy, have a total GNP of 1 900 billion dollars with individual values all greater than 70 billion dollars. These nations are at mid-latitudes in the northern hemisphere. The next twelve countries in rank, with GNPs above 15 billion dollars each, have a combined value of the GNP of 200 billion dollars and include India, Poland, Austria, Sweden, Netherlands, Spain, Democratic Republic of Germany, Brazil, Mexico, Belgium, Switzerland and Czechoslovakia. Of these, India and

Table 1. *Some fluxes in the major sedimentary cycle* (*adapted in part from Goldberg, 1971*)

Material	Geosphere receiving material	Flux in 10^{14} g/year
Suspended River Solids	Oceans	180
Dissolved River Solids	Oceans	39
Continental Rock and Soil Particles	Atmosphere	1–5
Sea Salt	Atmosphere	3
Volcanic Debris	Stratosphere	0.036
Volcanic Debris	Atmosphere	<1.5
Wastes of Society (excluding fossil fuels)	Hydrosphere, lithosphere atmosphere	30
Wastes dumped from ships	Oceans	1.4
Carbon and fly ash from fossil fuel combustion	Atmosphere	0.25
Industrial particulates (Total)	Atmosphere	0.54
<2 μm		0.12

Brazil are in the tropics, while only Australia is in the southern hemisphere. Thus, as a first approximation, man's atmospheric injections take place under a single transporting agency, the prevailing westerly flow in the northern hemisphere.

The other important parameter governing the dispersion of solids about the atmosphere is the height of injection. Sea salt particles enter at the water-air interface while dusts from volcanoes are estimated to achieve heights of 50 km or more.

The salts of the sea are injected into the atmosphere with the spray and Eriksson (1959) estimates the amount to exceed 1 000 megatons per year. Most of these particles rapidly return to the sea surface. Eriksson computes that about 100 megatons fall upon land and are returned to the oceans in run-off. Assuming both that this latter value represents those salts transported over long distances and that a similar fallout on an areal basis occurs in oceanic domains, then the total amount of sea salt involved in the major sedimentary cycle is about 300 megatons per year.

There have been many estimates of the fluxes through the rivers based upon their flow and their measured dissolved and suspended burdens. On the other hand, only recently has data become available to ascertain the rates of mobilization of rock and soil debris through the atmosphere. Present approaches involve the rates of accumulation of solids in permanent snow fields, rates of accumulation of eolian materials in deep sea sediments, and the standing crops of dusts in the atmosphere.

Windom (1969) determined the accumulation rates of detrital solids in the Greenland and Antarctic ice sheets and in five temperature glaciers, all of which had their upper levels dated by Pb-210 geochronologies. On the bases of size* and mineral distributions, locally derived solids could be distinguished from those that had been transported from distant places. An average value for the accumulation rate of the global component appeared to be around 0.1 mm per thousand years. Taking this rate as representative of the earth's surface and giving such materials a density of 2 g/cm^3, the annual rate of mobilization of continental soil and rock particles to the atmosphere is computed to be 10^{14} g.

---

* The distinction between globally dispersed particles and those introduced locally is most difficult to make. Many investigators base their definitions upon an upper limit in diameter with the concept that particles below some value, say 10 μm or 1–2 μm, have a high probability of being involved in long range transport. Windom (1969) introduced the refinement of considering both the size distributions of minerals and the composition of exposed surface solids near the sampling area. Here there will be no attempt to obtain a uniformity in the published values of globally transported dusts in the atmosphere. Any such effort would be difficult, if not impossible, to make. Also, the uncertainties in the reported values usually exceed any differences that might result from altering the size criterion.

Another estimate involves the average atmosphere dust burden, estimated by Goldberg (1971) to be of the order of 5 μg/m³. If this is representative of dust concentrations to heights of 5 000 m. into the atmosphere, and if from this zone there are 40 removals by rain each year, then a flux of 5×10^{14} g/year is found.

The rates of sedimentation in the open ocean provide means to evaluate the fluxes both of continental and of volcanic debris into and out of the atmosphere. The contributions of wind-borne terrestrial solids to the non-biogenous phases of deep-sea deposits are estimated to be about 50 % (Windon, 1969, Griffin et al., 1968). Their accumulation rates vary between 0.01 and 0.1 cm. per thousand years, or between 0.01 and 0.1 g/cm² per thousand years, since their average density is near 2 g/cm³ and the water content of the sediments averages around 50 %. If 0.1 g/cm² per thousand years is a representative value for both land and sea accumulation of wind-borne solids, then a world flux of 5×10^{14} g/year is found for the mobilization of such continental debris to the atmosphere.

Recent volcanic activity appears to have latitudinal zonations (Cronin, 1971). Over the past several decades, volcanic explosions which have ejected ash and gases into the stratosphere have taken place in two latitudinal belts. One is located in a narrow zone just below the Arctic Circle ($56° - 65°$N) and includes the volcanoes of Kamchatka, the Aleutian Islands, Alaska and Iceland. The other, a broader region, spans the equator from 8°S to 15°N and includes the volcanoes of Indonesia, the Phillipines, Central America, Ecuador, the Galapagos and the Caribbean.

There is a periodicity to these events. During the last two decades there have been two periods of intense volcanic activity, 1950–1956 and 1963–1970 with a quiet period intervening. In the former period, seven major events occurred, including perhaps the most violent eruption of the century, the Bezymianny explosion in central Kamchatka. In 1963, the major eruption of Agung on the Island of Bali placed great quantities of material into the stratosphere. Such periods of activity appear to influence the atmosphere turbidity.

Volcanic ashes rapidly degrade in the marine environment to montmorillonite as well as to some other less abundant phases. The montmorillonite contents in the sediments allow estimates to be made of the amounts of volcanic material annually injected into the atmosphere. The zones of highest montmorillonite concentration, the eastern equatorial and the south Pacific, have their deposits composed almost entirely of volcanic debris and their degradation products. Their measured rates of sedimentation, several tenths to a half of a mm per thousand years, represent an upper limit to the accumulation of atmospherically introduced volcanic debris. In other areas, wind, river and glacially transported continental materials dilute the volcanic solids. If the fallout of volcanic materials in pelagic sediments (density of solids taken as 2 g/cm^3 in a sediment composed of 50 % water) is characteristic of that over the surface of the earth, then up to 1.5×10^{14} g is calculated to be the amount of volcanic dust annually introduced to the atmosphere.

Mitchell (1970) found a stratospheric flux of 3.6×10^{12} g/year for volcanic debris with the following model: (*a*) the dust that reaches the stratosphere is 1 % of the material erupted and it has a residence time there of 14 months; (b) the remaining 99 % of the mass, after introduction to the atmosphere as larger particles, falls back to the earth's surface in much shorter time periods; and (c) the contribution of each eruption is taken as one half of its stratospheric injection mass in the first year. He derived a loading of volcanic debris in the stratosphere of 4.2×10^{12} g.

The major fluxes in the sedimentary cycle range between tenths and tens of billions of tons per year (Table 1). Although the individually calculated numbers rest upon tenuous assumptions or data, nevertheless, their containment within these two order of magnitude provides a basis to understand man's influence upon the cycle.

Detailed compilations of material and energy utilization data have been published in the United States. Such considerations can be extended globally in the following approximate way. The U.S. is responsible for about 35 % of the world's energy consumption. A similar figure applies to resource utilization. As a first approximation, then, the world's utilization of energy and matter can be taken as thrice that of the U.S. For example, the U.S. society utilizes 5 tons of mineral, food, and forest products per person per year. This can be extrapolated to a world usage of 3×10^{15} g/year. Since the world society disposes of, rather than accumulates, the materials necessary for its ways of life, this utilization is somewhat equivalent to the annual global waste problem —a cube about a kilometer on a side. But more important, its magnitude is comparable to fluxes in the major sedimentary cycle.

In addition, landscape alteration may have altered the intensity of the sedimentary cycle. Judson (1968) offers several lines of reasoning to indicate that the rate of continental erosion (and consequentially the delivery of suspended and dissolved solids to the oceans) has increased by a factor of 2 or 3 due to man-induced changes in land use. The transformation of forests to croplands and grazing areas seems to increase the erosion rate tenfold. With one fourth of the U.S. area now so involved, the erosion rate may be larger by a factor of slightly greater than 3.

Judson approaches the global problem in another way by noting that for areas unaffected by the activities of man the erosion rate appears to be about 3.6 cm per thousand years. Continental areas of 151 million square kilometers include 100 million square kilometers whose weathered products are carried to the sea by rivers (areas like the interior of Australia and the western U.S. have no rivers to carry erosion products to the oceans). With a density of eroded materials of 2.6 g/cm³, this weathered material brought to the marine environment is 93×10^{14} g. The total flux of materials to the oceans is about 220×10^{14} g (Table 1; river bed load is not included here but it is probably about 5% or less of the total load carried by rivers). Thus, man appears to have more than doubled rate of erosion.

About 48 million tons of wastes are dumped from ships at sea in the U.S. during 1968 (Table 2). Dredge spoils account for the bulk of this disposal and include besides sediments, industrial, domestic and agricultural wastes.

Only a small portion of the domestic solid wastes, 26 000 out of 190 000 tons, is subject to oceanic disposal. Trebling these figures, a global value of 1.4×10^{14} grams of oceanic dumping per year is estimated. This may be compared with a suspended river input of 180×10^{14} g/year. Whereas the river discharge areas are fixed, the ship disposal sites can vary. The increasing volumes of oceanic dumping (CEQ, 1970) may cause extensive damage to the inshore marine environment.

Man's contribution to atmospheric dust loads has been investigated by Parkin et al. (1970) in airs above the temperate north Atlantic. The eolian solids were grey to dark grey in color resulting from contents of fly ash and carbon from the combustion of fossil fuels. These materials constituted 60% of the dusts near land and 5% over the open ocean. Goldberg (1971) used the data to attain a value of 0.25 micrograms of fly ash per cubic meter of air over the north Atlantic. A sedimentation rate to the earth's surface may be based on a removal of the particles every ten days with rain. For a 5 km column, 1 m² in cross section, there would be a standing crop of 1 250 micrograms of man-introduced solids. This yields a sedimentation rate of 0.05 mm per thousand years, where the solid phases have a density of 2 g/cm³ and the sediments contain fifty percent water. This is much lower than the rates of accumulation of continental and volcanic solids which amass at levels of millimeters or fraction of millimeters per thousand years.

Table 2. *Ocean dumping in the U.S. for 1968 (CEQ, 1970)*

Waste Type	Amount in tons	Percent
Dredge spoils	38 428 000	80
Industrial wastes	4 690 500	10
Sewage sludge	4 477 000	9
Construction and demolition debris	574 000	1.2
Solid waste	26 000	< 1
Explosives	15 200	< 1
Total	48 210 700	100

Table 3. *Sources of U.S. particulate emissions from stationary operations. In percent* (*Shannon et al., 1971*)

Fuel Combustion	33
Crushed stone, sand and gravel	25.6
Agriculture	9.8
Iron and steel	7.5
Cement	5.2
Forest, Products	3.7
Lime	3.2
Clay	2.6
Primary non-ferrous metals	2.6
Fertilizer & phosphate rock	1.9
Asphalt	1.2
Ferroalloys	0.9
Iron foundries	0.8
Secondary non-ferrous metals	0.7
Carbon black	0.5
Coal cleaning	0.5
Petroleum	0.25
Mineral acids	0.1

About 18×10^{12} grams of particulates per year are broadcast about the atmosphere from stationary sources[1] in the U.S. (Shannon et al., 1970). The fine particle component (sizes less than 2 μm) is estimated to be about 22 % of this figure, 4×10^6 tons per year. The major sources are fuel combustion, the crushed stone industry, agriculture and related operations, the iron and steel industry and the cement industry (Table 3). If the U.S. represents one third of the world's inputs of such solids, then on a global basis the total and fine particle emissions are 54×10^{12} and 12×10^{12} g/year respectively. The smaller particles are preferentially emitted from operations involving combustion, condensation and vaporization as compared to those from mechanical processes. The most abundant particles are oxides of silicon, iron, aluminum, calcium and magnesium and calcium carbonate.

Fossil Fuels

The direct introduction of crude oil and petroleum products to the marine environment through human activity far exceeds natural seepages (Table 4). The annual influxes due to man appear to be of the order of 2.1×10^{12} g. On the other hand, an upper limit of natural seepages, 10^{11} g/year, was obtained by Revelle et al. (1970) with the argument that, if such an amount did enter the marine environment, the total estimated oil reserves would be depleted within a few million years.

---

[1] The particles from moving sources, primarily transportation, would increase these figures almost 5 percent (SCEP, 1970).

Table 4. *The involvement of petroleum with the marine environment (Data from SCEP, 1970)*

World Oil Production (1969)	1.82×10^{15} g/year
Oil transport by tanker (1969)	1.18×10^{15} g/year
Direct injections into marine environment through man's activities.	
Tanker operations	0.5×10^{12} g/year
Other ship operations	0.5×10^{12} g/year
Off-shore oil producton	0.1×10^{12} g/year
Accidental spills	0.2×10^{12} g/year
Refinery operations	0.3×10^{12} g/year
Industrial and automotive wastes	0.45×10^{12} g/year
Total	2.1×10^{12} g/year
Torrey Canyon Discharge	0.118×10^{12} g
Santa Barbara Blowout	$0.003–0.011 \times 10^{12}$ g
Atmospheric input from continents through vaporization of petroleums products	90×10^{12} g/year
Natural seepage into ocean	$<0.1 \times 10^{12}$ g/year

The direct hydrocarbon entries to the world's waters may be dwarfed by those from the atmosphere following the vaporization of petroleum products on the continents, estimated to occur at about 90×10^{12} g/year. Although a substantial portion of such gases may be oxidized in the atmosphere, the resistant part can fall to the land and sea surfaces subsequent to sorption on dust particles or with rain.

The heaviest influxes occur near or between man's habitats. Hydrocarbon fallout from the atmosphere takes place primarily in the mid-latitudes of the northern hemisphere, the band of heavily industrialized populations and the zone of the transporting system, the jet streams. The leakages of oils from ship and nearshore drilling operations have stained the waters of our coastal areas and shipping lanes quite conspicuously. The ofttimes spectacular ship disasters or blowouts can introduce amounts of oil which are substantial fractions of the chronic injection rate. For example, the breakup of the tanker *Torrey Canyon* dispersed oil about the sea at a level equal to 5% of the annual injection rate (Table 4). It is revealing to note that the annual world oil production of 1.82×10^{15} g, if spread over the entire oceanic area of 3.6×10^{18} cm², would produce a film of but 0.5 mg/cm².

The veneer of petroleum accumulating at the sea surface is extending the natural film of fatty acids and alcohols. Such a coating, perhaps a hundred to a thousand Å thick, may act as a concentration site for oil soluble substances, such as DDT, freon and the polychlorinated biphenyls, being dispersed by human activities to our surroundings.

The combustion of fossil fuels, coal, oil, lignite and natural gas, can potentially mobilize many elements into the atmosphere at rates in general less than, but comparable to, their rates of flow through natural waters during weathering cycles (Bertine and Goldberg, 1971). The world production of fossil fuels, and presumably their utilization, in 1967 was (SCEP, 1970):

coal	1.75×10^{15} g/year
lignite	1.04×10^{15} g/year
fuel oils	1.63×10^{15} g/year
natural gas	0.66×10^{15} g/year

The computed fluxes assume (1) about 10 % of the total ash produced escapes to the atmosphere (fly ash) with the remainder (bottom ash) collected in the combustion apparatus; and (2) about half of the coal mined is burned with the other half utilized in the manufacture of coke (Table 5).

The amount of an element yearly entering the world's oceans from rivers can be obtained from water discharge and composition data or from rates of sedimentation in marine areas. Both numbers are usually given in the Table 5. The river data consider only the transfer of dissolved phases, while the sedimentation numbers take into account both the dissolved and the particulate loads of rivers. Both methods depend upon obtaining global averages of geological parameters, numbers which have some uncertainty in them.

Table 5. *The mobilization of elements during the combustion of fossil fuels and during weathering processes* (*Bertine and Goldberg, 1971*) (10^9 g/year)

Element	Fossil fuel mobilization	Weathering mobilization	Element	Fossil fuel mobilization	Weathering mobilization
Be	0.41	5.6	Cu	2.1	80–250
B	10.5	360	Zn	7	80–720
Na	280	57 000–230 000	Ga	1	3–30
			Ge	0.7	12
Mg	280	42 000–148 000	As	0.7	72
			Se	0.45	7.2
Al	1 400	14 000–140 000	Sr	70	600–1 800
S	3 400	140 000	Y	1.4	25–60
Ca	1 400	70 000–540 000	Mo	2.3	28–36
Sc	0.7	0.14–10	Ag	0.07	0.03–11
Ti	70	108–9 000	Sn	0.28	11
V	12	32–280	Ba	70	360–500
Cr	1.5	36–200	La	1.4	7.2–40
Mn	7	250–2 000	Ce	1.6	2.2–90
Fe	1 400	24 000–100 000	Er	0.085	1.8–5.0
			Hg	1.6	1.0–2.5
Co	0.7	7.2–8	Pb	3.6	21–110
Ni	3.7	11–160	U	0.14	8–11

Selective volatilization can introduce the readily distillable materials at levels as much as twenty times greater than those indicated in Table 5. Observations of emissions from the d. c. arc spectrograph both for elemental states and for the oxides, sulfates, carbonates, silicates, phosphates and sulfides indicate a preferential transfer of As, Hg, Cd, Sn, Sb, Pb, Zn, Tl, Ag and Bi to the atmosphere during fuel burning.

The mid-latitudes of the northern hemisphere are the principle sites of fossil fuel combustion and the consequential alterations in the compositions of rivers, lakes and coastal sea waters should evidence themselves there.

About 30×10^{12} grams of sulfur dioxide are discharged annually into the U.S. atmosphere as a result of fossil fuel burning and a world figure of around 100×10^{12} g/year is a reasonable estimate. Such an input appears to have been identified in atmospheric fallout over the natural SO_2 background by Koide and Goldberg (1971). The sulfate contents in Greenland glacial ices (after correction for contributions from sea salt) doubled within the past decade, a phenomenon attributed to fuel combustion. Thus, society seems to compete now with nature on an equal basis with respect to sulfur emissions. The natural injections come from volcanic activity and from the bacterial decomposition of organic matter in soils and coastal sediments. Sea spray, on the basis of the chloride contents of these glacial ices, does not contribute significant quantities of sulfate compared to these other two sources. The sulfur dioxide has a short residence time in the atmosphere; estimates range from hours to several days.

On the other hand, selenium, the vertical periodic table neighbor of sulfur, is mobilized to a much lesser extent through the atmosphere, a difference most probably related to the chemical behavior of their respective tetravalent oxides (Weiss et al., 1971 b). Sulfur dioxide is a moderately stable gas; selenium dioxide, a white solid, reacts readily in air to form red elemental selenium. There has been no evident increase of selenium in the Greenland ice sheets during the last decade, indicating it has not been globally dispersed in the manner of sulfur following fossil fuel burning.

The input of nitrogen oxides from fuel burning 20.6×10^{12} grams into the U.S. atmosphere or perhaps around 60×10^{12} grams on a worldwide basis (SCEP, 1970). NO is very rapidly oxidized by ozone to NO_2 which is one of the building blocks of photochemical smog through its reactions with hydrocarbons in the presence of sunlight. NO_2 can be decomposed by the adsorption of visible radiation. The influence on the nitrogen cycle by man-made oxides is as yet undetermined.

The fate of the 13.4×10^{15} grams of carbon dioxide produced by world fossil fuel combustion has been considered in the SCEP report (1970) upon which the following summary is based. The CO_2 content in the atmosphere is increasing at about 0.5 % annually, i.e. the present concentration of about 320 ppm on a volume basis rises 0.7 ppm each year. There is about 1 ppm more CO_2 in the most northerly samples (Point Barrow, Alaska) than in the Antarctic samples. Distinct seasonal oscillations occur, higher at higher latitudes (about 9 ppm at Point Barrow, Alaska) and at higher altitudes.

About 50 % of the CO_2 that has been added to the atmosphere in the past decade has remained there; the reservoirs for the other 50 % are probably identified properly as the biosphere, the mass of living and non-living organic matter in the oceans and on land, and the oceans. The biosphere could take up additional CO_2 by growing faster but the quantitative aspects of this have not been developed. The relative importance of these two sinks remains to be resolved. It is interesting to note that the input of carbon dioxide by fossil fuel burning is about equal to the amount fixed annually by photosynthesis on land and on sea, 50×10^{15} g/year.

The estimated injection rate of carbon monoxide (world) into the atmosphere is 2×10^{14} g/year. Measurements in the Atlantic and Pacific Oceans have indicated these waters are the largest natural sources of carbon monoxide (Swinnerton et al., 1970). Conservatively, the amounts introduced are of the same order as those generated by fuel combustion (Seiler at this symposium).

The soil micro-organisms are capable of removing carbon monoxide from the atmosphere. On the basis of laboratory experiments with natural soils, Inman et al. (1971) concluded that metabolism by soil bacteria is a major sink for CO.

About 9×10^{13} grams of uncombusted hydrocarbons annually enter the atmosphere and can be involved in the photochemical formation of aerosols. The absorption of solar ultraviolet light by gaseous molecules including nitrogen dioxide produce ozone and nitric oxides which react with the hydrocarbons to produce "photochemical smog".

Halogenated Hydrocarbons

Of the thousands of synthetic organic compounds made each year, only data on the chlorinated hydrocarbon pesticides are comprehensive enough to allow flux calculations. Such substances as DDT and its degradation products (hereafter referred to as DDT residues), dieldrin, endrin, heptachlor, and benzene hexachloride, are not produced in measurable amounts by marine organisms, but have been detected in all levels of the food web. The DDT residues have been extensively analyzed and this treatment will emphasize them. The polychlorinated biphenyls (PCBs) have been used much longer (since the 1930s whereas the pesticides came into use after 1946) and have been detected in many members of the marine biosphere. However, not enough measurements on them have been carried out to formulate mass balances.

The total amount of DDT so far produced in the world is about 2×10^{12} grams with a present yearly production rate of 10^{11} grams (SCEP, 1970).

The atmosphere is most probably the major route of transfer of the DDT into the oceans from the continents (NASCO, 1971). DDT residues can be enveloped within wind systems during their aerial or ground application to plants or can volatalize from surfaces which have accommodated them. Once in the atmosphere they primarily return to the earth's surface in rains.

Analyses of western U.S. rivers give 100 parts per trillion as a maximum concentration of DDT residues. If the total world river discharge of 3.7×10^{19} cm³/year contained this amount, then an upper limit of 3.7×10^9 g of DDT residues would be annually transported by the rivers to the sea, about 3 % of the world production.

The DDT residue movement through the atmosphere can be estimated by considering its content in rains. The most extensive measurements were carried out in Great Britain where the average of 80 parts per trillion was found in samples measured at 7 stations between August 1966 and July 1967. DDT residues in south Florida precipitation averaged 1 000 parts per trillion in 18 samples taken at 4 sites between June 1968 and May 1969. If the annual precipitation over the ocean, 3.0×10^{20} cm³, contained the English content of DDT residues, a total of 2.4×10^{10} g/year would be transported to the oceans, about one quarter of the estimated DDT annual production.

The PCBs are ubiquitously distributed in the members of the marine and terrestrial biosphere and on the basis of present analyses may be the most abundant group of synthetic organic chemicals in the environment. They are used industrially as insulating fluids in electrical equipment, as heat exchangers, plasticizers and in a variety of other ways. They exist in a large number of homologues and isomers with 210 different chlorinated biphenyls possible. The following discussion is based upon the results of A Study on Marine Enivironmental Quality, held under the auspices of the Ocean Affairs Board of the National Academy of Sciences-National Research Council at Durham, New Hampshire, August 9–13, 1971.

Production figures are in general not released by manufacturers. Recent estimates of global production are based upon Japanese production figures. A yearly output of these chemicals in the range of 0.05 to 0.1 megaton now appears reasonable with an integrated production of a megaton. These figures are very similar to those for DDT.

Leakage to the environment probably takes place through discharges to water systems such as rivers and sewage outfalls, through the atmosphere following volatilization or through incineration, or through dumping. The relative importance of these methods of dispersion is not as yet known.

Analyses of plankton and fish indicate that the PCBs now exceed the DDT residues in concentration. Such was the case with freshwater fish monitored by the U.S. Bureau of Sport Fisheries and Wildlife (Henderson et al., 1969) and with marine zooplankton and fish from the Atlantic analyzed at the Woods Hole Oceanographic Institution (Vaughan Bowen, personal communication) and from the Pacific analyzed at the Fishery Oceanography Center, La Jolla, California (Izadore Barrett, personal communication).

Metals

The metals that are disseminated to the atmosphere in discharges from manufacturing, mining operations, power production and agriculture can have altered environmental concentrations on both global and regional scales. There are increased lead concentrations in surface ocean waters and elevated levels of mercury in recent glacial strata (see following sections). Most probably the atmospheric and hydrospheric burdens of other metals have been similarly affected, although there is little evidence to strengthen this argument. An entry to the problem may be found in an examination of atmospheric aerosol compositions, which can provide indications, if not estimates, of man's environmental impact.

A useful model assumes that atmospheric particulates are removed by rain every nine days (or forty times a year) from a column 5 000 m in height. Although the mid-latitudes of the northern hemisphere are the sites of broadcast for most of man's wastes, nonetheless, a fallout over the surface of the earth is assumed. This does overestimate global fallout somewhat, but it does take into account the effects of atmospheric mixing. Examples of such calculations are given in Table 6.

The Na, Mg, Ca, K and Sr concentrations in the atmospheric particulates bear a strong resemblance to their sea water values, strongly indicating a marine source for these metals. On the other hand, the other metals are markedly enriched in the atmospheric dusts and clearly must have different sources. Compared to the aluminum and iron concentrations, the Pb, Cu, Mn and V are too high for an origin in soils or crustal rocks. It is reasonable that these latter metals had sources in human activities—lead in lead alkyl combustion, vanadium from the burning of diesel oils, etc.

It is comforting to see the agreement between these computations with independent estimates of atmospheric mobilizations. For example, the computed sodium washout (350 megatons per year) agrees with that previously

Table 6. *Atmospheric mobilizations of some metals*

Metal	Concentration in air as atmospheric particulates[a] (ng/m³)	Concentration in seawater (mg/l)	Atmospheric rainout Megatons/year
Na	3 500 ± 2 000	10 500	350
Mg	410 ± 240	1 350	40
Ca	160 ± 90	400	16
K	120 ± 60	380	12
Sr	2.4 ± 1.5	8	0.24
Fe	12.0 ± 9.0	0.01	1.2
Pb	3.0 ± 2.8	0.00003	0.3
Cu	1.9 ± 2.1	0.003	0.2
Mn	0.19 ± 0.14	0.002	0.02
Al	6.7 ± 7.2	0.01	0.7
V	0.16 ± 0.11	0.002	0.02

[a] Collected from a tower on the windward coast of Oahu, Hawaii when the tradewinds had been blowing at least 24 hours before the start of sampling and during the entire sampling period. From unpublished Ph.D. thesis of G. L. Hoffman, Trace metals in the Hawaiian marine atmosphere, University of Hawaii, 1971. An average of at least 56 samples for all elements.

obtained from sea salt fluxes (300 megatons per year). The lead value of 0.3 megatons per year is in conformity with the lead alkyl production and presumably lead discharge to the atmosphere of 0.31 megatons per year (Table 8).

Heavy Metals: Mercury

There is one indication that substantial quantities of mercury are being mobilized over large expanses of the earth by the activities of man: the mercury contents in snows deposited on the Greenland Glacier have increased in recent years (Weiss et al., 1971 a). This mercury, presumably removed from the atmosphere in precipitation, has levels ranging from 30 to 75 ng/kg of water (average 60) during the period 800 BC to 1952 and from 87 to 230 ng/kg of water (average 152) between 1952 and 1965. If this increase is man-caused, how did he bring it about? An examination of environmental mercury fluxes (Table 7) suggests that the mercury burden of the atmosphere arises from the degassing of the earth's crust and that, if there is an impact by man, it must be through an enhancement of this degassing process.

The flow of mercury from the continents to the atmosphere is calculated to be in the region of 2.5 to 15×10^{10} g/year (Table 7). The mercury content in unpolluted airs ranges from less than 1 to 10 ng/m³. A conservative average of 1 ng/m³ yields a total atmospheric burden of 0.4×10^{10} g. Rain effectively washes the mercury out of the air. Taking an average time between rains of 10 days, the annual flux of mercury is 1.5×10^{11} g. A complementary calculation

Table 7. *Environmental mercury fluxes* (*Weiss et al., 1971*)

	Flux in g/year
Natural flows	
Continents to atmosphere	
Basis of precipitation with rain	8.4×10^{10}
Basis of atmospheric content	1.5×10^{11}
Basis of content in Greenland Glacier	2.5×10^{10}
River transport to oceans	$< 3.8 \times 10^9$
Flows involving man	
World Production (1968)	8.8×10^9
Entry to atmosphere from fossil fuel combustion	1.6×10^9
Entry to atmosphere during cement manufacture	1.0×10^8
Losses in industrial and agricultural usage	4.0×10^9

involves the mercury content of rain. The mercury concentration in rain water averages 0.2 parts per billion. An annual world precipitation of 4.2×10^{17} liters gives a flux of 8.4×10^{10} g/year. Using the pre-1952 glacier water as representative of typical fallout, a flux of 2.5×10^{10} g/year is calculated.

The principle transfer of mercury from the continents to the oceans most probably takes place through the atmosphere. The mercury carried by the rivers to the oceans is at least one order of magnitude less than the amount volatilized from the earth to the atmosphere (Table 7).

A survey of industrial activities has not revealed any mercury releases to the atmosphere that rival that of the natural degassing rate (Table 7). Thus, increased fluxes through the actions of man probably come about as a result of the enhancement of this degassing process. Landscape alterations that result in disturbances to surface solids, agriculture, mining, construction, etc., can allow more mercury vapor and more gaseous mercury compounds to enter the atmosphere.

Heavy Metals: Lead

Lead, like mercury, is being introduced to the marine environment through man's activities in amounts that begin to rival those brought in by the rivers (Table 8). The primary source of lead from society is its emission from internal combustion engines where it is used as an anti-knock additive in the fuel. Fourteen percent of the lead consumed in the U.S. is released in this way (CEQ, 1971).

The dispersion of lead to the surroundings by man has been taking place for at least several millenia in measurable amounts. The concentrations of lead that precipitate from the atmosphere are recorded in the annual layers of permanent snowfields. Murozumi et al. (1969) found lead increasing in a north

Table 8. *Annual lead budget (Murozumi et al., 1969)*

	10^{12} g/year
World lead production (1966)	3.5
Northern hemisphere production	3.1
Lead burned as alkyls	0.31
River import of soluble lead to marine environment	0.24
River input of particulate lead to marine environment	0.50

Greenland glacier 25-fold from 800 BC to 1750 as a result of smelting operations. By 1940 the lead levels were 175 times greater than the pre-historic
values, whereas in 1966 they were 500 times greater. Up to 1940, the increases
are attributed to smelting, and subsequently to the combustion of lead tetraethyl. The lead emitted from internal combustion engines, in the micron (μm)
and sub-micron ranges, is removed primarily by precipitation from the atmosphere.

Surface ocean concentrations of lead have dramatically increased as a consequence of the rainout of man-introduced lead from the atmosphere.
Contents in surface waters of the northern hemisphere today are about 0.07
micrograms of Pb per kg of sea water compared with estimated pre-historic
values of 0.01 to 0.02 μg/kg (Chow and Patterson, 1966).

Most probably the greater portion of the lead burned in internal combustion
engines eventually enters the marine environment. That which rains down upon
the continents can be transferred to the ocean by the rivers. The effect of this
increased lead upon surface marine organisms is unknown as yet. If the use
of lead in gasolines is curtailed, the concentration in surface waters will probably revert to much lower values within a decade, as the residence time of
this element in surface waters appears to be of the order of several years, with
removal primarily through biological activity.

Artificial Radioactivities

The natural radioactive background of the atmosphere and of the oceans has
been increased by man's introduction of artificially produced radionuclides
through fission and fusion explosive devices and through the production of
energy by nuclear fission. The bomb detonations have not occurred uniformly
with time, although there has been an increasing number of nuclear power
plants established. The nuclear explosions have introduced far more artificial
radioactive species to the oceans than have the reactors or nuclear fuel reprocessing plants up to the present. The oceanic burdens in 1970 were (Preston et al.
1971):

Source of radioactivity	Amount in oceans in Curies
Nuclear explosions:	
Fission products exclusive of H-3	2–6×10^8
H-3	10^9
Reactors and fuel reprocessing	
Fission and activation products	
exclusive of H-3	3×10^5
H-3	3×10^5
Total	10^9
Natural radioactivities	
K-40	5×10^{11}

The artificial radioactivities attain but 1/1000 of the total natural radioactivity in the oceans. This level will probably not increase very much in the foreseeable future (Preston et al., 1971). Weapon tests appear to be decreasing in number. Although nuclear power programs and the concommittant fuel reprocessing operations will increase, improvements in the management of radioactive wastes and their containment on land, will lessen the chances of any global contamination. These remarks do not apply to some individual isotopes like tritium, H-3, whose environmental levels are expected to rise primarily as a result of leakage from nuclear reprocessing plants, and to plutonium.

Synthetic Organics Other than Halogenated Hydrocarbons

Volatile synthetic organics can escape to the atmosphere at rates of the order of millions of tons per year during their production or utilization. For example, about 2.5 % of the total U.S. production of gasoline is lost by volatilization during transfer processes, from production site to vehicles and to storage tanks, and from carbureators. This amounts to 1.75×10^{12} g/year (Duprey, 1968). The evaporation of dry cleaning solvents reaches levels of 3.3×10^{11} g/year (Duprey, 1968) about equal to the production rate of the most widely used one, perchloroethyelene, 2.1×10^{11} g/year. Global values might reach two to three times the above values. The fates of such vapors in the atmosphere are not known.

The production of synthetic organics involves about 5 % of the annual petroleum production or about 10^{14} g/year on a worldwide basis. Many of these substances have low boiling points and high stabilities and can be expected to enter and to persist in the atmosphere and oceans. Table 9 lists the production of such substances in the U.S. in order of rank and with boiling points and water solubilities.

There are already evidences that such substances may be entering our surroundings in substantial amounts. With production rates of 10^{10} to 10^{12}

Table 9. *U.S. production of synthetic organic chemicals and their properties*
(*Anonymous, 1970*)

Substance	Annual production $\times 10^{12}$ g	Boiling point °C	Water solubility[a]
Boiling points between <0 to 30°C			
Formaldehyde	2.0	−21	s
Vinyl chloride	1.4	−14	ss
Ethylene oxide	1.2	13–14	s
Acetaldehyde	0.72	21	vs
Ethyl chloride	0.26	13	ss
Dichlorodifluoromethane	0.15	−29	s
Methyl chloride	0.14	−24	s
Glycerol tri-ether	0.10	0.95	
Trichlorofluoromethane	0.09		
Methyl amine	0.050	− 6	vs
Boiling points between 30 and 60°C			
Acetone	0.62	56	vs
Propylene oxide	0.44	35	vs
Carbon disulphide	0.36	45	s
Methylene chloride	0.14	40–41	ss
Diethyl ether	0.050	35	s
Boiling points between 60 and 100°C			
1,2-dichloroethane	2.2	84	ss
Methanol	1.7	65	vs
Ethanol	0.96	78.5	vs
Cyclohexane	0.93	81	i
Boiling points between 60 and 100°C			
Isopropyl alcohol	0.93	82	vs
Acrylonitrile	0.46	90–92	s
Carbon tetrachloride	0.35	77	i
Vinyl acetate	0.33	71–72	i
Trichloroethylene	0.24	87	ss
2-Butanone	0.21	80	vs
Methyl chloroform	0.14	74	i
Chloroform	0.082	61	s
Ethyl acetate	0.081	77	s
Ethyl acrylate	0.075	100	

[a] vs, very soluble; s, soluble; ss, slightly soluble; i, insoluble.

grams per year, losses in the percent range could contribute measurable amounts to the environment. Some recent work indicates that such losses are detectable. Trichloro-fluoromethane, one of the freons used as a propellant in dispensers and fire extinguishers and in refrigerant fluids, has been measured in winds over southwest Ireland in July and August 1970 with contents of 2×10^{-10} and 1×10^{-11} volume per volume of air coming from the directions 225°–315° and 45°–135° respectively (Lovelock, 1971). Corwin (1970) found acetone, butyraldehyde and 2-butanone (methyl-ethyl ketone) in surface waters from the Florida Straits, eastern Mediterranean (no butyraldehyde found) and the Amazon estuary. These low molecular weight species, with relatively low boiling points and high water solubilities, may leak to the surroundings during production or utilization by man.

Discussion

The amounts of materials that man is introducing into the sedimentary cycle are approaching, and in a few cases exceeding, those of geological processes. Sometimes the impacts of man are readily detectable, lead in surface sea waters, increasing contents of carbon dioxide in the atmosphere, or petroleum in marine organisms. For substances alien to the surroundings, such as DDT or artificial radioactivities, man's invasion can easily be identified.

On the other hand, global scale impingements of society may be difficult to observe, especially where there are large background fluctuations in the material under consideration. The site of the measurements also can be most significant as both man's and nature's injections can have zonal or regional distributions.

Such may be the case with atmospheric turbidity. Ludwig et al. (1969) indicates the intrusion of man-injected detritus on nonurban air quality in the U.S. with a statistically significant increase from 25.4 $\mu g/m^3$ for the period 1962–1966. On the other hand, for U.S. cities a 7 % decrease was observed over about the same period. This latter effect was attributed to effective control measures applied by local agencies.

At Mauna Loa, Hawaii, measurements of solar radiation over a 13 year period (1957–1970) indicated no evidence of man's alteration of atmospheric turbidity (Ellis and Pueschel, 1971). This observation is not surprising. The site of observation (19°31'N and 155°35'W) is at the lower limit of the jet stream which would transport matter from human activities in Europe and Asia. A decrease in insolation occurred in 1963, an event which coincided with the eruption of Mount Agung in Bali. The return of atmospheric transmission to the 1963 level took 7 years. This long recovery period was attributed to a continued fallout of particles from the stratosphere, a continuous production of atmospheric aerosols from volcanic gases, such as sulfuric acid from SO_2, an input of particles from subsequent volcanic explosions, or a combination of any of the three.

The changes in composition of three U.S. rivers, the Illinois, the Mississippi, and the Ohio and of Lake Michigan during the past century have been chartered by Ackerman et al. (1970). There has been a significant increase in their dissolved loads since the beginning of the century as follows:

Species	Average % change per year— Time Interval given in parenthesis		
Chloride	2.0	(52 years)–4.3 (70 years)	
Sulfate	2.0	(43 years)–2.5 (62 years)	
Nitrate	1.1	(50 years)–2.3 (70 years)	
Dissolved solids	0.17 (108 years)–0.7 (71 years)		

Lake Michigan has shown a decline in nitrate concentrations in recent years, a phenomenon that may be related to the change in sampling sites. The long

Table 10. *Sulfate fluxes in rivers. Chloride, sulfate and discharge data from Livingston (1963). Table adapted from Berner (1971)*

| | Total Cl$^-$ (mg/l) | Total SO$_4^{2-}$ (mg/l) | Pollutant SO$_4^{2-}$ (mg/l) | Flux to Oceans in 10^{12} g/year | | |
				H$_2$O	SO$_4^{2-}$ (natural)	SO$_4^{2-}$ (pollution)
Europe	6.9	24	17	2.5×10^6	17	45
N. America	8.0	20	12	4.6×10^6	37	55
S. America	4.9	4.8	0	8.2×10^6	39	0
Africa	12.1	13.5	0	6.0×10^6	81	0
Asia	8.7	8.4	0	11.2×10^6	94	0
Total				32.5×10^6	268	100

term changes in alkalinity were not of a substantial nature in any of the four areas.

A similar sense was reached by Berner (1971) through an examination of the dissolved sulfate concentrations in rivers flowing through areas of high and low levels of industrialization. The argument is made that most of the world's sulfur pollution arises in the northern hemisphere, primarily Europe and North America. On the other hand, the rivers flowing through Asia, Africa and South America are assumed to receive trivial amounts of sulfur as a result of man's activities. Thus, by accepting a SO$_4^{2-}$/Cl$^-$ ratio for unpolluted waters equal to the average of the rivers of Asia, Africa and South America, a correction factor can be applied to European and North American rivers to take into account pollution caused by man (Table 10). Utilizing the discharge data of Livingston (1963), Berner calculated the flux of natural and pollution sulfate for each continent (Table 10). On a global basis, it appears that 1.0×10^{14} grams of the 3.68×10^{14} grams of sulfate annually brought by the rivers to the oceans can be attributed to man. Since many of the analyses for average river values were obtained before 1900, the sulphate pollution value of 27 % [$(1.00/3.68) \times 100$)] is probably a lower limit.

It is interesting to note that the 100 megatons of sulphate pollution presumably carried by the rivers compares favorably with the 150 megatons of sulphate (100 megatons of SO$_2$) released annually to the atmosphere through the combustion of fossil fuels.

References

Ackermann, W. C., Marmeson, R. H. & Sinclair, R. A., Some long-term trends in water quality of rivers and lakes. EOS, *51*, 516 (1970).

Anonymous, Synthetic organic chemicals, U. S. Production and Sales, 1968 U. S. Tariff Commission Publication 327 (1970).

Berner, R. A., Worldwide sulfur pollution of rivers. J. Geophys. Research, *76*, 6597 (1971).

Bertine, K. K. & Goldberg, E. D., Fossil fuel combustion and the major sedimentary cycle. Science, *173*, 233 (1971).

CEQ, Ocean dumping. A National Policy. U.S. Council on Environmental Quality 45 p. (1970).

Chow, T. J. & Patterson, C. C., Concentration profiles of barium and lead in Atlantic waters off Bermuda. Earth Planetary Sci. Letters, *1*, 397 (1966).

Corwin, J. F., Volatile organic materials in sea water. In "Organic Matter in Natural Waters", Ed. Donald W. Hood, Institute of Marine Science Occasional Publication No. 1. University of Alaska, pp. 169–180 (1970).

Cronin, F. J., Recent volcanism and the stratosphere. Science, *172*, 847 (1971).

Duprey, R. L., Compilation of air pollutant emission factors. U.S. Public Health Service Publication No. 999-Ap-42, 67 p. (1968).

Ellis, H. T. & Pueschel, R. F., Solar radiation: Absence of air pollution trends at Mauuna Loa. Science, *172*, 845 (1971).

Eriksson, E., The yearly circulation of chloride and sulfur in nature; Meteorological, geochemical and pedological implications I. Tellus, *11*, 375 (1959).

Goldberg, E. D., Atmospheric dust, the sedimentary cycle and man. Comments in Earth Sciences: Geophysics, *1*, 117 (1971).

Goldberg, E. D. & Bertine, K. K., GNP/Area ratio as a measure of national pollution. Marine Pollution Bull., *2*, 94 (1971).

Griffin, J. J., Windom, H. & Goldberg, E. D., The distribution of clay minerals in the world ocean. Deep-Sea Research, *15*, 433 (1968).

Henderson, C., Inglis, A. & Johnson, W. L., Organochlorine insecticide residues in Fish—Fall, 1969. Pesticides Monitoring Journal, *5*, 11 (1971).

Inman, R. E., Ingersol, R. B. & Levy, E. A., Soil, a natural sink for carbon monoxide. Science, *172*, 1229 (1971).

Judson, S., Erosion of the land. Amer. Scientist, *56*, 356 (1968).

Koide, M. & Goldberg, E. D., Atmospheric sulfur and fossil fuel combustion. J. Geophys. Research, *76*, 6589 (1971).

Livingston, D. A., Chemical composition of rivers and lakes. U.S. Geol. Surv. Prof. Paper 440-G, 64 p. (1963).

Lovelock, J. E., Atmospheric fluorine compounds as indicators of air movements. Nature, 230, 379 (1971).

Ludwig, J. H., Morgan, G. B. & McMullen, T. B., Trends in Urban Air Quality. Trans. Amer. Geophys. Union, *51*, 468 (1970).

Mitchell, J. M., Jr., A preliminary evaluation of atmospheric pollution as a case of global temperature fluctuation of the past century, in Global Effects of Environmental Pollution (ed. F. S. Singer). Reidel Publishing Co., Netherlands, 97 (1970).

Murozumi, M., Chow, T. J. & Patterson C., Chemical concentrations of pollutant lead aerosols, terrestrial dusts and sea salts in Greenland and Antarctic snow strata. Geochim. Cosmochim. Acta, *33*, 1247 (1969).

NASCO, Chlorinated hydrocarbons in the marine environment. National Academy of Sciences Report (1971).

Parkin, D. W., Phillips, D. R., Sullivan, R. A. L. & Johnson, L., Airborne dust collections over the North Atlantic. J. Geophys. Research, *75*, 1782 (1970).

Preston, A., Fukai, R., Volchok, H., Yamagata, N. & Dutton, J., Radioactivity. In seminar on Methods of Detection, Measurement and Monitoring of Pollutants in the Marine Environment. FAO, Rome, Dec. 4–10, 1970.

Revelle, R., Wenk, E., Corino, R. & Ketchum, B. H., Ocean pollution by petroleum hydrocarbons. Manuscript presented at SCEP (1970).

SCEP, Man's Impact on the Global Environment. The Massachusetts Inst. of Technology, 319 p. (1970).

Shannon, L. J., Vandegrift, A. E. & Gorman, P. G., Assessment of small particle emissions. Midwest Research Institute Report on Contract CPA-22-69-104 with the Air Pollution Control Office, Environmental Protection Agency (1970).

Swinnerton, J. W., Linnenbom, V. J. & Lamontagne, R. A., The oceans: a natural source of carbon monoxide. Science, *167*, 984 (1970).

Weiss, H. V., Koide, M. & Goldberg, E, D., Mercury in a Greenland ice sheet: evidence of recent input by man. Science, In press (1971a).

Weiss, H. V., Koide, M. & Goldberg, E. D., Selenium and sulfur in a Greenland ice sheet: relation to fossil fuel combustion. Science, *172*, 261 (1971b).

Windom, H. L., Atmospheric dust records in permanent snowfields, implications to marine sedimentation. Bull. Geol. Soc. Amer., *80*, 761 (1969).

Determination of Natural Levels of Toxic Metals in a Terrestrial Ecosystem

By Clair C. Patterson

There is a horizontal row of metals in the periodic table located at the position of K which can be termed the nutrient row. Underlying these nutrient metals in each group are chemically related metals whose physiologic character changes progressively downward in such a way that the third metal down is usually toxic. Thus, there is a toxic row of metals at the Cs position. The bonding characteristics of these metals within inorganic and biological systems change progressively from strongly ionic bonds in Group I to strongly oriented coordinate covalent bonds in Group IV.

The aim of the geochemical research which I and my colleagues at the California Institute of Technology propose to carry out in a closed ecosystem of rock, soil, plant, herbivore and carnivore contained in an alpine valley of the Sierra Nevadas is to develop the concept of looking at the occurrences of toxic metals in relation to nutritious metal internal standards and noting the changes in ratios of nutrient to toxic metals which occur as the metals flow between related phases of an ecosystem.

This concept may be illustrated in the following table, where the relative abundances of the Group II metals, Ca, Sr, Ba, in the related phases rock, soil, plant, herbivores, are predicted from an interpretation of literature data.

	ppm of Sr and Ba in the Ca of the following materials			
	Canyon Wall	Soil	Grass	Voles
Ca	1 000 000	1 000 000	1 000 000	1 000 000
Sr	7 000	8 000	3 000	1 500
Ba	7 000	9 000	1 000	500

It can be seen that the abundance of the toxic metal Ba in the Ca of plants is less than that in soils and that herbivore Ca is probably freer of Ba than plant Ca. It is likely that the discrimination by organisms against Sr is less than that against Ba because Sr occupies an intermediate position in the Group II metals between Ca and Ba. We wish to find whether this is so for a closed ecosystem because such information has not yet been obtained; furthermore, we wish to discover whether similar relationships may exist for metals in other periodic groups such as Group II*b* which contains Zn, Cd, Hg and Group IV which contains Ge, Sn, Pb.

We believe that natural levels of a toxic metal cannot be determined as concentrations in wet tissue, dried material or ash because the undefined bulk has little relevance to the matter of understanding whether we are dealing with a natural or a polluted substance. We believe instead that knowledge of the occurrence of a toxic metal must be placed in a context of knowledge concerning other metals reacting in an ecosystem.

The valley we have chosen to study is located in a remote and inaccessible region of Yosemite National Park in California at an elevation of 3 000 m. The walls of the valley are comprised of a monotonous quartz monzonite and the floor consists of glacial till. The meadow grass covers most of the floor of the valley and this grass is eaten by a mountain vole. In addition to studying the occurrences of 18 metals in the rock, mineral, soil, grasses and voles of the valley, we also propose to determine the input via snow, rain and dry fallout and output via stream runoff of these metals to and from the valley.

Geological, Geochemical and Environmental Implications of the Marine Dust Veil

By Roy Chester

Introduction

The various geological and geochemical processes which have been operative during the history of the oceans are by no means fully understood. Many of the unsolved problems are intimately related to the supply and removal of material, both dissolved and detrital, which is brought to the oceans from the land areas. The present paper attempts to make a quantitative estimate of the amount of one kind of land-derived material, i.e. eolian dust, brought to the Atlantic Ocean. Some of the geological, geochemical and environmental effects of this dust are also examined, and it is suggested that eolian material, which is introduced into the oceans in a 'dry' state may behave differently in its reactions with sea water to river detritus, which is brought to the oceans in a 'wet' state.

Eolian Material in Deep-Sea Sediments

Darwin (1846) was one of the first scientists to recognise that the movement of dust by the wind was an important pathway for the transport of land-derived material to the deep-ocean areas. Wind-transported dust particles in deep-sea sediments were identified by Murray and Renard (1891) in samples collected by the *Challenger Expedition* (1873–1876). One of the first detailed studies of the areal distribution of eolian material in deep-sea areas was made by Radczewski (1939) in sediments collected off the coast of West Africa during the *Meteor Expedition* (1925–1927). Other investigations of wind transport followed these initial surveys. For example, a study of deep-sea sedimentation carried out by Rex and Goldberg (1958) established the effectiveness of long-range eolian transport, and showed that quartz particles could be carried from surrounding arid land areas to the mid-ocean Pacific. In these investigations eolian material in deep-sea areas had been identified from bulk samples of bottom sediments, and it was not until Parkin et al. (1967) collected dust directly from the atmosphere that the overall importance of eolian transport was fully recognised. These collections were followed by others, and it is now known that there is a dust veil over most oceanic areas.

This dust veil is more concentrated in some oceanic areas than in others, and its concentration depends on a number of factors. Some of these are listed below

(i) The geological nature of the land over which the winds pass, e.g. loose desert soils are in a form which is readily susceptible to wind movement.

(ii) The strength and circulation patterns of the various major wind systems, i.e. the equatorial easterlies (the trades), the temperate westerlies and the polar easterlies.

(iii) The mechanism by which dust particles are removed from the atmosphere, i.e. either rainfall wash-out, or gravitational settling.

(iv) The occurrence and magnitude of volcanic eruptions.

(v) The atmospheric input of man-made pollutants from adjacent land areas.

The material collected over deep-sea areas can conveniently be divided into a number of genetic classes. *Extra-terrestrial* material consists largely of cosmic spherules, but makes up only a small fraction of the dusts. *Biological material* includes fresh-water organisms, fungus-hyphae, spores, pollen, various insects and humus. *Land-derived inorganic material* makes up the bulk of most eolian dusts, and consists chiefly of clay minerals, quartz and feldspars with minor amounts of other minerals such as calcite, dolomite, pyroxenes etc. Volcanic material is also included in this class. *Man-made contaminants* include industrial waste products which have been expelled into the atmosphere, e.g. carbon and metal flakes; nuclear bomb debris; pesticides and other agricultural chemicals; and products of social activities, e.g. particulate lead from petrol fumes.

Dusts from the atmosphere over the Atlantic Ocean have been more extensively sampled than those from other areas, and the present discussion is confined to this ocean. The results of various recent studies now permit a tentative overall estimate of dust-loadings in the lower atmosphere over the Atlantic to be made. Dust-loadings are usually expressed in $\mu g/m^3$ of air, and in order to assess the validity of the published results it is necessary to briefly describe the collection technique. Most collections reported in the literature have been made on terylene or nylon meshes suspended in the lower atmosphere, either from a land-based tower or from on board ship. Dust particles adhere to the fibres of these meshes, i.e. an impingement as opposed to a filtration collection. The meshes suffer from the disadvantage that their collection efficiency is poor for small-sized particles. For example Parkin et al. (1970) have calculated that the collection efficiency of the meshes is only ca 50% for particles 2 μm in size. However, mesh collection does offer a simple technique which provides sufficient sample for detailed analytical investigation, and for this reason it continues to be used. The overall collection efficiency of the meshes, i.e. the particles collected as a percentage of the total number of particles in the possible collection size range, has been shown to be 50 % (Parkin et al., 1967). The collection efficiency of the meshes has also been experimentally checked by Goldberg (1971) who used membrane filters for comparison. Membrane filters offer a more efficient technique for particle collection, but are limited in that they can sample only small volumes of air compared to meshes. The results of Goldberg's experiments indicated that the efficiency of the membrane filters is ca ten times greater than that of the uncorrected meshes. For the data which is given in the literature the weight of dust collected has been mutiplied by two (to correct for overall mesh efficiency), and the dust-loading calculated from this corrected concentration. Dust-loadings obtained in this manner are used in the present paper. However, it now appears that these dust-loadings must be regarded as a lower limit for the concentration of particles in the dust veil,

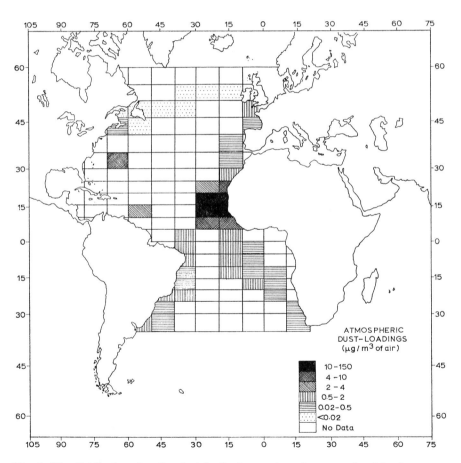

Fig. 1. The distribution of eolian dust in the lower atmosphere over the Atlantic ocean. The dust-loadings, which are given in μg/m³ of air, are the lower limit estimates of the dust concentration over the Atlantic—see text. The values are taken from Delany et al. (1967), Parkin et al. (1970), Chester and Johnson (1971*a* and *b*), Chester et al. (1971), Parkin, D. W. (unpublished results), and Chester, R. (unpublished results).

and to give an estimate of the upper limit the dust-loadings have been multiplied by a factor of five, i.e. equivalent to the Goldberg correction.

A summary of the various dust-loadings found in the lower atmosphere over the Atlantic Ocean is shown in Fig. 1. In this figure the ocean is divided into units each 5° of latitude by 10° of longitude. The dust-loadings for each unit are indicated by the relevant shading, and are an average when more than one result is available. It is evident that the highest dust-loadings are found in the north-east trades off the Sahara Desert coast of West Africa, and for the various major wind systems the dust-loadings decrease in the order north-east trades > south-east trades > the westerlies.

The presence of this dust veil over the Atlantic Ocean has a number of geological, geochemical and environmental implications, some of which are considered below:

1. The Transport of Land-Derived Solids to the Oceans, and Its Effect on Deep-Sea Sedimentation

From the data at present available it is possible to estimate the accumulation rate of this eolian material onto the deep-sea floor. As an example the accumulation rate of solids from the north-east trades has been calculated using the following data:

(i) Average dust-loadings are assumed for that portion of the North Atlantic lying between 5°N and 35°N. In the *Eastern Atlantic* a yearly average lower limit dust-loading of 10 μg/m^3 of air was obtained from 38 atmospheric samplings. In the *Western Atlantic* a lower limit average of 2 μg/m^3 of air was found by Parkin et al. (1967) over a period of one year on the island of Barbados. Over the *Mid-Atlantic Ridge* area a lower limit average dust-loading of 4 μg/m^3 of air had been assumed. This is a 'biased' average because the ridge is closer to Barbados than to the African Coast off which most of the dust-loadings in the Eastern Atlantic were obtained.

(ii) The height of the dust column in the Atlantic North-east trades is ca 3.5 km (Prospero et al., 1970).

(iii) Two processes, i.e. gravitational settling and rainfall wash-out, control the removal of particles from the atmosphere. At the average trade wind speed of ca 25 km/hr it would take <10 days for a particle to be transported across the Atlantic from the coast of West Africa. Calculations show that only those particles >8 μm in size will be significantly affected by gravitational fall-out within this period from a dust column in which there is a uniform distribution of particles (Prospero et al., 1970). The majority of particles, i.e. >70%, collected from the marine atmosphere are <4 μg in size. In view of this it is assumed that particle removal occurs by rain wash-out, and that the atmosphere is cleaned of its particle load every ten days (Flohn, 1963).

Table 1. *The accumulation rates of eolian material from the North-East trades of the Atlantic Ocean*

	Eastern Atlantic	Mid-Atlantic ridge	Western Atlantic
Lower limit of dust accumulation[a]	0.85	0.34	0.17
Upper limit of ust accumulation[b]	4.25	1.70	0.85
Accumulation rate of the land-derived fractions of deep-sea sediments[c]	1–8	0.70	1–8

Rates in mm/10^3 years
[a] Based on the weight of dust collected corrected for overall mesh collection efficiency, i.e multiplied by a factor of two.
[b] Based on the weight of dust collected multiplied by a factor of ten, i.e. the Goldberg factor.
[c] From Griffin et al. (1968).

Making the assumptions given above the sea floor accumulation rates of eolian dusts deposited from the north-east trades have been calculated. The results are given in Table 1 from which it is evident that in the area of the Mid-Atlantic Ridge and ridge flanks the minimum eolian contribution of land-derived material to the deep-sea sediments is ca 50 %. This is in agreement with the predictions made by Griffin et al. (1968) who concluded that eolian contributions will be greatest in the mid-ocean ridge areas which are protected by distance and topography from receiving a significant accumulation of river detritus. It has also been shown that the minerology of the dusts is similar to that of the land-derived fractions of the deposited deep-sea sediments—see Table 2.

The sea floor accumulation rates of eolian material given in Table 1 are based on the amount of dust falling onto the sea surface. Therefore, the calculations involve a further assumption; that the particles reach the sea floor without significant lateral spread by current action. This raises one of the most important current problems in marine sedimentology, i.e. the subsequent fate of small-sized material brought to the oceans. The question which needs resolving is whether or not small-sized land-derived detritus in sea water is thoroughly

Table 2. *The clay mineralogy of eolian dusts and Mid-Ocean Atlantic sediments*[1]

	Average, Barbados dusts	Average, Mid-Atlantic ridge and ridge flank sediments
Kaolinite	30	32
Illite	39	41
Montmorillonite	18	16
Chlorite	13	10

[1] Data from Delany et al. (1967); the clay mineral analyses are expressed in terms of a 100 % clay sample, and those of the sediments are for the <2 μm fractions.

mixed, or whether it retains the inter-mineral relationships of the surrounding source areas.

Several authors, e.g. Biscaye (1965), Griffin ct al. (1968), have shown that in some areas there are specific patterns in the distribution of clay minerals in the <2 μm fractions of deep-sea sediments. In the Atlantic Ocean there are two regions where these specific patterns are most strongly in evidence.

(i) Off the mouths of various South American rivers, where tongues of high illite concentration extend seawards.

(ii) Off the coast of West Africa where well-defined kaolinite concentration gradients extend seaward, decreasing westwards. Between ca 20°N and the equator the long-shore currents flow southwards, and Griffin et al. (1968) attributed the kaolinite distribution in the deep-sea sediments of this region to eolian transport from the Sahara Desert area where the surface deposits are rich in kaolinite.

The presence of these kaolinite concentration gradients in the deep-sea sediments of this region implies that if the major transport mechanism is eolian then the particles have reached the sea floor in a relatively short time, and so have escaped significant lateral transport and dispersion by oceanic currents.

An alternative hypothesis is that the concentration gradients do not result from eolian transport but are a function of processes such as turbidity currents and lutite flows. In this hypothesis it is considered that the sedimentary material is originally deposited on the shelf areas and is subsequently transported to deep-sea areas by turbidity currents and slumping processes and may be further redistributed by lutite flows. However, this does not appear to offer a satisfactory explanation for the kaolinite concentration gradients off the Atlantic coast of West Africa. Here, the concentration gradient decreases systematically westwards away from the African mainland to ca 70°W, i.e. across the Mid-Atlantic Ridge. This is shown in Table 3, in which the distribution of clay minerals in the <2 μm fractions of a series of deep-sea sediments in a trans-Atlantic section is listed. It is difficult to reconcile this kind of distribution with particle supply by turbidity currents since it appears to be independent of sea floor topography.

This region of the North Atlantic underlies the north-east trade winds, and the minerology of the dusts is similar to that of the deposited deep-sea sediments. Further, it has been shown above that the amount of dust falling onto the sea surface in mid-ocean areas is sufficient to make up at least 50 % of the land-derived fractions of the underlying sediments. The various data at present available suggest that the dusts reach the sea floor in a relatively short time and that their inter-mineral relationships are preserved. However, there is as yet no satisfactory explanation for this. For example, from Stokes'

Table 3. *The clay mineralogy of a series of North Atlantic deep-sea sediments.*[1]

	E 1	E 2	E 4	E 5	F 2	F 1
Kaolinite	37	37	32	30	19	11
Illite	34	40	40	46	50	52
Montimorillonite	18	11	14	12	13	14
Chlorite	11	12	14	13	18	24

Deep-sea sediment locations

E 1	22° 06′ N, 20° 29′ W
E 2	22° 03′ N, 28° 29′ W
E 4	22° 04′ N, 42° 57′ W
E 5	22° 04′ N, 49° 58′ W
F 2	25° 09′ N, 65° 13′ W
F 1	25° 01′ N, 72° 20′ W

[1] The Clay mineral analyses are expressed in terms of a 100 % clay sample and are for the <2 μm fractions of the sediments. Analyst J. J. Griffin.

law considerations a 4 μm particle would take about 100 days to fall 100 m, by which time it could have been transported some 4 000 km by the North Equatorial Current (Deleny et al., 1967).

In order to overcome this difficulty Deleny et al. (1967) have suggested the possibility that filter feeding organisms in the upper water layers injest the dust particles which are then excreted in as aggregates in fecal pellets which rapidly sink. This concept has been considered in detail by Smayda (1971) who has concluded that fecal pellets do provide a possible means to bring about the accelerated sinking of phytoplankton remains to depth in the water column. Another line of evidence which suggests that the rate of sinking of organic and inorganic material in the oceans is in excess of that predicted by Stokes' law has been given by Osterberg et al. (1963). These authors found that certain radionuclides with a relatively short half-life, e.g. ^{95}Zr (half-life, 65 days), could be detected in bottom feeders at a depth of ca 2 800 m in Pacific Ocean waters. They suggested that one possible explanation for this was the sinking of fecal pellets. In the size range found in sea water these pellets apparently sink at a rate which, depending on size, varies between ca 36 and ca 376 m/day (Smayda, 1969), i.e. to fall 3 000 m would take ca 10–100 days. The pellets can decompose, or be further utilized in the marine food chain, at depth in the water columns. However, it may be that mineral particles will have become aggregated together during pellet formation and so after pellet decomposition will sink much faster than the original non-aggregated grains.

At present this problem has not been resolved, and it is yet to be shown that mineral aggregates exist at depth in the water column.

However, the considerations listed above indicate an important implication of the marine dust veil, and lead to the general concept that there are at least three genetically different kinds of particle brought to the oceans from the land areas.

(I) Those particles deposited initially on the shelf areas, mainly by river run-off, some of which may be subsequently redistributed to, and within, deep-sea areas by sea-floor processes such as slumping, turbidity currents and lutite flows.

(II) Those particles introduced mainly by river run-off which, because of their small size, escape deposition on the continental shelves and which are transported to deep-sea areas by current transport in the water column. These may subsequently be redistributed on the sea floor by processes such as lutite flows, but the important distinction is that initially they were transported in the water column and not along the sea floor.

(III) Those particles which are brought directly to deep-sea areas by eolian transport, and which are originally in the upper water layers irrespective of particle size. Most eolian dusts in marine areas consist largely of particles <4 μm in size, but samples have been reported in which 25 % of the total particles were >10 μm in size (Prospero et al., 1970), and in dust storms particles >50 μm have been found over deep-sea areas (Game, 1964). Once eolian particles have reached the sea floor they may be redistributed by processes such as lutite flows.

2. The Effect of Eolian Material on the Trace Element Geochemistry of Deep-Sea Sediments

Certain trace elements, e.g. Mn, Ni, and Co are enriched in deep-sea clays compared to near-shore sediments, and in the Atlantic Ocean they are most strongly enriched in those deep-sea clays deposited in mid-ocean areas. Other trace elements, e.g. Cr and V, have similar concentrations in near-shore sediments and deep-sea clays. It is of interest to compare the contribution made by eolian material to the content of these geochemically contrasted trace elements in mid-Atlantic deep-sea clays.

The average contents of these trace elements in mid-Atlantic deep-sea clays and north-east trade wind dusts is given in Table 4. From this table it is evident that the sediments have a higher concentration of Mn, Ni, and Co than the dusts, but that the contents of Cr and V are reasonably similar in both. The rates of accumulation of the trace elements in the sediments and the deposited dusts can be calculated from the various data given above. In these calculations the following accumulation rates of total solids have been assumed; land-derived fraction of deep-sea clays, 0.7 mm/10 years (Griffin et al., 1968), eolian dust, 0.35 mm/10^3 years (i.e. a minimum contribution of 50 % of the land-derived material in the clays). The trace element accumulation rates are listed

Table 4. *The trace element contents of Atlantic North-East trade wind dusts and Mid-Atlantic deep-sea sediments*[1]

Trace element	North-east trade dusts	Mid-ocean sediments[a]
Mn	1 558	5 912
Ni	41	418
Co	14	138
Cr	160	120
V	197	240

[1] Contents in p.p.m, analyses from Chester and Johnson (1970c).
[a] Data from Chester and Messiha–Hanna (1970). The analyses, which are on carbonate-free basis, are for the following cores: J4 (37° 22′ N, 38° 47′ W): 14 (34° 06′ N, 38° 55′ W); H4a (31° 02′ N, 45° 13′ W); F5 (24° 56′ N, 39° 30′ W).

Table 5. *The accumulation rates of trace elements in Mid-Ocean Atlantic sediments and deposited North-East trade wind dusts*

Trace element	Mid-ocean sediments[a]	Eolian dusts
Mn	621	82
Ni	44	2.1
Co	15	0.7
Cr	13	8.4
V	25	10

Rates in $\mu g/cm^2/10^3$ years.
[a] For sediment core locations—see Table 2.

in Table 5, from which it can be seen that the Ni and Co required by the sediments is more than an order of magnitude in excess of that deposited by the dusts.

3. The Introduction of Land-Derived Material Directly into Sea Water

Adsorption onto the surfaces of detrital particles has been considered an important mechanism for the removal of trace elements from natural waters. For example, Krauskopf (1956) concluded from laboratory investigations that adsorption may control the concentrations of Zn, Cu, Pb, Bi, Cd, Hg, Ag and Mo in sea water. The laboratory investigations involved small scale experiments which were considered to have at least a qualitative application to the processes actually coccurring in sea water. Other workers, for example Chester (1965), have also shown that detrital material such as clay minerals can remove trace elements from sea water.

However, Kharkar et al. (1968) have experimentally examined the adsorption of trace elements by detritus in both the river and the marine environments. They concluded that when a trace element is adsorped from solution in river water it is always released to a greater or lesser extent on contact with sea water. While they agreed with the findings of Krauskopf (1956) that detritus placed in sea water can remove trace elements from it they postulated that this does not happen in the transport of river detritus to the oceans. In fact, river-transported particles are actually adding trace elements to sea water by desorption rather than removing them by adsorption.

From these considerations it would appear that one of the critical factors which controls the uptake of trace elements from sea water by detritus is the pathway by which the detritus is transported to the oceans. This is not un-expected. Chemical weathering occurs in the presence of natural waters. In this first stage in the sedimentary cycle the weathered material, particularly the weathering residues such as the clay minerals, will interact with dissolved trace elements in the ground waters. If the weathered material is subsequently transported by rivers in the form of suspended detritus, or bottom load, it will again interact with dissolved trace elements in the river water. If the trace element uptake is in the form of surface adsorption it will tend to reach an equilibrium state. In sea water a new equilibrium will be approached with the dissolved species in that medium, and according to Kharkar et al. (1968) this will involve the desorption of trace elements. However, material which is introduced directly into sea water from the land surfaces in a 'dry' state will tend to reach an equilibrium directly with sea water. Clearly, therefore, it is incorrect to assume that laboratory experiments in which previously dried clay minerals are allowed to react with trace elements dissolved in sea water are directly applicable to all actual processes which occur in the oceans. This is because the clays have not passed through the experimental equivalent of a river environment. The former type of experiment may, however, be applicable to material brought to the oceans in a 'dry' state, e.g. from eolian transport.

Since the trace element composition of rivers is apparently not very different from that of sea water it would not seem unreasonable that detritus should tend to reach the same equilibrium with respect to trace element uptake in the two waters. In practice, of course, the dissolved salts in sea water affect this equilibrium and it appears from experimental results that in river water trace element uptake is about two to three times greater than in sea water.

The possible role of trace element adsorption by land-derived detritus in sea water can be examined in terms of eolian material brought to mid-ocean areas in the Atlantic. That such dust is capable of removing Co from sea water has been shown by Aston et al. (1971). However, their experiments were crude because the concentration of dust was many times that of open-ocean waters and no account was taken of organic films which may form on particles in sea water. Experiments such as these can only be taken as evidence that the dusts are capable of trace element uptake under certain closed conditions, and cannot be extrapolated to the very different conditions occurring in the open oceans. It is inherently difficult to reproduce these open-ocean conditions in the laboratory, one particular difficulty being the very small amount of detritus present in open-ocean water, i.e. in the order of a few micrograms per litre. To overcome this, much more sophisticated laboratory experiments must be attempted than those previously described in the literature.

In the absence of such experiments it is useful to attempt to estimate trace element adsorption on eolian dusts by other means. One possible approach which may yield a tentative upper limit of such adsorption can be made by considering the distribution of a particular trace element between the sediment-suspended dust-sea water complex. For the trace element Co this estimate can be made in the following manner:

The concentration of Co in sea water is 0.1 μg/l (Goldberg, 1965).

The residence time of Co in sea water is 18×10^3 years (Goldberg, 1965)

A column of water extending above each cm^2 of sediment surface has an average height of ca 3 000 m in the Atlantic and adjacent seas. The column contains 300 l of sea water and therefore 30 μg of Co.

If it is assumed that all the Co in this column is removed by eolian dust then 30 μg of Co will be associated with the amount of dust deposited in 18×10^3 years. In the mid-Atlantic, where the dust has an accumulation rate of 0.35 mm/10^3 years, ca 0.9 g will be deposited in 18×10^3 years. This will yield a concentration of ca 33 p.p.m. adsorbed Co in the deposited dusts. Although this concentration is an upper limit it is useful in estimating, to a first approximation, the total amount of Co which could be supplied to the underlying sediments by the dusts. From Table 3 it can be seen that the average mid-Atlantic sediment requires a Co accumulation rate of ca 15 μg/cm^2/10^3 years. Eolian dust falling from the air has a Co accumulation rate of ca 0.7 μg/cm^2/10^3 years. With the additional maximum adsorption of 33 p.p.m. from sea water the total dust Co accumulation rate is ca 4 μg/cm^2/10^3 years. This is less than the expected contribution from river detritus which contains an average of ca 40 p.p.m. Co (Turekian and Scott, 1967); a concentration which will increase in the smaller-sized material transported to deep-sea areas. This manner of estimating the upper limit of trace element adsorption is useful, therefore, since it has shown that even if the dust removed the maximum possible amount of Co from sea water it could still not account for the high concentration of Co in mid-Atlantic deep-sea clays. However, a similar type of calculation showed that the maximum Ni which could be adsorbed on the dust was ca 660 p.p.m. which means that the total dust could supply ca 37 μg of the 44 μg/cm^3/10^3 years required by the sediment.

In practice, of course, it is extremely unlikely that the majority of Co and Ni in sea water is taken up by eolian dust. Other phases in deep-sea sediments e.g. authigenic precipitales, are extremely efficient in the scavenging of trace elements from the sea water. The most important of these authigenic phases are the oxides of iron and manganese, and ferro-manganese nodules. The nodules are deposited at a rate of mm/10^6 years, and have concentrations of ca 0.3 % Co and ca 0.4 % Ni.

It must also be stressed that in the simple calculation given above it is assumed that the trace elements are homogenously distributed in the oceans and are removed from the sea water in the deep-sea area. This is by no means certain, and processes which operate in near-shore areas may impose a stronger control on the removal of some trace elements from sea water than those in deep-sea areas (Turekian and Schutz, 1965).

It may be concluded, therefore, that although it is extremely unlikely that the deposition of eolian dusts provides a major worldwide mechanism for the removal of trace elements from sea water and their subsequent incorporation into deep-sea sediments, some trace element removal will occur when the dusts enter the water column. The extent of this removal is not at present known, and must be further investigated. Such an investigation is needed because eolian transport provides a sedimentary pathway which is genetically different from that of river transport, and the effect of the dust must, therefore, be considered when the input of pollutants to the oceans is evaluated.

4. The Introduction of Pollutants to the Oceans

The presence of the dust veil over the oceans offers a mechanism for the input of pollutants to sea water. Some pollutants are introduced directly into the atmosphere. Among these are included presticides from crop spraying, solids and gases as waste products of social and industrial activity, and volatile elements such as Zn, Hg, Pb and Cd.

The presence of pesticides in eolian dusts has been assumed from the identification of the mineral talc, which is used as a diluent for pesticides (Windom et al., 1967), and from measurements of D.D.T. and its degradation products (Risebrough et al., 1968). The latter authors concluded that the amount of chlorinated hydrocarbons brought to the Atlantic by the north-east trades are comparable to those brought to the sea by the major river systems. The fate of these pesticides in sea water is not clear. It has been shown that D.D.T. is strongly adsorbed by marine sediments (A. J. Murray, pers.comm.) It is possible, therefore, that D.D.T. introduced from the atmosphere will remain associated with dust particles in sea water and so follow the dust sedimentation cycle until pesticide decomposition occurs.

Solids which are produced as waste material in social and industrial activity and which are introduced into the atmosphere include elemental carbon, fly-ash and various minerals such as talc and asbestos. Carbon and fly-ash have been reported in eolian dusts from the mid-latitude North Atlantic (Parkin et al., 1970), and were shown to increase in concentration adjacent to industrially active coastal areas.

According to Goldberg (1971) man is now a rival to nature in the introduction of some heavy metals to sea water. For example, the injection of Pb into the oceans, as a result of the utilization of lead tetraethyl in internal combustion engines, is ca 2.5×10 g/year compared to ca 1.5×10 g/year from natural weathering processes. However, very little is known of the concentration of volatile elements such as Hg, Pb, Zn and Cd in eolian dusts over deep-sea areas. Such data that are available indicate that in some oceanic areas mans input of volatile elements may no longer be trivial. For example, Egarov et al. (1970) measured the concentrations of Pb and Cd in surface air over the U.S.S.R. and the Indian Ocean. The results are given in Table 6, and indicate that the air above the Northern Indian Ocean, which has a higher proportion of surrounding land area and more intensive industrial activity, contains considerably more Pb and Cd than the Southern Indian Ocean air. The results reported by Chow et al. (1969) for the concentration of Pb in Pacific Ocean air are also given in Table 6.

Table 6. *The concentrations of Pb and Cd in surface air of some land and sea areas* ($\mu g/m^3$ *of air*)

Location	Pb	Cd
USSR[a]		
Novaya Zemlya	0.00023	0.00028
Sevastopol	0.00825	0.00234
Tashkent	0.07840	0.12390
Semipalatinsk	0.55450	0.09615
Northern Indian Ocean[a]	0.00445	0.00196
Southern Indian Ocean[a]	0.00101	0.00014
USA[b]		
San Diego Harbour	0.18	—
Downtown San Diego	1.5–2.5	—
Scripps Pier, La Jolla	0.3–0.4	—
Lowest US Mainland value;		
Laguna Mountain, Calif.	0.004	—
Pacific Islands[b]		
Pago Pago harbour	0.016–0.061	—
Midway harbour	0.0175	—
North and Central Pacific		
Ocean[b]	0.0003–0.0015	—

[a] Data from Egarov et al. (1970).
[b] Data from Chow et al. (1969).

Conclusions

Recent work has shown that there is a veil of continentally-supplied dust over the oceans. The presence of this dust veil has important geological, geochemical and environmental implications. One of the most important of these may be that the atmosphere provides a transport pathway for solid material to the oceans which is genetically different from that of river transport. It is not simply that both pathways bring solid material to the oceans. What is important is that the solids brought by the two pathways will behave differently in their reactions with sea water. While it is true that eolian transport supplies only a fraction of the solids brought to the oceans by rivers, the implications of the presence of the dust may be far reaching and must be fully investigated.

In order to achieve this a world-wide monitoring programme must be established. The collected dust samples must be subjected to analysis for particle size, mineralogy, chemical composition (including both major and trace elements), and pollutants. Probably the most efficient, and perhaps the least expensive, method of atmospheric monitoring could be carried out on board ship. In this respect the commercial shipping lines of the world may be able to provide the potential sampling facilities. In addition to monitoring the atmosphere the fate of eolian material in the oceans must be studied, both in the laboratory and in sea water itself, and an attempt must be made to establish levels of concentration above which pollutant imput is considered harmful to the eco-system.

Financial support for the collection of eolian dust samples (see Figure I) was provided by the Royal Society of London (Government Grant for Scientific Investigations). Facilities for collection were provided by H. E. the Governor of St. Helena Island, and the directors of the Union Castle Line and the Blue Funnel Line (Ocean Fleets Limited).

References

Aston, S., Chester, R., and Johnson, L. R., In preparation. (1971).

Biscaye, P. E., Geol. Soc. Am. Bull. 76, 803 (1965).

Chester, R., Nature, Lond., 206, 884 (1965).

Chester, R., Elderfield, H. and Griffin, J. J., Nature, Lond., In press (1971).

Chester, R. & Johnson, L. R., Nature, Lond., 229, 105, (1971 a).

Chester, R., & Johnson, L. R., Marine Geol., In press (1971 b).

Chester, R. & Johnson, L. R., Nature, Lond., In press (1971 c).

Chester, R. & Messiha-Hanna, R. G., Geochim. Cosmochim. Acta, 34, 1121 (1970).

Chow, T. J., Earl, J. L., & Bennet, C. F., Environmental Science and Technology, 3, 737 (1969).

Darwin, C., Q. J. Geol. Soc. Lond., 2, 26 (1864).

Deleny, A. C., Deleny, A. C., Parkin, D. W., Griffin, J. J., Goldberg, E. D. & Reimann, B. E. F., Geochim. Cosmochim. Acta, 31, 885 (1967)

Egarov, V. V., Zhigalovskaya, T. N., & Malakhov, S. G., Jour. Geophys. Res., *75* 3650, (1970).

Flohn, H., Cologne. Westdeutscher Verlag. (1963).

Goldberg, E. D., Comments in Geophysics: Earth Science, I, 117 (1971).

Goldberg, E. D., In Chemical Oceanography, Vol 2 (J. P. Riley & G. Skirrow, eds), Academic Press, Lond., 163 (1965).

Griffin, J. J., Windom, H. & Goldberg, E. D., Deep-Sea Res., *15*, 433 (1968 Kharkar, D. P., Turekian, K. K. & Bertine, K. K., Geochim. Cosmochim. Acta, *32*, 285 (1968).

Krauskopf, K. B., Geochim. Cosmochim. Acta, *9*, I (1956).

Murray, J. & Renard, A. F., Scient. Rep. Challenger Exped., *3* (1891).

Osterberg, C., Carey, A. G. & Curl, H., Nature, Lond., 200, I 276, (1963).

Parkin, D. W., Phillips, D. R., Sullivan, R. A. & Johnson, L. R., J. Geophys., Res., *75*, 1782 (1970).

Prospero, J. M., Bonatti, E., Schubert, C. & Carlson, T. N., Earth Plan. Sci. Lett., *9*, 287 (1970).

Radczewski, O. E., In Recent Marine Sediments, (P. D. Trask, ed.), Am. Assoc. Petrol. Geol., Tulsa, 496 (1939).

Rex, R. W. & Goldberg, E. D., Tellus, *10*, 153 (1958).

Risebrough, R. W., Huggett, R. J., Griffin, J. J. & Goldberg, E. D., Science, *159* 1233 (1968).

Smayda, T. J., Marine Geol., *11*, 105 (1971).

Smayda, T. J., Limnol. Oceanog., *14*, 621 (1969).

Turekian, K. K., & Schutz, D. F., Univ. Rhode Island, Occ. Publ., (3), 41, (1965)

Windom, H., Griffin, J. J., & Goldberg, E. D., Environmental Science and Technology, *I*, 923 (1967).

Manganese Nodules and Budget of Trace Solubles in Oceans

By S. Krishnaswamy and Devendra Lal

Introduction

Studies of chemical behaviour and budget of trace elements in the oceans, although realised to be important by chemical oceanographers, geochemists and cosmochemists, have lagged behind because of several reasons. Lack of proper reliable techniques for sampling and estimating element concentrations at trace levels contributes only partly to the present status of this field. The main reason for the slow development seems to be due to problems presented by the requirement of ascertaining separately the dissolved amounts in sea-water and the authigenic (or hydrogenous) amounts in sediments, of a given trace element. In the case of sediments, chemical leaching techniques have been adopted to estimate non-lithogenous component (c.f. Goldberg and Koide 1962; Chester and Messiha-Hanna, 1970). Another method for calculating authigenic part from the *total* measured concentration values is to subtract lithogenous contribution by a comparison of trace element concentrations in marine sediments with shale, for instance, which may be assumed to represent typical lithogenous contribution (Turekian and Wedepohl, 1961). None of these approaches is satisfactory for several elements. In the former case it is known that even mild chemical treatment can often contribute appreciably, (by leaching trace elements from detrital phases) whilst in the case of the latter method the magnitude of corrections is some times very large to reduce the value of such estimates. The complexities involved can be easily judged by the fact that even pelagic sediments are $>75\%$ lithogenous (Goldberg, 1971).

Ferro-Manganese Nodules as Indicators of Authigenic Deposition

In this paper, we explore the possibility of using manganese nodules for studying the rates of authigenic removal of trace elements to the ocean floor, i.e. considering only trace elements in hydrogenous phases (Goldberg, 1964) in sediments. Our present attempts followed the recent detailed investigations of physiochemical properties of manganese nodules (Bhat et al., 1971; Krishnaswami, 1971, Somayajulu et al., 1971). The observations made by these authors lend high credibility to a slow and nearly entirely authigenic growth of manganese nodules derived from open ocean regions. Before discussing their interpretations, it seems pertinent to briefly discuss the current theories of their origin and growth. "At least ten different theories have been advanced ranging from the nodules being the end product in a leaching process that removes the silica, alumina and other gangue materials, to bacterial oxidation and precipitation of the various metals" (Mero, 1969).

Three theories currently under consideration are (1) the authigenic theory i.e. chemical precipitation of manganese and associated elements from sea water (Goldberg, 1954; Goldberg & Arrhenius, 1958 & references therein), (ii) the volcanic i.e. leaching of manganese and iron from the submarine lavas and their subsequent precipitation, (Arrhenius, Mero & Korkish 1964; Bonatti & Nayudu 1965) and (iii) biogenic i.e. dissolution of calcareous skeletal material containing iron and manganese, at depths in the ocean and their subsequent oxidation (Graham 1959). The second and third mechanisms necessitate that these ferromanganese deposits should be accumulating fairly rapidly on the ocean floor. Hence a knowledge of the accumulation rates of these deposits is very vital for delineating their growth mechanism.

Radiometric dating of nodules indicates their slow growth in the range of $mm/10^6$ yrs. (Bender, Ku & Broecker, 1966; Barnes & Dymond, 1967; Somayajulu, 1967; Ku & Broecker, 1969) which leads on to the problem of their escape from burial (Menard, 1964; Bonatti & Nayudu, 1965) in the faster depositing marine sediments ($mm/10^3$ yrs.). As an attempt to resolve this problem, it was suggested that the radioactive nuclei of interest are not incorporated in the matrix at the time of their growth but adsorbed later on their surface and the adsorbed nuclei may even diffuse inwards into the matrix and thus feign their radioactive decay with depth (for a review see Arrhenius, 1967). This indeed seemed to be a valid criticism since (i) the conventional dating methods employing ionium, protoactinum and uranium radionuclides apply only to the top few hundred microns of these deposits and (ii) since the nodule surfaces being very irregular, sub-surface scrapings may in fact represent a part of surface adsorbed activities resulting in an apparent radioactive decay with depth.

The above doubt has been satisfactorily answered by the analyses of Be^{10} activity in three nodules upto depths of 13–30 mm (Somayajulu, 1967; Bhat et al. 1971). As seen from Fig. 1, Be^{10} activity persists inside the nodules. The decrease with depth corresponds to rates of accumulation of 0.8 ± 0.1 (Zetes-3D), $3.8 \pm^{1.8}_{1.0}$ (Tripod-2D) and $1.8 \pm^{0.5}_{0.2}$ (DODO-15-1) $mm/10^6$ yrs. In the first two of these nodules, Th^{230} (excess) and Th^{230} (excess)/Th^{232} ratios were determined; the corresponding growth rates are found to agree well with those based on Be^{10} data. (See Fig. 1 where Th^{230} (excess)/Th^{232} data are plotted

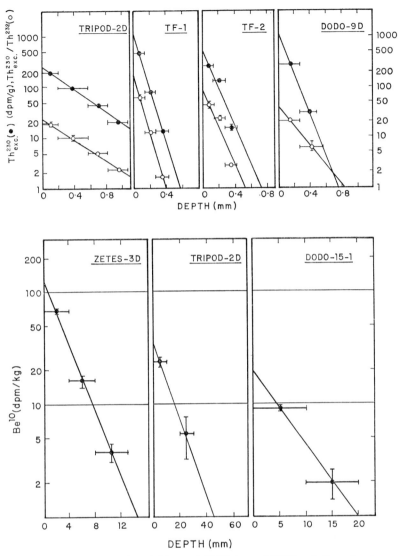

Fig. 1. Be^{10}, Th^{230} (excess) activities and Th^{230} (excess)/Th^{232} activity ratios in manganese nodules (see Table 1 for locations). The deduced Be^{10} growth rates are given in text for the three nodules. The corresponding values based on Th^{230} (excess)/Th^{232} activity ratios for Tripod-2D, TF-1, TF-2 and DODO-9D are 4.0, 0.9, 1.0 and 2.1 mm/10^6 yrs respectively. (After Bhat et al., 1971).

for Tripod-2D and three other nodules. Location and physical data on the nodules are given in Table 1.)

The Be^{10} data in Fig. 1 form the basis for believing in the slow growth rates of the three nodules and confirm the general conclusions based on Th^{230} (excess) measurements (Bhat et al. 1971) for the top mm layers.

The other two observations in manganese nodules pertinent to our present

Table 1. *Relevant details of nodules studied*

Nodule	Location		Water depth (m)	Sample description	Source
	Latitude	Longitude			
E-17-36	55° S	95° W	4 770	Nodules of irregular shapes due to aggregation of smaller accretion.	Dr W. S. Broecker Lamont Geological Observatory
TF-1 TF-2 TF-3 TF-4	13° 52′ S	150° 35′ W	3 623	Nearly spherical nodules of about 3–6 cm diameter with a well defined nucleus.	Prof. G. O. S. Arrheniu Scripps Institution of Oceanography
2P-50	13° 53′ S	150° 35′ W	3 695	Several small nearly spherical nodules of 1–4 cm diameter.	D. Macdougall Scripps Institution of Oceanography
2P-52	9° 57′ N	137° 47′ W	4 930	Several small nearly spherical nodules of 1–4 cm diameter.	D. Macdougall Scripps Institution of Oceanography
Dodo-9D	18° 16′ N	161° 50′ W	5 500	Nodule with irregular surface diameter 8–9 cm. Well defined off-centred basaltic nucleus of about 3 cm diameter.	Dr B. K. L. Somayajul Tata Institute of Fundamental Researc
Dodo-15-1	19° 23′ N	162° 20′ W	4 160	Flat encrustation of about 2 cm thick covering a base of altered basalts.	Dr B. L. K. Somayajul Tata Institute of Fundamental Researc
6A	19° 39′ N	113° 44′ W	4 000	Discoidal or cauliflower shaped with distinctly different surface textures.	Dr W. S. Broecker Lamont Geological Observatory
Tripod-2D	20° 45′ N	112° 47′ W	3 000	Flat encrustation with visible nucleus.	Dr B. L. K. Somayajul Tata Institute of Fundamental Researc
V21-D2	34° 54′ N	160° 19′ W	5 400	Aggregation of small flat nodules.	Dr W. S. Broecker Lamont Geological Observatory
Zetes-3D	40° 16′ N	170° 20′ E	3 000	Encrustation with layer structure. Approximate size, 24 × 17 × 10 cms.	Dr B. L. K. Somayajul Tata Institute of Fundamental Researc

discussions are: (i) the approximately equal rates of deposition of manganese and some trace elements (g cm^{-2} yr^{-1}) in the nodules and in the sediments (authigenic phase only) at the same location (Bender, Ku & Broecker, 1970; Somayajulu et al., 1971), and (ii) an order of magnitude smaller integrated activity ($\sum$ dpm/cm^2)[1] for the radionuclides Be^{10} and Th^{230} (excess), (Ku and Broecker, 1969; Bhat et al., 1971).

---

[1] $\sum$ dpm/cm$^2 = K\varrho \int N_x dx$ where ϱ is the in-situ density of the nodule material (taken to be 2.5 g/cm^3), N is the measured Be^{10} or Th^{230}(excess) activity (dpm/g) at depth x (cm). K is a constant ($=4$ for a spherical uniformly growing nodule and $=1$ for a rectangular slab shaped nodule growing on one face).

The above laed to fairly compelling conclusion that the open ocean manganese nodules studied usually represent growth by accumulation of hydrogenous components, and that their growth is often not continuous in time (Bhat et al., 1971; Krishnaswamy & Lal, 1971). Based on Th^{230} (excess) and Be^{10} data Bhat et al., 1971 have postulated that on the average, nodules seem to be buried in sediments (and do not grow during this period) for 90 % of their life time. It has been suggested that the mechanism which keeps the nodules from sinking in the sediments is the gentle stroking and rearrangements of sediment material and nodule due to bottom currents. As discussed by Bhat et al., 1971, such a mechanism is not inconsistent with the photographic evidence (Mero, 1965); fingerprints of bottom currents are clearly seen in several of the photographs showing extensive nodule occurrences.

It should be pointed out here that although manganese-nodules have dormant periods (when growth = 0), the estimated ages of different nodule strata on the basis of calculated apparent growth rates (cf. Fig. 1) still remain correct; the nodules thus represent long term accumulations but on an average they accumulate at the rate of about few cms/10^6 yrs. when they grow.

Experimental Techniques for the Measurements of Trace Elements in Manganese Nodules and in Sediments

In view of the various arguments presented above regarding a slow and possibly entirely authigenic growth of manganese nodules, we have been led to the measurements of a host of trace elements in several radiometrically dated nodules (Table 1) and sediments (Table 3).

Sampling for the analysis of various major and minor elements was done by powdering nodule material chipped off from the top one cm layer. Care was taken to avoid the incorporation of nucleus material in the sample.

Be^9 concentration were measured by fluorometry using morin reagent (Sill et al., 1961). A preliminary separation of beryllium from the matrix was made by acetylacetone extraction in presence of EDTA at pH = 5–6. Carrier free Be^7 tracer was added to estimate the chemical yield of extraction.

For Sc, Cr, Co, Cu, Mo and La neutron activation was done, followed by radiochemical separation and gamma counting using a $3'' \times 3''$ Na (Tl) I crystal coupled to a 400 channel pulse height analyser. The samples (about 100 mg) were sealed in quartz vials and irradiated along with 100 microgram standards of all elements for 6–12 hrs at a flux of 10^{12} neutrons per cm^2 and sec. Irradiated samples were cooled for two days and processed for the various isotopes after adding suitable amount of stable carrier for each element. The details of radiochemical separation as well as the procedures for the estimation of Fe, Mn, Ni and Ti will be discussed elsewhere (Krishnaswamy, Ph.D. Thesis, to be submitted).

Results and Discussions

Radioactive Nuclides

Th^{232}, Th^{230} (excess) and U^{238} concentrations in five of the nodules in Table 1, Zetes-3D, Tripod-2D, TF-1, TF-2 and DODO-9D, were reported earlier (Bhat et al., 1971). The new data for 2P-50 and 2P-52 are similar to others. Th^{232} and U^{238} concentration values are listed in Table 2. Typical data on Th^{230} (excess) and Be^{10} concentrations are plotted in Fig. 1.

Major and Minor Elements

The major and minor element composition of the manganese nodules studied are given in Table 2. The listed concentrations refer to the nodule sample as a whole, i.e. uncorrected for any insoluble matter (found to vary between 5%–25% by weight). To check on the reliability of the data, duplicate analysis was performed on Zetes-3D (0–10 mm section); the data agreed within ±10% for all elements excluding Sc. However there may exist systematic errors of ±15%.

The results of determinations of trace element concentrations in four Pacific sediment cores which have been previously dated by the Th^{230} (excess) or Be^{10} methods (Amin, Kharkar & Lal, 1966; Amin 1970), are presented in Table 3.

In order to compare our data on the average major and minor element concentration values, we have considered published data (Goldberg & Arrhenius, 1958; Riley & Sinhaseni, 1958; Wedepohl, 1960; El-Wakeel & Riley, 1961; Skornyakova, Andruschenko & Fomina, 1962; Wills & Ahrens, 1962; Goldberg, Koide & Griffin, 1963; Mero, 1965; Sackett, 1966; Barnes, 1967; Buchowiecki & Cherry, 1968; Ku, Broecker & Opdyke, 1968) for the following regions:

Pacific: 40°N − 20°S; 160°E − 120°W
Atlantic: 40°N–20°S; 70°E–0°W

for both nodules and sediments considering the locations of our radiometrically dated samples (Tables 1 and 3). For manganese nodules, only those occurring at depths greater than 3 000 m were considered in order to avoid cases of preferential accumulations of elements due to variations in the mineralogy of nodules (Barnes, 1967). In case of sediments, only clays have been considered (i.e. no calcareous and siliceous oozes to avoid corrections for $CaCO_3$ and opal; at present one is but sure about the incorporation mechanisms for most of the elements in biogenous phases).

The results are given in Table 4 along with average concentrations in crustal

Table 2. *Chemical composition of radiometrically dated Pacific manganese nodules*

Code no. Nodule	Concentrations in ppm dry weight, unless stated														Rate of accumulation (mm/10⁶ yrs)
	Be	Sc	Ti	Cr[a]	Mn(%)	Fe(%)	Co	Ni	Cu	Mo	La	Th[b]	U[b]	H₂O(%)	
E–17–36			7 200		36.0	15.6	1 660		2 800	650	176	54.5	9.0	17.2	2.4
TF–2	2.9	11.8	11 400	26	18.6	20.0	4 200	3 020	1 940		350	22.0	15.0	21.4	1.0
2P–50		14.4	13 400		18.0	20.5	3 900	3 140	1 450	760	232	20.0	10.5	20.5	1.0
2P–52			2 740		27.8	4.9	1 720	14 400	9 500	940	76		7.4	12.5	7.3
Dodo–9D	4.2		12 000		39.8	20.4	5 200		618	1 050	244	35.0	9.0	24.0	2.1
6A	4.7	18.9	2 690		25.8	9.4	1 270	11 700	9 270	1 020	100	24.5	7.0	10.8	4.1
Tripod–2D	2.4	10.2	6 450	0.7	18.9	8.6	3 670	2 530	211	590	370 (300)	38.0	18.0	6.9	4.0
V21–D2	3.1		7 600		15.8	15.4	3 220	5 260	3 680	660	229	122.0	5.8	13.1	4.0
Zetes–3D	1.9	8.5	6 450	22	26.5	17.4	5 450	4 800	455	2 750	405	40.0	17.0	21.1	2.0
	(1.9)	(13.9)	(6 950)		(26.6)	(17.95)	(4 900)	(4 640)	(415)		(412)			(18.4)	
Mean Pacific average[c]	3.2	12.8	7 770	—	25.2	14.7	3 370	6 410	3 325	1 053	242	45	11.0	16.4	Mean average rate of accumulation = 3 mm/10⁶ yrs
		10	7 500	—	23.8	12.0	3 080	9 100	7 000	430	160	—	—	—	
Adopted mean values	3	12	7 500	—	25	14	3 200	7 000	4 000	700	200	45	11	16.4	

[a] Chromium values are upper limits since the observed Cr⁵¹ activity levels were usually very small, ≤5% of the background.
[b] The data for Th, and U concentrations and the rates of accumulations for TF–2, Dodo–9D, Tripod–2D and Zetes–3D are from Bhat et al. (1971) and for E–17–36, 6A, V21–D2 are from Ku and Broecker (1969). Numbers in parenthesis of Zetes–3D and Tripod–2D refer to duplicate determinations.
[c] See Table 4.

Table 3. *Trace element composition of Pacific sediment cores studied*

Sediment core code no.	Location (Lat.; Long.)	Concentration of element in ppm wt (for Fe wt. %)												Sedimentation rate[a] (mm/10^3 yrs)	
		Be	Sc	Ti	Cr	Mn	Fe	Co	Ni	Cu	La	Th[a]	U[a]	Be^{10}	Io/Th
MSN-96	57° 35′ S; 175° 15′ W	1.9	26	3 940	65	3 980	4.15	86	84	87	15	7.4	1.5	3.6	2.6
NOVA-13	03° 55.6′ N; 178° 47.3′ W		23	3 540	61	5 780	6.00	58	156	330	40	7.9	1.3	—	—
NOVA III-16	0° 14.1′ N; 179° 7.9′ W			3 960 (4 050)		6 050 (5 950)	5.80 (5.90)		117 (120)	278	37			2.2	1.6
MSN-147G	8° 20′ N; 145° 24′ W		31	4 000	64	1 030	5.36	31	83	256	34	12.3	1.6	3.9	1.9
i) Average of above sampls		1.9	27	3 860	63	4 210	5.33	58	110	238	32	9.2	1.5	Mean sedimentation rate = 3 mm/10^3 yrs	
ii) Average of above and Cap 23 HG, MP-38, WW-5[b]			28	4 770	70	6 930	4.9	144	269	474	94	12.4	1.5		
iii) Pacific average (Table 4)			28	4 500	—	7 800	5.1	132	242	430	115	12.3	2.2		
Adopted mean values		2	28	4 000	65	6 000	5	70	200	300	100	10	1.5		

Numbers in paranthesis refer to duplicate analyses.

[a] Data from Amin (1970).
[b] Data from Goldberg and Arrhenius (1958). Cap 23 HG (16° 58.5′ S, 161° 35′ W), MP-38 (19° 01′ N, 177° 19′ W), WW-5 (27° 37.8′ N, 124° 25.7′ W).

rocks, shales and near-shore sediments. In the case of Pacific Ocean, the mean values based on the present determinations in *radiometrically dated samples of nodules and sediments* agree fairly well with the averages based on available data (Tables 2 and 3).

We now wish to study the implications of the observed major and minor trace element concentrations in nodules and sediments. The sediments are known to contain large amounts of lithogenous trace elements (see Fig. 3 in Goldberg & Arrhenius, 1958). The elements Fe, Ti, Mg, Sr, Ga, for instance, are present in pelagic sediments at levels similar to those in igneous rocks. On other hand Mn, Cu, Co and Mo exist in considerably larger concentration in pelagic sediments (cf. Table 4). Authigenic concentrations, C_s (auth.), of any of these elements in sediments may be deduced to a first approximation, from the total concentration, C_s (total), in sediments, using the following relation:

$$C_s \text{ (auth.)} = C_s \text{ (total)} - C_s \text{ (shale)} \tag{1}$$

where C_s (shale) refers to average concentrations in shale assumed to be the material closest to the lithogenous component in sediments.

On the other hand, if we make the assumption that manganese nodules primarily represent an accumulation of hydrogenous components and further that the rate of deposition, P of any trace element (authigenic part alone) is the same as in sediments, then we have:

$$P_N = \frac{K}{\varepsilon} \varrho_N G_N C_N \tag{2}$$

Table 4. *Average abundances (in ppm wt) of elements in various samples*

Element	Crustal[a] rocks	Shales[b]	Near shore[c] sediments	Pacific[d] sediments	Pacific[d] nodules	Atlantic[d] sediments	Atlantic[d] nodules
Sc	22	13	13	28	10	13	20
Ti	4 400	4 600	4 600	4 500	7 500	5 100	6 950
V	135	130	130	200	540	—	700
Mn	950	850	850	7 800	238 000	4 100	166 000
Fe	50 000	47 200	48 000	51 000	120 000	57 000	187 000
Co	25	19	13	132	3 080	47	4 200
Ni	75	68	55	242	9 100	165	4 050
Cu	55	45	48	430	7 000	152	2 320
Zr	165	160	160	161	630	134	540
Mo	1.5	2.6	1.0	21	430	11	390
La	30	92	92	115	160	107	—
Pb	13	20	20	88	1 400	61	1 430
Th	7.2	12	—	12.3	44	16	—
U	1.8	3.7	—	2.2	11	2.9	—

[a] Mason, B., 'Principles of Geochemistry', John Wiley and Sons Inc., New York, 45 (1966).
[b] Turekian, K. K. and Wedepohl, K. H., Geol. Soc. Am. Bull. 72, 175 (1961).
[c] Wedepohl, K. H., Geochim. Acta, 18, 200 (1960).
[d] Published values: see text for references, sample selection criteria and locations for which average values quoted here.

$$P_s \text{ (auth.)} = \varrho_s \, G_s \, C_s \text{ (auth.)} \tag{3}$$

where ϱ and C are in-situ specific gravity and concentrations respectively, G is the *time averaged* growth rate of nodule or sediment strata, the subscripts N and s refer to nodule and sediment respectively. K is the geometric factor for the nodule (discussed earlier) and ε is the fraction of time the nodule grows on the average. If

$$P_N \simeq P_N \text{ (auth.)} \tag{4}$$

and

$$P_N \simeq P_s \text{ (auth.)}, \tag{5}$$

as hypthesised above, equating 2 and 3:

$$R_{NS} = \frac{C_N}{C_s(\text{auth.})} = \frac{G_s \, \varrho_s \, \varepsilon}{G_N \, \varrho_N \, K} \tag{6}$$

In Table 5, we have calculated the value of the ratio R_{NS} for several elements using Eqn. 1 to estimate average C_s (auth.) for Pacific ocean. The various trace elements have been grouped in 4 classes depending on the magnitude of the shale correction.

For class I elements, i.e. when the shale correction is 0–20%, the experimentally determined values of R_{NS} lie between 15–48. Similar values are found for Ni and Pb where shale correction is about 30%. For most other elements,

Table 5. *Trace elements in manganese nodules and sediments in Pacific Ocean*

Element	C_s (auth.) reliability class and magnitude of shale correction	Concentration (ppm Wt.) in Pacific sediments	Shale	C_s (auth.) deduced using equation (l)	$R_{NS} = C_N/C_s$ (auth.)	C_s (auth.)[a] based on $R_{NS} = 25$
Mn	Class I (0–20 %)	6 000	850	5 150	48	10 000
Cu		300	45	255	15.5	160
Mo		21	2.6	18.4	38	28
Ni	Class II (20–50 %)	200	68	132	53	280
Pb		88	20	68	21	56
Sc		28	13	15	1	0.5
Co		70	19	51	63	128
V	Class III (50–80 %)	200	130	70	8	22
Fe	Class IV (> 80 %)	50 000	47 200	2 800	?	5 600
Ti		4 000	4 600	?	?	300
Zr		161	160	?	?	25
La		100	92	?	?	8
Th		10	12.0	?	?	1.8
U		1.5	3.7	?	?	0.4
Be		2	3	?	?	0.1

[a] C_N values in last two columns are based on data in Tables 2 and 4. The value of C_s (auth.) is given in ppm wt. For elements Mo, Pb, Zr and Be, their average values are taken from Table 4; for others the mean adopted values summarised in Table 3 are used.

particularly those in class IV, it does not remain meaningful to calculate R_{NS} values because of uncertainties in C_s (auth.).

For radionuclides, Be^{10} and Th^{230} (excess), we can obtain R_{NS} without recourse to Eqn. 1, since these nuclides are injected in the oceans entirely as dissolved. The available data (Fig. 1, Amin, Kharkar & Lal, 1966, Ku & Broecker, 1969, Bhat et al., 1971) yield:

$R_{NS} (Be^{10}) = 15 (6-35)$
$R_{NS} (Th^{230} excess) = 10 (5-20)$

considering in both cases the surface extrapolated activity values, i.e. the concentrations in nodules/sediments at deposition (the central value of R_{NS} and its approximate range (within parenthesis) are given above for Be^{10} and Th^{230}).

The theoretically expected ratio, R_{NS} on the basis of hypotheses 4 and 5 is 10 using the following average values for the parameters:

$G_s = 3$ mm/10^3 yrs (Table 3)
$G_N = 3$ mm/10^6 yrs (Table 2)
$\varrho_s = 0.5$ gm $\cdot$ cm^{-3}
$\varrho_N = 2.5$ gm $\cdot$ cm^{-3}
$\varepsilon = 0.1$
$K = 2$

The rate constants used above are based on radiometric determinations but since the chemical data refer to several undated specimens for both nodules and sediments and because of uncertainties in values of ϱ, K and ε, we conclude that the theoretical value of 10 for R_{NS} is in fact in good agreement with the value of about 30 observed for class I elements (which are chemically quite dissimilar). The data points are few for Be^{10} and Th^{230} (excess), but the available data are not inconsistent with the value of 30 for R_{NS} in these cases. In view of this, we believe that the hypotheses under Eqns. 4 and 5 hold for a fairly widely different geochemical group of elements: Be, Th, Mn, Cu, Co, Mo and possibly Ni and Pb (Table 5). Thus it seems that essentially all hydrogenous phases alone are effectively incorporated in the nodules (at least of elements listed in Table 5). This result is quite in accord with the earlier suggestions made by Bender, Ku and Broecker, 1970 and Somayajulu et al., 1971 but there exist subtle differences in details.

Authigenic Concentrations of Stable Trace Elements in Pacific Sediments

In last column of Table 5, we have given the estimated average values for C_s (auth.) in Pacific sediments based on $R_{NS} = 25$ and C_N values in Tables 2 and 4;

the assumption of validity of Equation 6 for class III and IV elements seems a reasonable one since these elements have shorter residence times compared to those in class I (Goldberg, 1965) and for Be^{10} and Th^{230}, the two highly active species, an experimental verification could be made.

We believe that the values of C_s (auth.) given in the last column of Table 5 represent the best estimates of the average authigenic concentrations in Pacific pelagic sediments (for the belt 20°S–40°N latitude and 165°E–120°W). Implications of these estimates of the authigenic concentrations of a suite of geochemically different trace elements in marine sediments will be discussed elsewhere (Krishnaswamy and Lal, 1971). As an example, we may point out here that the value of 0.44 ppm for authigenic uranium in sediments corresponds to a residence time of 2×10^7 yrs., which is one to two orders of magnitude larger than the previous estimates based on budget estimates and comparisons of U^{234}/U^{238} ratios in rivers and sea-water (Goldberg & Arrhenius, 1958; Moore, 1967; Bhat & Krishnaswamy, 1969).

Other Geochemical/Geophysical Considerations

Having established that the open ocean manganese nodules often represent growth from hydrogenous marine phases and grow at a slow rate (*time averaged value of about (1–4) mm/10⁶ yrs.*), albeit discontinuously, we decided to look for evidences of temporal changes in ocean chemistry. Nodules of Zetes-3D size, if they grew at the same rate in the past beyond the range of Be^{10} method, would represent an existence of about 100 million years on the ocean floor. Preliminary conclusions (Bhat et al., 1971) based on analyses of depth variation of U^{238} and Th^{232} activities in Zetes-3D show that during the last 15 million years, no appreciable changes have occurred in the U^{238} concentrations in the oceans (less than 10 %) but those of Th^{232} have increased steadily till the present time (by about 30 %). On a longer term basis, the U^{238} concentrations varied in the past (lower by 50 % at 100 million years) but of Th^{232} however, remained constant during 15–100 million years before present. Further work is in progress to study the chemical records in manganese nodules.

The presently described work would not have been possible without the generous supply of nodule and sediment samples by Professors G. O. S. Arrhenius and W. S. Broecker, Mr D. Macdougall and Dr B. L. K. Somayajulu. Authors are grateful to Dr M. Sankar Das and Mr A. V. Murali of Bhabha Atomic Research Centre, Trombay for assistance with neutron irradiations. We thank Miss A. G. Padhye for skillful assistance in the stable beryllium determinations. Acknowledgment is made to the donors of The Petroleum Research Fund, administered by the American Chemical Society, for partial support of this research.

References

Amin, B. S., Kharkar, D. P. & Lal D., Deep Sea Res. *13*, 805 (1966).

Amin, B. S., Dating of ocean sediments by radioactive methods, M. Sc. Thesis, Bombay University, 100 pp. (1970).

Arrhenius, G., Mero, J. & Korkish, J., Science. *144*, 170 (1964).

Arrhenius, G. & Bonatti, E., Neptunism and Volcanism in the ocean, in Prog. in Oceanography (ed. F. Koczy and M. Sears) Pergamon Press, (1965).

Arrhenius, G., Deep Sea sedimentation. Trans. Am. Geophys. Union, U. S., National Report (1963–1967), 604 (1967).

Barnes, S. S., The formation of ferromanganese minerals, Ph.D. Thesis, University of California, 57 pp. (1967).

Barnes, S. S. & Dymond, J. R., Nature, *213*, 1218 (1967).

Bender, M. L., Ku, T. L. & Broecker, W. S., Science, *151*, 325 (1966).

Bender, M. L., Ku, T. L. & Broecker, W. S., Earth Planet Sci. Lett., *8*, 143 (1970).

Bhat, S. G. & Krishnaswamy, S., Proc. Ind. Acad. Sci. *LXX*, 1 (1969).

Bhat, S. G., Krishnaswamy, S., Lal, D., Rama & Somayajulu, B. L. K., Radiometric and trace elemental Studies of ferromanganese nodules. To be published in the proceedings of the International Symposium on Hydrochemistry and Biochemistry, Tokyo (1970).

Bonatti, R. & Nayudu, Y. R., Am. J. Sci., *263*, 17 (1965).

Buchowiecki, J. & Cherry, R. D., Chem. Geol. *3*, 111 (1968).

Chester, R. & Messiha-Hanna, R. G., Geochim. Cosmochim. Acta, *34*, 1121 (1970).

Cronan, D. S., Geochim. Cosmochim. Acta, *33*, 1562 (1969) .

El-Wakeel, S. K. & Riley, J. P., Geochim. Cosmochim. Acta, *25*, 110 (1961).

Goldberg, E. D., J. Geol. *62*, 249 (1954).

Goldberg, E. D. & Arrhenius, G., Geochim. Cosmochim. Acta, *13*, 153 (1958).

Goldberg, E. D. & Koide, M., Geochim. Acta, *26*, 417 (1962).

Goldberg, E. D., Koide, M. & Griffin, J. J., A geochronological and sedimentary profile across the north Atlantic ocean in 'Isotopic and Cosmic Chemistry' (eds. H. Craig, S. L. Miller and G. J. Wasserburg) North Holland Publishing Company, 211 (1963).

Goldberg, E. D., The oceans as a geological system. Trans. N.Y. Acad. Sci. 2, *27*, 1 (1964).

Goldberg, E. D., Minor-Elements in Sea Water in Chemical Oceanography (ed. J. P. Riley and G. Skirrow), Academic Press (1965).

Goldberg, E. D., private communication (1971).

Graham, J. W., Science. *129*, 1428 (1959).

Krishnaswamy, S. & Lal, D. In preparation (1971).

Ku, T. L., Uranium series disequilibrium in deep sea sediments, Ph.D. Thesis, Columbia University (1966).

Ku, T. L., Broecker, W. S. & Opdyke, N., Earth Planet Sci. Lett., *4*, 1 (1968).

Ku, T. L. & Broecker, W. S., Deep Sea Res., *16*, 625 (1969).

Manaheim, F. T., Manganese-iron accumulations in the shallow marine environment; in Symposium on marine geochemistry; Narragansett marine Laboratory, University of Rhode Island Occassional Publication *3*, 217 (1965).

Mason, B., Principles of Geochemistry, John Wiley and Sons, Inc., New York, (1966).

Menard, H. W., Marine geology of the Pacific, Macgraw Hill, New York (1964).

Mero, J. L., 'The mineral resources of the sea', Elsevier Publishing Company, Amsterdam (1965).

Mero, J. L., "The Manganese nodules" in Encycl. of Oceanography, *I*, (ed. R. W. Fairbridge), Reinhold Publishing Corporation, New York (1966).

Moore, W. S., Earth Planet Sci. Lett. *2*, 231 (1967).

Riley, J. P. & Sinhaseni, P., J. Mar. Res., *17*, 466 (1958).

Sackett, W. M., Science, *154*, 646 (1966).

Sill, C W., Willis, P. C. & Flygare, J. K., Anal. Chem. *33*, 1671 (1961).

Skornyakova, N. S., Andruschenko, P. F. & Fomina, L. S., Okeanologia, *2*, 264 (1962).

Somayajulu, B. L. K., Science, *156*, 1219 (1967).

Somayajulu, B. L. K., Heath, G. R., Moore, T. C. & Cronan, D. S., Geochim. Cosmochim. Acta, *35*, 621 (1971).

Turekian, K. K. & Wedepohl, K. H., Geol. Soc. Am. Bull., *72*, 175 (1961).

Wedepohl, K. H., Geochim. Cosmochim. Acta, *18*, 200 (1960).

Willis, J. P. & Ahrens, L. H., Geochim. Cosmochim. Acta, *26*, 751 (1962).

Discussion 7a. Sedimentary Cycles. Manganese Nodules. Airborne Dust

Rickard

It may well be that you have underestimated the impact of man on the erosional cycle, especially for base metal production. Base metal production figures are not a measure of how much metal is dug out of the ground but only a percentage, perhaps as low as 50 % and as high as 90 %, because of losses at the concentration stage.

Goldberg

I agree with you.

Seiler

You said that the natural flux of mercury into the atmosphere is much higher than the flux made by man. How can you explain the increase of mercury in the Greenland glacial waters since 1952?

What is the normal mixing-ratio of mercury in the troposphere?

Goldberg

These questions are dealt with in the section on mercury in my article.

Ui

Where and how does the degassing process for mercury occur? How large is the proportion of oceanic emission of mercury in the atmosphere?

Have you any idea of the chemical form of these emissions of mercury?

Goldberg

The first questions are dealt with in the section on mercury in my article.

As regards to the last question the chemical form might be elemental mercury and compounds such as the sulphide, which are somewhat volatile.

Lal

This refers to your slide on global dispersion of heavy elements by burning fossil fuels. Here the most efficient and quickest way of global dispersion is probably by operation of air-crafts. Is this contribution important, however?

Goldberg

I have no data on aircraft introduction of materials. This is worth investigating.

Bowen

Guinn reported at ACS Summer Symposium 1971 that mercury analyses of museum specimens of large pelagic fish (dated from 1850 to 1970) show no concentration trend with time. Preston's point about artificial radioactivity releases: this is true *only* for beta-gamma nuclides; the rate of release of *alpha* activity, and specifically of plutonium and other transuranics, has increased (for instance, specifically at Windscale) each year from each fuel reprocessing facility. There are both economical and technical reasons for this.

Rickard

Chester has shown that the total metal content of eolian dust plus the weight metal adsorbed during sedimentation (assuming *all* possible metal is removed) is commonly less than the metal concentration in the sediment. Does this not mean that the net effect of the addition of eolian dust to sediments is a dilution of sedimentary metal concentrations?

Chester

I think that in this context dilution is the wrong term. Without the detrital component from river and wind transport there would be negligible amounts of land-derived deep-sea sediments deposited. The alternative is the formation of hydrogenous sediments rich in trace elements which have been removed from sea water. Such hydrogenous sediments do occur. However, in your context all detrital material must be regarded as diluting hydrogenous sediments which would otherwise cover the sea floor. This is an interesting concept.

Duursma

In comparing the trace element concentrations of marine sediments with those of any settling sediments (from dust or rivers) and relating this to adsorption or desorption processes during input and settling in the sea one has to know whether the marine sea floor itself is in equilibrium with the sea water above. With radionuclide tracer techniques it can be shown that all marine sediments do show adsorption-desorption processes whenever they are brought in contact with sea water. These results do not necessarily agree with parallel trace metal processes.

As example: Cobalt-60 is adsorbed while total stable cobalt is released. This indicates that apparent short time equilibria has to be compared or related to long term processes, which happen inside the bottom where diffusion (at low coefficients of less than 10^{-10} cm²/sec) occur with inside bottom pore water and sedimentary-partical reactions, as well as the (long term small) bottom-sea water intersurface reactions.

Chesselet

I should like to add some remarks to the data given by Chester. The concentrations of Co and Ni, for example, that we have found in suspended inorganic particles, collected in the North Atlantic *deep waters* are in complete agreement with his data for the dust load in the air (about 50 ppm for cobalt, about 30 ppm for nickel), what support to me the idea that those concentrations are *not* very much affected, when those particles are going from the "dry" state to the sea water surrounding. But here, I must point out that we find the *same* concentrations in the fraction of very small size particles (about 1–2 μm) which escape from estuaries to the ocean (for example, Gironde). Thus, we cannot, at this state of findings, rule out the important role played by the injection of particles by streams. What is evident, whatsoever are the origins for those particles, is that their "present day" contents in Ni and Co can *not* fully explain the values found for the average pelagic clay sediments in the Atlantic and, far less, for the Pacific and Indian Oceans.

Chester

I agree with Chesselet that the contribution of trace elements by river detritus is certainly important in the trace element budget. If, however, north-east trade wind dusts make a significant contribution to mid-ocean Atlantic sediments they cannot provide the excess, Mn, Ni and Co in these sediments. I suggested that adsorption from sea water was one possible mechanism by which the trace elements could be acquired. However, as I pointed out, it is unlikely to account for very much of the trace element enrichment. Therefore, I agree with Chesselet that other enrichment processes must be involved.

Bowen

Wangersky showed many years ago that in the subtropical Atlantic the horizontal distribution of foraminifera in sediments parallels that in the surface ocean, while that of Coccolithophorids (and other fine fractions) does not. This difference in size range resulted in great increase in horizontal velocity during sinking.

Namias

Are the atmospheric dust data adquate to assess the variations due a) to seasonal changes in the prevailing winds b) to anomalous wind patterns which bring about variable frequency of rains c) to changes in the character of soil (dry or moist) as occurring after periods of drought (e.g. U.S. "dust bowl" of the 1930's)?

Variable dust off Africa might assist or inhibit growth of hurricanes due to variations in coalescence of cloud droplets to form rain, as high density of cloud particles with many dust nuclei makes it harder to get rain and thus releases latent heat of condensation (ref. Twomey and Squires).

Chester

Seasonal changes in the movement of the Atlantic north-east trade dust "belt" have been shown to exist by Prospero. It would appear that in summer the dust "belt" moves southwards. I think the other comments raise extremely interesting questions. At present our data has not been taken over a continuous period which is longer than one year. Perhaps the dust-loadings at Barbados (the one year sampling point) could profitably be compared to the occurrence of weather phenomena such as hurricanes. Although the data available does not permit present changes in soil types to be correlated with dust-loadings, there is a possibility that a study of deep-sea cores in the Equatorial North Atlantic might evaluate post-changes in the nature of the Sahara Desert. "Fertile" periods in the history of the desert may possibly be identified from variations in both the concentration and kind of dust incorporated into the sediments.

Sorokin

When using the experimental approach to the study of absorption or sedimentation mechanisms and rates it should be taken into account the biological mechanisms of their assimilation by microorganisms and accumulation by filtering activity of animals. Animals are filtering out the total volume of the ocean in several years. The mechanism of filtration including not only mechanical separation but also electrostatical adsorption at the mucoid surfaces. So animals can separate with high efficiency even inorganic hydrosoles such as $[Fe(OH_{2.7}Cl_{0.3}]_x$.

Chester

This question is closely bound up with the production of fecal pellets and their utilization in the marine food chain. I discussed this briefly as a possible mechanism for accelerating inorganic particle sinking rates. I certainly feel that Sorokin is correct in stressing the importance of biological mechanisms in the cycle of inorganic particles in the oceans.

Chesselet

An oceanic survey that we made in the Atlantic shows that for waters, from 500 m depths down to the bottom, the weights of suspended matter are extremely constant 30 ± 20 μg/1. Those values are the same for the Pacific (Arrhenius and Sackett).

Below 500 m, the percentage of suspended organic matter which can be destroyed by H_2O_2 attack is fairly constant: 30 to 40 % of the total suspended matter. At the bottom layer (100 to 200 m *above* the sediment) this fraction increases to 70 %. The distributions of humic acids change completely for suspended organic matter collected above (in the 4 km column) and in this layer. This could show that the organic matter in the bottom layer is quite *younger* than the other, indicating a much more recent departure from the continental source.

Comparisons made between the quantities of mineral particles in the 4 km deep water column and the sedimentation rates (given by recent radiochronology) show "residence time" for those particles much less than 100 years, which seems to us very *short*, regarding the settling velocities for those particles that one can compute from experiments and from optical observations on their population/size distributions.

One of our working hypothesis, that at least a fairly large fraction of the pelagic sediment could have for origin pulses of small size particles, released by turbidity currents on the shelves, and carried far away from this source by even slow bottom-water-currents (about 15 cm/s), is substantiated by many evidences. This process could explain the lead of modern origin that you find even in pelagic sediments. Also, this process could represent a very fast pathway to the pelagic sediments for many other pollutants coming by the rivers.

Anyway, I think that we should have to take, very soon, into consideration and study all those processes by which particles seem to be driven very fast to the pelagic oceanic sediments.

Patterson

It is not generally recognized that the observed worldwide pattern of isotopic compositions of lead in pelagic sediments reflects local differences among leads in the soils of nearby onshore drainages. More than half of this lead is contained in authigenic chemical precipitates and must have passed through a dissolution-in-sea water step before deposition. In order for leads of different isotopic compositions not to be thoroughly homogenized before deposition, the residence time must be very short.

We do not know how to account for this except to postulate the incorporation of lead in surface waters into the biomass, where it is formed with very large particles, such as testes and fecal pellets, which fall rapidly to the bottom where subsequent local dissolution processes occur. It is also not generally recognized that fine clay dust particles can dissolve in a few months in pure water. If such particles are aggregated and settled rapidly by mechanisms similar to those required for lead, then they would be protected against dissolution and complete homogenization so as to display pelagic deposition patterns of different chemical and mineral species.

Grasshoff

Should one not find a remarkable function of the manganese nodules in the top layer of the sediments buried in areas with a high surface concentration of the nodules? According to the literature there are hardly any nodules below the surface.

Lal

It is well known that nodules are not restricted to the top surface; the evidence is strong especially for smaller nodules. It is mainly due to the inadequacy of coring techniques that larger nodules are not reported from subsurface layers.

Grasshoff

I did not completely understand the mechanisms of bringing the nodules, especially rather large ones, up to the surface again.

Lal

In areas where extensive nodule deposits are found, one nearly always sees an evidence for bottom currents which manifest as fingerprints on the sediment surface. Probably nodules are retained on the surface of sediment by the gentle stroking action due to bottom currents.

Bowen

Sorokin's ideas about the importance of bacteria in Mn-nodule formation seem to me to contribute to the clarification of the difficult question how nodules or slabs so often over-grow (and so include) layers of carbonate sediment.

Olausson

A model for manganese nodule formation was published by Olausson and Uusitalo (Compt. Rend. Soc. Géol. Finlande *XXXV*, 101 (1963)). The vibration from earth quakes (if the intensity is greater than 0.5 *g*) may be sufficient to move the nodules upwards in fine-grained sediments.

Lal

I think that the mechanism suggested by you may indeed be an important one particularly to bring a nodule up, once it is buried.

Odum

Perhaps the rolling and agitation of the manganese nodules which your theory requires may be supplied by animals. Most bottoms are continually reworked in this way. In the deep sea, you would only need one action per 1 000 yrs.

Lal

Organisms may even continually keep the nodules above the sediments if it is in their interests, but this point needs to be checked.

The Acceleration of the Hydrogeochemical Cycling of Phosphorus

By Werner Stumm

Introduction

Phosphorus plays a governing role in the life cycles; its hydrogeochemical transformations are interwoven with those of other biogenic elements. Solar energy recirculates carbon, nitrogen, phosphorus, sulfur and other elements together with water through the biomass thus synthesizing carbohydrates and other organic nutrients; it thereby maintains the biogeochemical parity of the biomass. In the aquatic environment the stoichiometry of the photosynthesis reaction and the biological oxidation (respiration) of the photosynthetic products—the reverse reaction as long as sufficient O_2 is available—can be given by the simplified reaction (Redfield, Ketchum and Richards, 1963):

$$106\,C + 16\,N + 1\,P + n\,H_2O +$$

$$mH^+ + \text{trace elements} + h\nu \underset{\text{Respiration}}{\overset{\text{Photosynthesis}}{\rightleftarrows}} C_{106}\,N_{16}\,P_1\,H_xO_y + 138\,O_2 \qquad (1)$$

Hence, according to the average composition of plankton, one phosphorus atom may—under suitable conditions—"drive" ca 138 oxygen or 106 CO_2 molecules and thus affects redox intensity and acidity.

Acceleration of P Circulation

The energy fixed by all plants on the surface of the earth is approximately 8×10^{17} Kcal per year. Man's metabolism ($\sim 3 \times 10^{15}$ Kcal per year) plays a minor role in the physiology of the biosphere. Man in his capacity to manipulate nature dissipates from 10 to 20 times (in developed countries 50–100 times) as much energy as he requires for his metabolism. Much of the energy utilized by our industrial society for its own advantage, though still much smaller than the total energy flow within the biosphere, causes localized simplification of the ecosystem and tends to accelerate the cycling of individual elements.

The mining of phosphate and its application in agriculture, industry and household have increased nearly exponentially over the last few decades (Fig. 1). The flow of P from land to water has increased because of various tech-

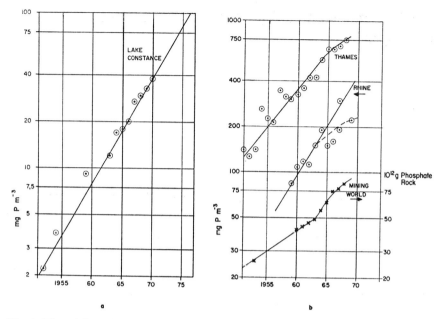

Fig. 1. The mining of phosphate and the increase of its concentration in inland waters. Total P in Lake Constance during circulation period in spring (*a*), in the Rhine (border Netherlands/Germany) and in the Thames (at Laleham) (*b*).

nological measures (clearing land, deforestation, establishing monocultures; municipal waste disposal and urban drainage); the consequences are reflected in the progressively increased concentrations of P in rivers and lakes (Fig. 1).

It is the purpose of this inquiry to evaluate and to assess the civilizatory impact on terrestrial and oceanographic transformations of phosphorus.

Global Phosphorus Circulation

Phosphorus liberated by weathering by oxidation of biota and by mining is carried to the sea where its distribution is controlled primarily by biological and physical processes. Much of the P supplied to the ocean becomes incorporated in plankton and settles into the deeper portions of the sea. In the Atlantic the deep water layer consists of water sunken in the northern latitudes. While this water moves toward the Antarctics, to the Indian Ocean and eventually to the Pacific, its P content progressively increases as a result of differential advection and of accumulation of sinking decomposition products of organic debris.

Fig. 2 gives a simplified scheme of the distribution and circulation of phosphorus. The data on P distribution are from the following sources: The P content of the earth crust has been estimated by Tailor (1964). The P content of the sediments has been calculated from a geochemical balance. Values for P

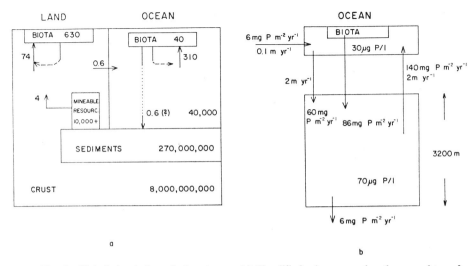

Fig. 2. Global circulation of phosphorus. (*a*) Simplified scheme on abundance and transfer rates (for basis of data see text). Units are 10^{11} moles for abundance and 10^{11} moles year^{-1} for transfer rates. (*b*) Simplified steady state model patterned after Broecker (1971).

in biota have been estimated from Bolin's (1970) figures for carbon in standing biomass by assuming atomic C/P ratios of 100 and 500 for land and marine biota, respectively. The extent of mining of phosphate rocks is given in the United Nations Handbook (1970); the P content of the rock has been assumed to be 13.3 %. Figures for the annual consumption of P by biota on land and in sea have been estimated from productivity data evaluated by Vallentyne (in print) using the C/P ratios mentioned above.

Values for the annual transfer of phosphorus from land to sea have been arrived at by the following considerations: Judging from the solubility constants of apatite, $FePO_4$ and $AlPO_4$ in fresh water, weathering should give concentrations of phosphate phosphorus averaging about 20 μg P/l (Stumm and Morgan, 1970). An equivalent amount of P may be assumed to be present in the form of organic phosphorus. The rivers draining the more developed countries have substantially higher concentrations (see Fig. 1); in rivers of USA (Verduin, 1967) and Europe the P concentration usually exceeds 200 μg/l. Averaging this civilizatory P contribution over the water volume of all the rivers of the world adds another 15–20 μg/l P to the average water draining from land to sea. The composite value of 0.6×10^{11} moles P (3.3×10^{16} liter of 1.8×10^{-6} M) is nearly three times higher than the values quoted in recent compilations on average P abundance in river waters (Riley and Chester, 1971; Turekian, 1969) but is in accord with some earlier estimates (Conway, 1942). Because no data appear to be available on the annual amount of phosphorus lost from the sea to the sediments, the assumption of Emery, Orr and

Rittenberg (1955), that P is deposited in the sediments in approximate balance to the P brought to the ocean, has been adopted for the scheme of Fig. 2.

Progressive Accumulation of Phosphorus on Land

Although P is found in reasonable amounts in the earth crust and is relatively abundant in soil, its movement is restricted because of its limited solubility and because it is retained by components of soil and sediments. Sorption of phosphates onto clay minerals appears to involve at least two mechanisms: chemical binding of the anions to positively charged edges of the clays and of other aluminum and iron (III) oxides, and substitution of phosphates for silicate in the clay structure. The application of phosphate fertilizers has increased ten-fold over the last 50 years and must be assumed to continue to increase exponentially with a similar rate, because modern agricultural technology is fast expanding toward developing countries. Today extraction of P from mineable deposits exceeds the quantity of P washed into the sea. Significantly higher P levels are being built up in a few percent of the earth's total land surface. This progressive accumulation of P and other nutrients, together with other activities necessary to maintain a productive soil monoculture are incompatible with and counteract measures designed to keep inland waters in a non-productive, non-polluted state.

Oceanic P Regeneration

The annual uptake of P by phytoplankton in the sea far exceeds the annual contribution of P to the oceans; hence most of the phosphorus flowing through the phytoplankton is continuously being regenerated from organic debris. Because the average residence time of P in non-biotic form (~ 130 years) is small compared to the time it takes for the average water molecule to return to the surface, much of the regeneration must occur in the upper layers of the oceans. This is in accord with the observation that phosphate and other regeneration products resulting from the oxidation of organic debris (carbon dioxide and nitrate) increase rapidly with water depth, reaching a maximum at the lower end of the permanent thermocline. The redissolution of organic debris in the deeper portions may depend on pH and the availability of dissolved oxygen.

A quantitative evaluation of the P transformations is not yet possible because the rate of incorporation of P into sediments is not known. If the P cycle in the oceans were at steady state, the rate of accumulation of P in sediments should equal the rate of P supply to the ocean. If organisms assimilate P from the sea water much faster than P is supplied to the ocean by rivers (Fig. 2), then a large fraction of the biogenic P must be regenerated and redissolved while a small fraction of biogenic P becomes deposited. If this material were uniformly distributed over the entire ocean floor, the sediments would contain phosphorus to the extent of 0.2 % as P_2O_5. However, P deposition is favored in restricted shallow areas because the tendency for redissolution of any biogenic (skeletal) apatite structures increases with depth (due to lower pH and higher pressure). It is well established that skeletal apatite slowly dissolves on the deep-ocean floor (Arrhenius, 1963).

The Ocean as a Sink for Phosphorus

To what extent can the ocean serve as a sink for phosphorus and other nutrients? In order to assess the influence of an accelerated P flux to the sea, the mechanisms operative in the control of phosphorus concentration need to be understood. The solubility product of apatite (carbonato fluoro hydroxo apatite) for sea water conditions is not known with sufficient precision (Pytkowicz and Kester, 1967), but it appears unlikely that the mean P content of the oceans is controlled by apatite solubility. The latter however, as will be shown later, may control formation and deposition of biogenic and autogenic phosphate minerals in selected shallow areas of the ocean.

Broecker (1971) has recently proposed a simple steady state box model according to which the mean P content of the ocean depends on vertical mixing, on the rate at which P enters the sea and the proportion of biogenic P which escapes dissolution. Figure 2*b* has been patterned according to Broecker's model. Specifically an upwelling rate $V_D = 2$ m yr^{-1} has been adopted; the sinking velocity must be of the same magnitude. Hence the downward and upward transport are given by V_D [$P_{surf.}$] and V_D [P_{deep}], respectively. The areal loading from the river input, given in Figure 2*a*, corresponds to 6 mg P m^{-2} yr^{-1} ($= V_R$ [P_{river}] where the areal hydraulic loading of the ocean $V_R = 0.1$ m yr^{-1}). Assuming, as before, that P is removed into the sediments at the same rate that rivers bring it to the sea, all transfer rates are determined by steady state balance.

The model assumes relatively constant compositions for the upper water layer and for the deep ocean. In the case of P, the composition of the upper layer is not uniform; P increases rapidly with depth near the thermocline. I assume [$P_{surf.}$] ≈ 30 μg/l, a value significantly higher than that suggested by Broecker.

According to this model, the deep portions of the ocean receive phosphate in two forms: (1) the preformed phosphorus, P_{pr} (60 mg P m^{-2} yr^{-1}), i.e., phosphate that enters the deep water as such and remains there as a conservative parameter (cf. Redfield et al., 1963, and Culberson and Pytkowicz, 1970); (2) phosphorus in the form of biogenic debris, P_{debris} (86 mg P m^{-2} yr^{-1}). Most of the latter is being oxidized to form phosphate of oxidative origin, P_{ox} (80 mg P m^{-2} yr^{-1}).

Oxygen Utilization

Enrichment of the sea with algal nutrients, if it occurred homogeneously throughout the ocean or locally in some nutrient deprived regions, is not un- desirable. But because the oxygen concentration in the deep ocean depends on the amount of organic debris settling and the amount of O_2 advecting to the deeper portions, any *excess* fertilization may decrease the oxygen reserves of the deeper waters. According to Eqn. 1, for every phosphorus atom of oxidative origin found, 276 oxygen atoms have been consumed. Hence the flux of P_{ox} is paralleled by a flux of oxygen utilization, OU, equivalent to 11.4 g oxygen m^{-2} yr^{-1}. Hence in the deep waters, where $[P_{ox}] \approx 40$ μg P/l, the average oxygen deficit is $[OU] = 5.7$ mg O_2/l. This corresponds to a mean O_2-saturation of 49 %. In the deep waters of the North Atlantic and North Pacific, oxygen satur- ation values in the magnitude of 81 % and 44 % respectively (Redfield et al., 1963) are typical. In some regions, e.g. the east tropical North Pacific Ocean or in less deep portions where advection of O_2-rich water is small, anoxic or nearly anoxic conditions prevail.

Consequences of Increased P Supply

Any increase in the supply of P to the sea, even if its effect on the mean P content of the ocean is relatively small, will increase the fraction of ocean floor covered by anaerobic waters. As pointed out by Broecker (1971), the oceanic system may respond to such a perturbation by reestablishing a balance between loss and gain of P; for example with reduced O_2 reserves a larger fraction of organic debris would escape decomposition and thus tends to restore the mean P content to the earlier value. While doubling of the P input into the ocean may occur within some decades, regulatory response may be 100 to 1 000 times slower; hence a larger fraction of the ocean, especially coastal waters, will become excessively enriched with P, so as to cause dramatic and mostly un- desirable charges in plant and animal life. Under anaerobic conditions all higher forms of life are eliminated.

Sources of Phosphorus

By mining, man restores incipiently marine phosphorus in increasing quantities to the land. Because the rate of mining exceeds the rate of transport to the sea (Fig. 2), ecological unbalance results causing pronounced pollution in inland and coastal waters.

Vollenweider (1968) has reviewed the various nutrient sources extensively and has attempted to analyze them. His report should be consulted for the detailed accounting of the various factors involved. Obviously, the quantity of phosphorus introduced into a surface water from a given drainage area is dependent on density of population and livestock, on the methods and intensity of fertilization, on the type of cultivation (e.g., forests, grassland, cropland) on the pedological characteristics of the soil and on the type of sewage and waste treatment system involved. The daily per capita excretion of P is 1.5 gram. Other loadings in municipal waste can be attributed primarily to phosphates in detergents. As Fig. 3 shows, extent of fertilizer application in countries of modern agricultural technology is related to population density. A reasonable figure for the total municipal discharge in the USA and Europe is ca 3 g P per capita per day; or related to the population density on an annual basis, 1 mg P year^{-1} m^{-2} per population density (inhabitants km^{-2}). Table 1 gives estimates on the application of nutrients and their runoff from an area representative for Europe. The nutrient loading of lakes can then be estimated by relating the drainage area to the lake surface (Table 1, Part III).

Vollenweider (1968) has shown convincingly on the basis of data on 20 lakes that a valid correlation can be established between areal limiting nutrient

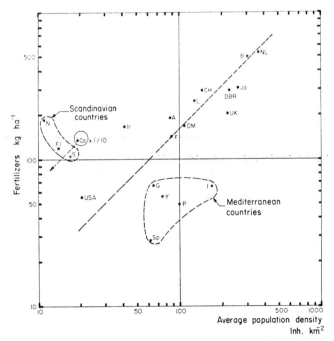

Fig. 3. Fertilizers used (N + P$_2$O$_5$ + K$_2$O) per unit of arable land surface in relation to population density (from Vollenweider, 1968). Letters refer to countries, i.e., G = Greece, DBR = German Federal Republic, A = Austria and CH = Switzerland, etc.

Table 1. *Sources of phosphorus. Loading of land, export to the water and loading of inland waters*

The figures given are estimates representative for the European situation. With minor modifications the data given are also typical for USA. Some of the background information is from Vollenweider (1968). Specifically, a population density of 150 inhabitants km^{-2}, a land utilization of 30 % for crop and 30 % for grassland production have been assumed.

I. *Application and "production" of nutrients per unit area*

	N gram m^{-2} yr^{-1}	P gram m^{-2} yr^{-1}
Agricultural		
Animal wastes	5.3	0.9
Fertilizer	2.4	1.2
Rain	0.4	0.04
Municipal		
Human wastes	0.7	0.08
Detergents	—	0.08
Industrial wastes	0.1	0.01
Highways	0.1	0.01

II. *Export from unit area of land*

A washout of approximately 15 and 3 %, respectively, of the N and P, applied to the land, and a connection to sewers of 80 % of the municipal sources have been assumed.

	N gram m^{-2} yr^{-1}	P gram m^{-2} yr^{-1}
Agricultural	1.2 (63 %)	0.06 (30 %)
Municipal	0.7 (37 %)	0.14 (70 %)
Total	1.9	0.20
After mechanical and biological waste treatment[a]	1.6	0.16
After "complete" waste treatment[b]	1.5	0.08

III. *Representative loading of lakes per unit lake area*

These estimates are based on a surrounding factor (= drainage area/lake surface) of 20.

	N gram m^{-2} (lake) yr^{-1}	P gram m^{-2} (lake) yr^{-1}	N/P by atoms
without waste treatment	38	4.0	21
with mechanical and biological treatment	32	3.2	22
with "complete" waste treatment[b]	30	1.6	42

[a] Waste treatment reduces N and P contributions of municipal wastes only.
[b] "Complete" treatment means mechanical and biological treatment supplemented by a chemical precipitation process for phosphate elimination (> 80 %).

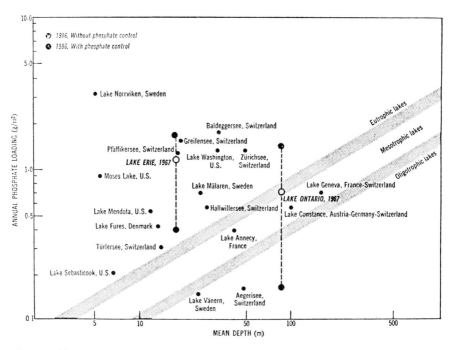

Fig. 4. Critical phosphorus loading as a function of depth (from Vollenweider, 1968).

loading and mean lake depth on one hand, and degree of enrichment on the other. In Fig. 4 this relationship is plotted with phosphorus as a limiting nutrient. The demarcation line indicated in this figure gives perhaps the most relevant collective reference values on permissive phosphorus loadings.

Present day aerobic biological waste treatment mineralizes substantial fractions of bacterially oxidizable organic substances but is usually not capable of eliminating more than 30 to 50 percent of phosphate components, because most municipal wastes are nutritionally unbalanced (deficient in organic carbon) for a heterotrophic enrichment process.

An estimate of the extent of possible ecological effects of algal nutrients (potential fertility) is obtained from the schematic stoichiometry equation of production and respiration (Eqn. 1). If phosphorus is the limiting factor, 1 mg of P allows the synthesis of approximately 0.1 g of algae biomass (dry weight) in one single cycle of the limnological transformation. This biomass, after settling to the deeper layers, exerts for its mineralization a biochemical oxygen demand of approximately 140 mg. This simple calculation demonstrates that the organic material that is introduced into the lake with domestic wastes (20–100 mg organic matter per liter) may be small in comparison to the organic material that will be biosynthesized from fertilizing constituents (3–8 mg P per liter which can yield 300–800 mg organic matter per liter).

More complete phosphate removal can be accomplished readily by treating wastes with lime, iron or aluminum salts leading to chemical precipitation of phosphate (Leckie and Stumm, 1970). However, even if it were possible to eliminate all phosphorus discharged from the sewage system, substantial nutrient loading from less controllable sources would remain (Table 1).

Pollution of Inland Waters, Estuaries and Fjords

The addition of nutrients is one of the major factors in the pollution of fresh and coastal waters of Europe, North America and Japan. The concentration of dissolved phosphate in natural waters gives little indication of phosphate availability; quite to the contrary, in a highly productive system, most of the soluble phosphorus has been taken up into the biomass. The phosphorus reserve in a lake is not a simple function of the supply of phosphorus to the body of water; its magnitude depends also on the residence time of phosphorus, t_p, relative to that of water, t_{H_2O}, which in turn is influenced by the biota, by the mixing relationships, by the morphometry of the basin and by the exchange with and retention by the sediments. Stratified waters often trap nutrients, i.e., t_p is larger than t_{H_2O}.

As Eqn. 1 predicts, phosphate and nitrate are eliminated from the water in

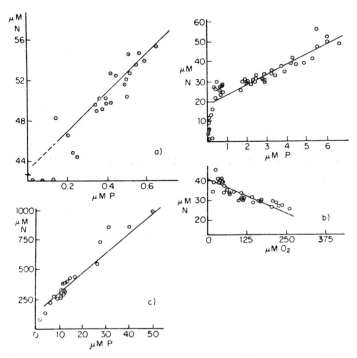

Fig. 5. Correlation of concentrations of soluble NO_3^-, P and oxygen (cf. Stumm and Stumm-Zollinger, 1968). (*a*) Lake Constance; (*b*) Lake Zurich (oxygen data only from hypolimnion); (*c*) Lake Norrviken (ice-covered, winter stagnation).

a fixed ratio during photosynthesis; in the deeper water layers, as a result of mineralization of biogenic debris, these elements are liberated in the same fixed ratio. If the concentration of NO_3 is plotted as a function of phosphate or oxygen, linear diagrams should be obtained with the coefficients required by Eqn. 1, provided that the rate of mixing is not fast in comparison to the transport of plankton. Fig. 5 gives some examples of such plots for European lakes, although for the cases illustrated the molar ratios differ somewhat from the ratios postulated in Eqn. 1.

The trapping of nutrients is most efficient in estuaries and fjords, because countercurrent systems are particularly effective in producing changes in the distribution of nutrients along the direction of flow; nutrients accumulate in the direction from which the surface current is flowing. Algae grown from nutrients that are carried seaward in the surface outflow eventually settle and become mineralized. The mineralization products are then carried landward by the countercurrent of more dense sea water that moves in to replace the water entrained in the surface outflow. An example on the distribution of salinity, of oxygen deficit and of total phosphorus in the lower Hudson River and estuary and in the waters of New York City illustrated by Ketchum (1969) is given in Fig. 6. Several of the Norwegian fjords (Føyn, 1970) and

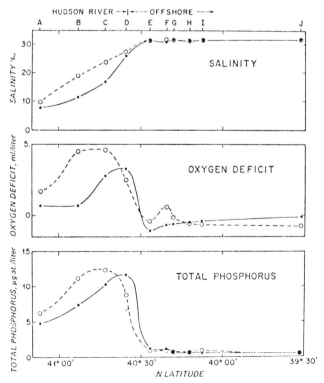

Fig. 6. Distribution of properties in the Lower Hudson River and Estuary and in the waters off New York City (from Ketchum, 1969).

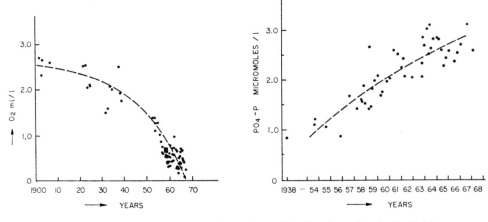

Fig. 7. Mean values of dissolved oxygen and phosphate of the Landsort deep in the Baltic Sea (from Fonselius, 1969). Data from below the halocline at station F 78.

parts of the Baltic Sea are known to have become anoxic (Fonselius, 1969, 1970) (Fig. 7).

   Localized effects of increased P contribution by rivers draining industrially developed areas can be significant. For example, total supply of P to the North Sea by the Rhine comes at present to 21 000 tons per year, enough for the production of 2 million tons of organic matter (dry weight). This is 10 times the amount of organic matter presently extracted from the North Sea by fisheries. This quantity of P is half the amount of marine P carried into the North Sea through the Strait of Dover (Postma, 1967).

Limiting Nutrients

For most inland waters phosphorus appears to play a major role in influencing productivity. In some estuaries and in many waters of the marine coast, nitrogen appears to be more limiting to algal growth than phosphorus.

   For the lakes considered in Fig. 5, the concentration of phosphorus approaches zero (intersection of correlation line with ordinate) when nitrate is still present in the water in substantial concentrations. In these particular lakes, therefore, the assumption is well justified that, besides localized and time-transient deviations, phosphorus, rather than nitrogen, limits biomass synthesis. Deficiency in trace elements occurs usually only as a temporal or spatial transient. Inorganic or organic "growth factors", especially hormones and chelators, may affect the composition of the algal community rather than its size.

   Table 2 illustrates the change in N/P ratios typically encountered in passing from the land to the sea. The data given and their comparison with the average

Table 2. *Variation in N:P ratios in passing from the land to the sea*

N:P (by atoms). Most commonly encountered values:

Municipal sewage 6–14	Inland waters 15–30	Coastal waters 2–25	Ocean 15	Phytoplankton 10–17
Change in ratio caused by:	Agricul- tural drainage	Denitri- fication	(N-fixation) P-sedimentation N in rain	

ratio in phytoplankton illustrate plausibly that fresh waters typically receive an excess of N over that needed. Agricultural drainage contains relatively large concentrations of bound nitrogen because nitrogen is washed out more readily from fertilized soil than phosphorus. In estuaries denitrification is frequently encountered because NO_3^- bearing waters may come into contact with organically enriched water layers; the N/P ratio can also be shifted by differences in the circulation rate of these two nutrients.

Formation of Marine Phosphorites

The term phosphorite is used to describe marine sedimentary deposits composed mainly of carbonate apatite. The geochemistry of phosphorite deposition has been discussed and reviewed by d'Anglejan (1968), Tooms, Summerhayes and Cronan (1969) and Kolodny and Kaplan (1970).

Phosphorites have been deposited on the continental shelf, in the uppermost parts of the continental slope in water depths less than 1 000 m and in regions where sedimentation is very slow or negligible. The relative rarity of these deposits indicates that special conditions must be met for the formation or deposition of phosphate minerals. There are essentially the following ways for phosphorus to be deposited or phosphorites to be formed: (1) Burying of detrital P; (2) chemical precipitation of apatite; and (3) diagenetic replacement of calcite (e.g., skeletal carbonate) by substitution of carbonate by phosphate.

Although the solubility product of apatite is not known for sea water conditions, precipitation of calcium phosphate (carbonato, fluoro apatite) in the deep sea is unlikely. Phosphorite formation can only occur where the relative degree of apatites saturation has been increased and where favorable conditions for heterogeneous nucleation prevail.

Accumulation of P regenerated from detritus as it occurs most extensively in shallow areas and under conditions of countercurrent systems, however, does not in itself lead to an increase in the relative apatite saturation because the regeneration of one phosphorus atom is accompanied by an increase in acidity caused by the formation of ca 106 CO_2 molecules. In order to exceed the critical ion product, the excess of CO_2 formed must be lost or neutralized. Such conditions are encountered in areas of upwelling, where excess CO_2 is lost to the atmosphere and under reducing conditions where denitrification and sulfate reduction consume hydrogen ions. Indeed phosphorite nodules are found generally in areas of upwelling and have been deposited under conditions that are at least mildly reducing.

Pytkowicz and Kester (1967), by comparing two North Pacific regions, in one of which phosphorites are found, have shown that seawater is more saturated (but not necessarily oversaturated) with calcium phosphate in regions where phosphorites are found than where they are not found. The greater degree of saturation in waters where phosphorites were formed was not due to a higher phosphate concentration, but due to a higher pH.

Most of the phosphorites dredged from the present sea floor, however, are old (probably older than 10^5 years) and are at the present being eroded rather than deposited. It has been suggested (cf. Kolodny and Kaplan, 1970) that the higher temperatures prevailing during the Miocene enabled the formation of phosphorites at that time.

Nucleation and Growth of Apatite

Although geologically recent phosphorites are rare, marine apatite is still being formed under restricted conditions. In our laboratory (Leckie, 1969, Stumm and Leckie, 1971) investigations on the kinetics of interaction between calcite and phosphate have been carried out. One of the interesting results of these studies is that in the pH range 6.8–8.3 apatite is formed epitaxially on the calcite surface, i.e. the calcite becomes overgrown with a thin layer of carbonate hydroxy apatite (Fig. 8). The apatite structure of this overgrowth has been confirmed by grazing angle electron diffraction.

Fig. 9 shows representative results obtained in systems where $CaCO_3(s)$ is maintained in equilibrium with a partial pressure of CO_2; i.e., for a given CO_2 pressure, the concentration of Ca^{+2}, HCO_3^-, H^+ remains constant, while the concentration of soluble phosphorus may vary. Representative curves on the kinetics of apatite formation illustrate that the reaction involves three steps: (1) chemisorption of phosphate accompanied by heterogeneous formation of nuclei of a presumably amorphous calcium phosphate; (2) a slow transformation of these nuclei into crystalline apatite; and (3) crystal growth of apatite. The experimental results of all three reaction steps can be interpreted kinetically in terms of accepted models on heterogeneous nucleation and crystal growth. The lag period during which a phase transformation occurs in the

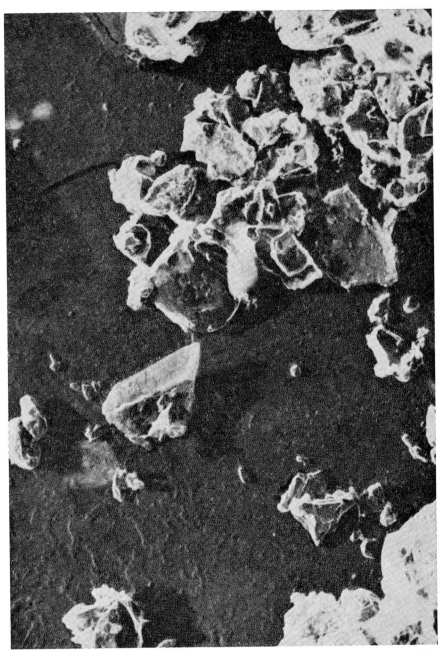

Fig. 8. Electron micrographs of platinized surface replicas of calcite covered with crystallites of hydroxyapatite.

calcium phosphate nuclei, as well as the subsequent apatite crystal growth reaction depend strongly on the $[CO_3^{-2}]/[PO_4^{-3}]$ ratio. Competition of CO_3^{-2} and PO_4^{-3} for adsorption at the growth sites most likely accounts for the reduced

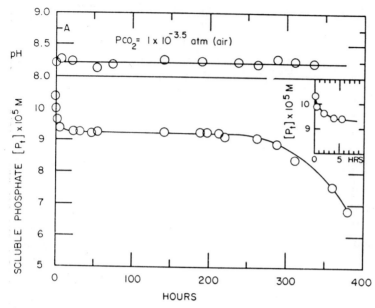

Fig. 9. Heterogeneous nucleation and crystal growth of apatite on calcite. Kinetic data for equilibrated heterogeneous reactions at 25°C. pH remains stable throughout the reaction. Solution composition: pH 8.25, $[Ca^{+2}] = 4.5 \times 10^{-4}$ M, $[HCO_3^-] = [C_t] = 8.9 \times 10^{-4}$ M, $[P_t]_0 = 10.27 \times 10^{-5}$ M, Calcide surface: 3.65 m²/l.

rates of reaction at high $[CO_3^{-2}]/[PO_4^{-3}]$ ratios. The rate of crystal growth is much slower than it would be if it were controlled by transport (diffusion) of the ions from the bulk of the solution. Most likely, surface diffusion on the surface of the crystal determines the rate of crystal growth.

Fluoride, even in trace concentrations (5×10^{-5} M) enhances the rate of apatite precipitation. Because F⁻ can substitute for OH⁻ in the apatite structure, adding F⁻ has partially the same effect as raising the pH. On the other hand, apatite formation is retarded significantly by Mg^{+2}. Organic adsorbates also inhibit the crystallization reactions.

As the results indicate, calcite will convert into apatite in sediments under suitable conditions, although this conversion will be extremely slow at the concentrations and pH values typically encountered at the sea-sediment inter- face. Although data from freshwater sediments are lacking, information from estuary and ocean sediments indicate that diagenesis should also occur in fresh waters; because of lower $[Mg^{+2}]$ the reaction might be faster in fresh water sediments. A recent example of diagenesis of carbonate sediment has been reported by d'Anglejan (1968) where the dissolved inorganic P concentra- tions averaged 3.5×10^{-6} M at the sediment water interface.

Conclusions

By mining phosphorus in progressively increasing quantities man disturbs the ecological balance and creates undesirable conditions in inland waters, estuaries and coastal marine waters. The civilizatory increase in phosphorus supply to the oceans, although of little consequence to the oxygen reserves of the deep sea, augments markedly the marine environments with intermittent or permanent oxygen deficient conditions. Because most aquatic food resources are produced in estuaries and coastal areas, the deterioration in water quality of these regions decreases the potential harvest of marine animal protein.

Our present agricultural practice of excessively fertilizing land needs to be reexamined; our present agricultural technology must not without modification be exported to tropical areas. Our present drainage systems for sewage, industrial wastes and storm water runoff accelerate the transport of nutrients and other pollutants to the rivers and the sea; waste treatment plants are remarkably inefficient in mitigating this civilizatory flux.

References

d'Anglejan, B. F., Can. J. Earth Sci., *5*, 81 (1968).

Arrhenius, G., in The Sea (ed. M. N. Hill), Vol. 3, p. 655. Wiley-Interscience, New York 1963.

Bolin, B., Sci. American, *223*, Sep. p. 125 (1970).

Broecker, W. S., Quaternary Research, *1*, 188 (1971).

Conway, E. J., Proc. Royal Irish Acad., *48 B*, 119 (1942).

Culberson, C. & Pytkowicz, R. M., J. Oceanogr. Soc. Japan, *26*, 95 (1970).

Emery K. O., Orr, W. L. & Rittenberg, S. C., in Essays in Natural Science in Honor of Captain Allan Hancock, p. 299. Univ. So. Calif. Press, Los Angeles (1955).

Fonselius, S. H., Hydrography of the Baltic Deep Basins. Vol. III, Report No. 23 Fishery Board of Sweden, Lund 1969.

Fonselius, S. H., Environment, *12*, No. 6, 2 (1970).

Føyn, E., in Eutrophication in Large Lakes and Impoundments, p. 447. Report by OECD, Paris 1970.

Ketchum, B. H., in Eutrophication, Causes, Consequences, Correctives. Nat. Acad. Sciences, Washington, D. C., 1969.

Kolodny, Y. & Kaplan, I. R., Geochim. Cosmochim. Acta, *34*, 3 (1970).

Leckie, J. O., Phosphate Exchange with Sediments. Ph.D. Thesis Harvard University, Cambridge 1969.

Leckie, J. O. & Stumm, W., in Advances in Water Quality Improvement (eds. E. Gloyna and W.W. Eckenfelder). Univ. of Texas Press, 1970.

Postma, H., in Chemical Environment in the Aquatic Habitat (eds. H. L. Golterman and R. S. Clymo). Noord-Hollandsche Uitgevens Maatschappij 1967.

Pytkowicz, R. M. & Kester, D. R., Limnol. Oceanogr., *12*, 714 (1967).

Redfield, A. C., Ketchum, B. H. & Richards, F. A., in The Sea (ed. M. N. Hill), Wiley-Interscience, New York 1963.

Riley, J. P. & Chester, R., Introduction to Marine Chemistry. Academic Press, London 1971.

Stumm, W. & Leckie, J. O., 5th Internat. Conf. Water Pollution Research. Pergamon Press, London 1971.

Stumm, W. & Morgan, J. J., Aquatic Chemistry. Wiley-Interscience, New York 1970.

Stumm, W. & Stumm-Zollinger, E., Chimia, *22*, 325 (1968).

Tailor, S. R., Geochim. Cosmochim. Acta, *28*, 1273 (1969).

Tooms, J. S., Summerhayes, C. P. & Cronan, O. S., Oceanogr. Mar. Biol. Ann. Rev., *7*, 49 (1969).

Turekian, K. K., in Handbook of Geochemistry, Vol. I, Springer, Berlin 1969.

Vallentyne, J. R., in Data of Geochemistry, U. S. Geological Survey (in print) quoted from Primary Productivity in Aquatic Environments (ed. C. R. Goldman), Univ. Calif. Press, Berkeley 1969.

Verduin, J., in Agriculture and the Quality of our Environment. Amer. Assoc. Adv. Science 1967.

Vollenweider, R. A., Scientific Fundamentals of the Eutrophication. OECD Report DAS/CSI/68.27 (1968).

Sulfate Reduction, Pyrite Formation, and the Oceanic Sulfur Budget

By Robert A. Berner

Introduction

Every year 368 megatons of dissolved sulfate are delivered to the ocean by rivers. Only two processes are of possible importance in removing this sulfate from sea water. One is the precipitation of calcium sulfate and the other is the bacterial reduction of sulfate to hydrogen sulfide which is precipitated as pyrite, FeS_2. Calcium sulfate is considerably undersaturated in normal sea water so that evaporation to salinities over three times the average is necessary to reach saturation. Although the geological record provides many examples of past evaporative marine basins of large areal extent, the present ocean contains essentially no quantitatively significant evaporite basins where calcium sulfate is precipitated. Therefore, dissolved sulfate must be removed from the ocean at present by the formation of sedimentary pyrite. The primary purpose of this paper is to discuss and illustrate, through the use of theoretical models, the principal factors which limit the amount of pyrite which may form in a marine sediment. In addition an estimate is made of the present oceanic sulfur budget. If nothing else is accomplished, it is hoped that this paper will point out the need for obtaining much more data on the contents and distribution of various forms of sulfur in marine sediments.

The overall process by which pyrite is formed in marine sediments (Berner, 1970) can be briefly summarized as flollows: in those sediments where organic matter accumulates faster than it can be destroyed, pore waters become anaerobic and the process of bacterial sulfate reduction begins. Hydrogen sulfide is formed and immediately some of it reacts with detrital iron minerals in the sediment to form black iron monosulfides, chiefly mackinawite, FeS, and greigite, Fe_3S_4. Some of the remaining H_2S is oxidized to elemental sulfur by aerobic or anaerobic bacteria. A part of this elemental sulfur then reacts with the iron monosulfides, by way of solution-reprecipitation reactions, to form pyrite. The remaining elemental sulfur is oxidized bacteriologically to sulfate so that it does not accumulate. This is all illustrated in Fig. 1.

From this discussion and Fig. 1, it can be seen that the primary limitations upon how much sulfate can be ultimately removed from sea water and fixed as pyrite are: 1. The availability of bacteriologically metobolizable organic

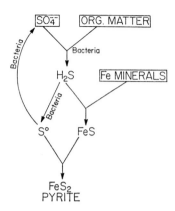

Fig. 1. Major steps in the process of sedimentary pyrite formation.

matter; 2. The concentration and rate of deposition of detrital iron compounds which can react with H_2S to form iron sulfides; 3. The rate of replenishment of sulfate in the sediment via diffusion from the overlying water. The role of each of these factors will now be discussed in detail.

Organic Matter

The presence of microbiologically decomposable organic matter is necessary for pyrite formation for several reasons. First, all dissolved oxygen must be absent for pyrite to be stable and removal of oxygen requires the presence of organic matter which, by means of biological metabolism acts as a primary reducing agent for the oxygen. Secondly, organic matter is required for bacterial sulfate reduction since these bacteria are heterotrophic. Furthermore, sulfate reducers are obligate anaerobes and require the previous removal of oxygen by other organisms. Without sufficient decomposable organic matter deposition there is no sulfate reduction, no H_2S formation, and, thus, no pyrite formation.

Deposition of Organic Matter

The deposition of high percentages of decomposable organic matter in sediments is favored by: low wave and current energy, high organic productivity, a rapid rate of deposition, and restricted bottom water circulation. Low wave and current energy allows dead organic matter, which has a low specific gravity, to settle out; otherwise, it does not accumulate. This is why beach sands are generally almost free of organics whereas fine grained muds are often organic-rich. Quiet near shore waters protected by reefs, barrier beaches, etc and deep waters below wave base, thus, are the characteristic environments of deposition of organic-rich muds.

High organic productivity obviously favors the deposition of higher quantities of organic matter and this leads to the observation that regions of up-welling and high surface productivity are commonly underlain by organic-rich, pyritic sediments. Several examples are provided by the basins off southern California (Emery, 1960).

If organic matter is deposited slowly in a sediment overlain by oxygenated sea water aerobic organisms may be able before burial to destroy all compounds which would otherwise be available for bacterial sulfate reduction. Thus, if the rate of destruction of potentially utilizable organic matter is faster than its rate of sedimentation, it cannot accumulate and pyrite formation cannot occur. This is the reason why most deep water sediments of the ocean are not organic-rich and do not contain pyrite. Only in those places where bottom waters are low in dissolved oxygen can organic matter be deposited slowly without being destroyed. A restricted circulation of the bottom waters favors stagnation and oxygen depletion and a classic example of this stiuation is the Black Sea. Of course, organic-rich pyritic sediments can also accumulate in fully oxygenated bottom waters if the rate of deposition is sufficiently rapid as shown by many nearshore subtidal and intertidal sediments.

Organic Matter and Bacterial Sulfate Reduction

Under anaerobic conditions heterotrophic bacteria, generally of the *Desulpho-vibrio* type, utilize dissolved sulfate ions as hydrogen acceptors and oxidize organic matter and reduce sulfate according to reactions of the types:
For carbohydrate:

$$2CH_2O + SO_4^{2-} \rightarrow H_2S + 2HCO_3^-$$

For amino acid:

$$4CH_2NH_2COOH + 4H_2O + 3SO_4^{2-} \rightarrow H_2S + 2HS^- + 8HCO_3^- + 4NH_4^+$$

Pyrite may also form from hydrogen sulfide derived from the breakdown of sulfur-containing organic compounds but this source of H_2S in marine sediments has been shown by many studies (eg. Skopintsev, 1961) to be negligible when compared to the abundant sulfate of sea water. The reason why sulfate is so more important is that it is mobile and able to diffuse into sediments undergoing sulfate reduction. As a result, amounts of pyrite build up in a sediment far in excess of the amount of organic sulfur or dissolved sulfate originally buried with the sediment. The sediment acts as an open system to the overlying water with regards to sulfate which can continually diffuse down gradients of concentration in the pore waters of the sediments to replace that which is reduced to H_2S.

Laboratory studies (Harrison and Thode, 1958; Kemp and Thode, 1968) have demonstrated that the rate of sulfate reduction is much more strongly dependent upon the concentration of bacterially metabolizable organic compounds than it is on the concentration of sulfate. In addition Zobell and Rittenberg (1948) and Sorokin (1962) have shown that the population of sulfate reducers in marine sediments decreases rapidly with depth most likely as a result of the loss of metabolizable organics during burial. When fresh organic materials are first deposited, sulfate reducers have available to them a wide variety of readily decomposable compounds such as amino acids, low molecular weight fatty acids, etc. As a result, the number of cells and rate of sulfate reduction is high. During burial, however, the readily decomposable material rapidly disappears and then the sulfate reducers become dependent upon other fermentative microorganisms to provide them with utilizable compounds by breaking down long chain polymers and other macromolecules which are otherwise not available to the sulfate reducers. Thus, a sulfate reduction ecology is set up (Sorokin, 1962). Ultimately with continued burial the fermentative microorganisms run out of decomposable material, and as a result sulfate reduction ceases.

If a knowledge of the concentration and type of organic compounds at each depth were known and the response, in terms of Michaelis-Menten or similar equations, (Dixon and Webb, 1964) had been determined for the bacteria, then exact expressions for the rate of sulfate reduction could be stated. In the absence of such data, the writer (Berner, 1964a) has constructed a simplified model which assumes that the disappearance of total organic carbon with depth is a measure of the organic material which becomes available to sulfate reducers, and that the rate of sulfate reduction at any given depth is directly proportional to the concentration of this "metabolizable" organic matter. In other words:

$$R = LkG \tag{1}$$

where: R = rate of sulfate reduction

G = concentration of metabolizable organic carbon

k = the first order rate constant for G (see below)

L = stoichiometric coefficient relating the number of atoms of carbon oxidized to the number of sulfate ions reduced (for the carbohydrate shown reaction above $L = 1/2$)

The distribution of metabolizable carbon G with depth is problematical but, as a first approximation, I have assumed that it is non-diffusable and disappears according to first order kinetics, so that at steady state the diagenetic equation (Berner, 1971a) is:

$$-\omega \frac{\partial G}{\partial x} - kG = 0 \tag{2}$$

where: x = depth in the sediment measured positively downward from the sediment-water interface

$\omega = dx/dt$ = rate of deposition (minus compaction)

Upon integration and substitution into Eqn. 1 one obtains:

$$R = LkG_0 \exp\left[\frac{-k}{\omega}x\right] \tag{3}$$

where G_0 is the value of G at $x = 0$. Then for steady state, the diagenetic equation for sulfate is:

$$D_s\frac{\partial^2 S}{\partial x^2} - \omega\frac{\partial S}{\partial x} - LkG_0\exp\left[\frac{-k}{\omega}x\right] = 0 \tag{4}$$

where: S = concentration of dissolved sulfate in the pore water

D_s = whole sediment diffusion coefficient (including tortuosity)

Solutions of (4) at constant ω and D_s for the appropriate boundary conditions yields the expressions:

$$S = (S_0 - S_\infty)\exp\left[\frac{-k}{\omega}x\right] + S_\infty \tag{5}$$

$$S_0 - S_\infty = \frac{\omega^2 LG_0}{\omega^2 + D_s k}$$

where: S_0 = concentration of sulfate at $x = 0$

S_∞ = asymptotic concentration of sulfate where $G \rightarrow 0$.

The above model can be tested against the data of Kaplan et al., (1963) for the sediments of the Santa Barbara Basin off southern California, which appear to represent a steady state diagenetic system. Using the measured values of $\omega = 0.16$ cm/yr with the data shown in Fig. 2, and assuming that $L = 1/2$ and that $G_0 = 0.28$ moles per liter of pore water which is the difference in total organic carbon content between the surface and the depth where S approaches S_∞, solution of Eqns. 5 yields $D_s = 2 \times 10^{-6}$ cm^2/sec and $k = 7.5 \times 10^{-11}$ sec^{-1}. This value for D_s is reasonable for the average diffusion coefficient of an anion in the top several meters of a fine-grained sediment.

A further test of the model is provided by the data of Sorokin (1962) for the Black Sea deep water sediments. The bottom conditions in the Black Sea are rather similar to those in the Santa Barbara Basin as shown in Table 1. On this basis it is assumed that the values of k and G_0 are approximately the same for the two localities. Using an average value for ω of 0.01 cm/yr based on the data of Ross et al. (1970), Eqn. 3 can be solved for the rate of sulfate reduction R as a function of depth. Calculated values are compared to those measured

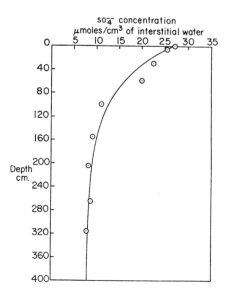

Fig. 2. Plot of dissolved sulfate vs depth for the interstitial water of a sediment core from the Santa Barbara Basin, California. Circles represent measurements of Kaplan et al. (1963). The curve represents equation (5) fitted to the data.

by Sorokin in Table 2. As can be seen, there is reasonably good agreement at each depth, especially considering the many crude assumptions of the model.

Although the sulfate distribution or rate of reduction in the Santa Barbara Basin and Black Sea bottom sediments is well described by the model, the distribution of pyrite is not. The problem is that pyrite is formed more rapidly than predicted by the model; i.e. high values are reached at very shallow depths in the sediment. In the case of the Black Sea this discrepancy can be explained in terms of formation of the pyrite from H_2S contained in the bottom waters. However, in the Santa Barbara Basin the bottom waters do not contain H_2S and a more reasonable explanation is that near the sediment-water interface, where much of the pyrite is formed, the rate of sulfate reduction is higher than predicted by the model. The probable reason for this has already been given. At and near the sediment-water interface, freshly deposited organic matter may by highly enriched in compounds which can be readily utilized by sulfate reducing bacteria thus enabling high metabolic rates and rapid pyrite formation. Below this zone the readily utilizable material disappears and the sulfate reducers become dependent upon the fermentative microorganisms to produce their

Table 1. *Comparison of the Black Sea and Santa Barbara Basins*

Basin	Depth (m)	Bottom water			Surface sediments	
		T °C	S %$_{00}$	O_2 (ml/l)	org. C %	Benthos
Santa Barbara	600	6	34	0.3	2.5–3.5	few to none
Black sea	2 000	9	22	0.0	1.3–5.0	none

Table 2. *Rate of sulfate reduction R in Black Sea central basin sediments*

	R in mole cm^{-3} sec^{-1}	
Depth cm	theoretical	measured (Sorokin, 1962)
0	1.0×10^{-14}	1.0–16×10^{-14}
5	0.3	0.0–4
10	0.08	0.0
20	0.007	0.0

organic source. It is this lower, much thicker zone of fermentation plus sulfate reduction to which the model applies. Unfortunately most of the pyrite is formed in the upper zone for which precise data are unavailable due to the problem of obtaining closely spaced samples near the sediment-water interface without disturbing the system. It is quite conceivable that, were the data available, the same type of model would apply to the upper zone, the only difference being changes in the values of k and G_0.

Another, less exact way of studying sulfate reduction in this upper zone is to sample the top few centimeters of relatively rapidly deposited sediment at different localities within a small geographical area and relate the content of total reduced sulfur, present as pyrite, monosulfide, and elemental sulfur, to that of originally deposited organic carbon. If the organic matter delivered to each site is derived from a common source of roughly constant biochemical composition, then original metabolizable organic matter should, as a first approximation, be directly proportional to original total organic carbon. If, also, the reduced sulfur content is a measure of the integrated rate of sulfate reduction, then the model predicts that for constant k, ω, and x a direct proportionality should exist between the concentration of total reduced sulfur and original total organic carbon. This can be seen by integration of Eqn. 3:

$$\sum S = LG_0 \left[1 - \exp \left(\frac{-k}{\omega} x \right) \right] \tag{6}$$

where: $\sum S$ = total sulfate reduced during burial to depth x.

A plot of total reduced sulfur vs "original" total organic carbon for the upper 2 cm of the intertidal and shallow subtidal sediments from the central Connecticut coast of Long Island Sound, USA is shown in Fig. 3. Original organic carbon is approximated by the sum of measured organic carbon plus the much smaller amount oxidized to produce the reduced sulfur. The reasonably good correlation shown in Fig. 3 suggests that sulfate reduction rate *is* proportional to organic carbon content[1] and, since a much poorer correlation is exhibited

---

[1] However, an exact theoretical interpretation of this correlation requires a more complicated model than that upon which Eqn. 6 is based because of mixing due to biological activity, etc.

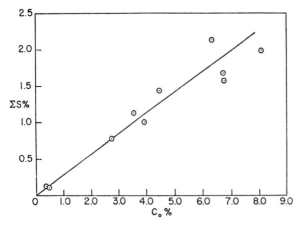

Fig. 3. Plot of total reduced sulfur, ΣS, vs original total organic carbon C_0 for the upper 2 cm of the intertidal and shallow subtidal sediments of the central Connecticut coast of Long Island Sound, USA Percentages are for $CaCO_3$-free, acid soluble iron-free dry weight.

between ΣS and reactive iron, it appears that the principal factor limiting pyrite formation in these sediments is metabolizable organic matter.

Iron

No matter how much hydrogen sulfide is produced in a sediment, no more pyrite can form than the amount of iron available for reaction with the H_2S. Thus, it is possible that in some sediments the amount of pyrite formed is limited by the concentration of reactive iron. A useful measure of reactive iron is that which is rapidly dissolved by boiling concentrated hydrochloric acid. It is reasonable to assume, and can be demonstrated, that iron not removed by such strong acid treatment does not react with H_2S to form iron sulfides. Thus, iron now present in pyrite, which is insoluble in boiling HCl, was originally in an acid soluble form, and the sum of prite iron plus HCl-soluble iron can be used as a measure of the original potentially reactive iron, here denoted as Fe_H. Extensive measurements from many different sedimentary environments made by the writer and others have shown that P, the fraction of Fe_H which has actually reacted to form pyrite, is always less than one and only very rarely exceeds 0.5, even in sediments containing high concentrations of H_2S. Thus, total iron is never a limiting factor in pyrite formation. Some typical examples of P vs depth plots are shown in Fig. 4.

Several studies (eg. Carroll, 1958) have shown that in terrigenous sediments the iron which reacts with H_2S to form iron sulfides consists mainly of adsorbed coatings of colloidal ferric oxides, such as hematite and goethite, on detrital clays and silt grains. In addition, finely crystallized iron-containing chlorites

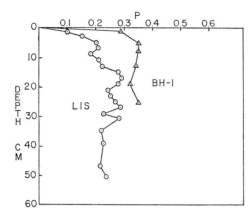

Fig. 4. Some typical plots of P vs. depth for intertidal and subtidal sediments of Long Island Sound, USA ($P = Fe_{pyrite}/Fe_H$ = the degree of pyritization of potentially reactive iron.)

are also generally reactive. By contrast, silt and sand sized grains of hematite, goethite, magnetite, and ferruginous silicates are quite non-reactive not only with H_2S, but also, in the coarser grain sizes, with boiling 12 N HCl (Berner, 1970). It is these mineral grains which account for much of the metastable iron in H_2S-rich sediments. Because the reactive iron minerals occur mainly as "rusty coatings", they are more abundant in fine grained clayed sediments containing grains of higher specific surface area for adsorption than they are in coarser grained sediments. This is why clays exposed to the same H_2S concentrations as silts and fine sands contain more pyrite.

In carbonate and other biogenic sediments which are low in detrital matter, few iron oxide-coated grains occur. As a result the reactive iron content, and consequently the pyrite content is much lower than in terrigenous sediments. This is shown in Table 3 for two H_2S-rich anaerobic sediments, one terrigenous and the other carbonate. Note that the organic carbon contents of the Long Island Sound terrigenous sediment and the Florida Bay carbonate sediment are similar, but that the values for pyrite sulfur, Fe_H, and P are markedly different.

Table 3. *Comparison of pyrite sulfur (Spy), potentially reactive iron (Fe_H), and degree of pyritization (P) between a carbonate sediment from Florida Bay and terrigenous sediment from Long Island Sound, each of which has a similar organic carbon concentration (C)*

Depth cm	C %	Spy %	Fe_H%	P
Florida Bay				
0–10	1.25	0.13	0.25	0.46
22–31	1.38	0.16	0.27	0.52
25–35	1.18	0.16	0.20	0.60
Long Island Sound				
10–12	1.08	0.48	1.98	0.21
18–20	1.24	0.92	2.75	0.29
34–36	1.06	0.76	2.99	0.22

Pyrite sulfur and Fe_H are lower in the Florida Bay sediment as expected but P is higher. Higher P indicates that the limited supply of iron to the carbonate sediments is more reactive than the iron minerals of terrigenous muds (there are almost no identifiable clay minerals or iron oxide coated grains in the Florida Bay samples). The identity of the reactive iron in terrigenous-free carbonate sediments is not known but may be that originally contained within organic compounds.

If a spectrum of reactivities towards H_2S exists in a sediment, then the higher the concentration of H_2S maintained during pyrite formation, the higher should be the proportion of iron converted to pyrite; in other words P should be proportional (although not necessarily directly proportional) to the concentration of H_2S. In a euxinic basin the concentration of H_2S in the bottom waters is generally laterally uniform due to mixing processes. If pyrite forms mainly from the H_2S contained in the bottom waters, rather than from that formed in the sediment pore waters from locally deposited organic matter, its concentration should be limited by the concentration of reactive iron deposited at each site; i.e. P should be relatively uniform and, thus, Fe_H should correlate with pyrite sulfur. Ostroumov et al. (1961) state that such a correlation exists for the topmost sediments of the Black Sea deep basin, which suggests that pyrite is formed from the H_2S of the bottom waters. By contrast a rather poor correlation between the concentrations of organic carbon and pyrite is found in the same sediment. Older, Pleistocene sediments of the Black Sea also show a direct correlation between pyrite sulfur and potentially reactive iron (Berner, 1972) but only in those layers where the iron monosulfides have been completely converted to pyrite.

Sulfate

Under conditions of very high rate of deposition and high metabolizable organic content bacterial reduction can cause the dissolved sulfate concentration in the pore water of a sediment to fall to zero at shallow depths. As a result no more H_2S is formed. In most marine sediments this is not a factor limiting pyrite formation because pyritization is completed long before the sulfate disappears, if it in fact disappears at all. However, in some polluted sediments and others of unusually high organic sedimentation rate, pyrite formation can be limited by the absence of sulfate and, consequently, H_2S. As a result the sediment remains black with depth due to a lack of transformation of iron monosulfides to pyrite. An example is provided by the black, sulfate-free sediments from a narrow, deep depression in a polluted Maine fjord (Somes Sound) shown in Fig. 5.

If sulfate itself becomes the rate limiting factor in bacterial sulfate reduction,

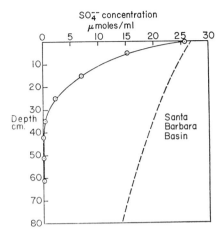

Fig. 5. Plot of dissolved sulfate vs depth for the interstitial water of the polluted sediment from a deep narrow depression in Somes Sound, Maine. For comparison the sulfate concentrations in the Santa Barbara Basin sediment taken from Fig. 2 are shown by the dashed curve.

then the Michaelis-Menten equation for sulfate reduction at constant temperature, pH, and organic substrate concentration reduces to that for simple first orders kinetics (eg. see Dixon and Webb, 1964). In other words:

$$R = k'S \tag{7}$$

where: k' = first order rate constant.

Thus, the steady state diagenetic equation is

$$D_s \frac{\partial^2 S}{\partial x^2} - \omega \frac{\partial S}{\partial x} - k'S = 0 \tag{8}$$

Solution of Eqn. 8 for constant D_s and ω and the proper boundary conditions yields:

$$S = S_0 \exp\left[\left(\frac{\omega - (\omega^2 + 4k'D_s)^{\frac{1}{2}}}{2D_s}\right)x\right] \tag{9}$$

where: S_0 = concentration of sulfate in the overlying water.

The total reduced sulfur present as pyrite plus iron monosulfides within a given layer by this model should be equivalent to the total sulfate reduced since deposition; i.e. there should be no excess H_2S which can diffuse out of the sediment. Thus:

$$\Sigma S = \int_0^T R \, dt = \int_0^X \frac{R}{\omega} \, dx \tag{10}$$

where: ΣS = total reduced sulfur
T = time since deposition do depth X

Substituting for R from Eqns. 7 and 9 and integrating:

$$\Sigma S = \frac{2k'D_s S_0}{\omega[(\omega^2 + 4k'D_s)^{\frac{1}{2}} - \omega]}\left\{1 - \exp\left[\left(\frac{\omega - (\omega^2 + 4k'D_s)^{\frac{1}{2}}}{2D_s}\right)x\right]\right\} \tag{11}$$

In general, $4k'D_s \gg \omega^2$. Therefore, Eqn. 11 can be approximated by the much simpler expression:

$$\Sigma S = \frac{S_0(k'D_s)^{\frac{1}{2}}}{\omega}\left\{1 - \exp\left[-\left(\frac{k'}{D_s}\right)^{\frac{1}{2}}x\right]\right\} \tag{12}$$

At a sufficiently great depth Eqn. 12 further simplifies to:

$$\Sigma S = \frac{S_0(k'D_s)^{\frac{1}{2}}}{\omega} \tag{13}$$

From the data of Fig. 5 for the Maine fjord and measurements of ΣS, Eqns. 9 and 13 can be solved for k' and ω, if a reasonable value for D_s is assumed (3×10^{-6} cm²/sec). The resulting value for ω of 3 cm/yr is not unreasonable for a narrow deep depression in a polluted near-shore body of water, but independent evidence is needed to serve as a true check on the model. A lack of mirror image symmetry between sulfate and ΣS with depth, as predicted by the model, indicates, as in the organic-limiting model, that a zone of higher H_2S production rate exists near the sediment-water interface. In addition, the stable isotope fractionation studies of Harrison and Thode (1958) suggest that sulfate does not become rate limiting until concentrations drop to a few millimoles per liter. Thus, it is probable that only the lower part of the curve for the Maine fjord shown in Fig. 5 is described by Eqn. 9.

Rate of Sulfur Uptake in Marine Sediments

The rate of sulfur uptake in marine sediments can be determined in several ways. The most direct is to measure the pyrite content and the rate of deposition. Some results, using this method, are shown in Table 4. In the absence of such data, measured or theoretically predicted curves of dissolved sulfate *vs* depth can be used, instead, to calculate the rate of diffusion of sulfate into the sediment. However, unless all the H_2S produced by reduction of the sulfate is trapped as iron sulfides, the sulfate diffusion rate gives only a maximum rate of uptake. This is because H_2S can build up in the sediment pore waters and diffuse back out of the sediment. The expression for diffusive uptake J, in terms of mass per unit area per unit time is:

$$J = -\phi_0 D_s \frac{\partial S}{\partial x}\bigg|_0 \tag{14}$$

where ϕ = porosity and the subscript 0 refers to the sediment-water interface. Reasonable values of ϕ_0 and D_s can be assumed and thus, from empirical or theoretical S vs x plots, J can be calculated. Results for several calculations are included in Table 4.

Table 4. *Rates of uptake of sulfate by marine sediments as determined by different methods. Units are in mg $S/cm^2/yr$. For discussion of methods see text*

Locality	J	Method	Reference
Black Sea Deep Basin	0.05–0.25	Pyrite content plus ω	(2), (3)
	0.35	Calculated sulfate gradient	(9)
	0.05–0.85	S^{35} uptake	(1)
Santa Barbara Basin	0.8	Pyrite content plus ω	(4)
	1.3	Measured sulfate gradient	(4), (9)
Gulf of California	0.5–0.8	Pyrite content plus ω	(5), (6)
Long Island Sound subtidal	0.4	Pyrite content plus ω	(7)
Polluted depression in		Measured sulfate gradient	(9)
Maine fjord	11.3		
Lindsley Pond, Conn. (freshwater mud)	2.0	S^{35} uptake	(8)

(1) Sorokin (1962)
(2) Ross et al. (1970)
(3) Ostroumov et al. (1961)
(4) Kaplan et al. (1963)
(5) Van Andel (1964)
(6) Berner (1964*b*)
(7) Berner (1970)
(8) Stuiver (1967)
(9) Model of the present paper

Another method for determining the maximum rate of sulfate uptake is to measure *J* directly using S^{35} tracer. This has been done for the Black Sea by Sorokin (1962) and for a fresh water pond by Stuiver (1967). Their data are also included in Table 4. Note the surprisingly good agreement between different methods for the Black Sea and for the Santa Barbara Basin.

Sulfur Budget in the Oceans

If more data for sulfur uptake rates for different sediment types and different areas were available, a good estimate could be made of the annual loss of sulfate from the ocean to form pyrite. Even without such data, however, certain conclusions can be drawn. First of all, large areas of the ocean are underlain by aerated sediments, such as the deep sea red clays, and these can be eliminated from consideration because pyrite cannot form in the presence of dissolved oxygen. Secondly, carbonate sediments, because of their low reactive iron contents, can also be eliminated. This then leaves a large volume of terrigenous deltaic, basinal, and hemipelagic sediments for which there is only scanty chemical data that can be used to calculate uptake rates. Using the average reduced sulfur content of 0.13 % determined by Clarke (1924) for 52 samples of hemipelagic "blue" clay, and a very approximate average rate of deposition for this sediment type given by Kuenen (1950) of 15 cm/1 000 yrs, an uptake rate of 0.01 mg $S/cm^2/yr$ is obtained. If one accepts the generous estimate of Kuenen (1950) that 15 % of the area of the oceans is underlain by similar hemipelagic sediment, then the annual removal of sulfur amounts to 6 megatons S per year. This value can be raised to 7 megatons if the Black Sea and lesser euxinic and semi-euxinic basins are included. Seven megatons per year is far less than the amount delivered by rivers, 123 megatons S per year, and no reasonable estimate of cyclic sulfur in river water can bring the sulfur budget into balance. Unless considerable sulfur is removed in shallow water, especially within deltaic complexes where there are high rates and large volumes of sedimentation, then it appears that the oceans are badly out of balance relative to the removal of sulfur. Before this conclusion can be fully accepted, however, much more data is needed especially on those sediments forming near the great sediment-carrying rivers of the world.

An alternative approach to the problem is to assume that the rate of pyrite formation is balanced by the rate of pyrite weathering on the continents. This then leaves all sulfate, delivered by rivers, that is derived from the weathering of $CaSO_4$, as well as all that arising from pollution as excess inputs. The writer (Berner, 1971b) has recently estimated the proportion of sulfate in river water that is derived from the weathering of $CaSO_4$ to be 22% of the total. This amounts to the addition of 27 megatons of sulfur to the ocean per year which is not removed by concommittant $CaSO_4$ precipitation. The pollutant addition has been estimated by Ericsson (1963) to be 50 megatons S per year, with 40 megatons due to the burning of fossil fuels and 10 megatons from the use of sulfur-containing fertilizers. Combining all sources, the total excess sulfur added per year is approximately 90 megatons. This strongly suggests that the sulfate content of sea water is increasing. Since the oceans contain 1 300 million megatons of sulfur, it would take, at the present rate of 90 megatons per year, about 14 million years to double its present value. However, judging from the geologic record, it is reasonable to assume that over periods of tens of millions of years new evaporite basins will form which would enable the ocean to maintain a more or less constant sulfate concentration. This is especially true since the pollutant contribution should rapidly fall off when the fossil fuel supply is exhausted.

References

Berner, R. A., An idealized model of dissolved sulfate distribution in recent sediments, Geochim. et Cosmochim. Acta, v. 28, p. 1497–1503 (1964a).

Berner, R. A., Distribution and diagenesis of sulfur in some sediments from the Gulf of California, Marine Geology, v. 1, p. 117–140 (1964b).

Berner, R. A., Sedimentary pyrite formation, Am. Jour. Sci., v. 268, p. 1–23 (1970).

Berner, R. A., Principles of Chemical Sedimentology, McGraw-Hill, New York, 240 p. (1971a).

Berner, R. A., Worldwide sulfur pollution of rivers, Jour. Geophys. Res. v. 76. p. 6597 (1971b).

Berner, R. A., Iron sulfides in the Pleistocene deep Black Sea sediments and their paleooceanographic significance, Am. Assn. Petroleum. Geol. Memoir (in press) (1972).

Carroll, P., The role of clay minerals in the transportation of iron, Geochim. et Cosmochim Acta, v. 14, p. 1–27 (1958).

Clarke, F. W., The data of geochemistry, U.S. Geol. Surv. Bull. 770, 841 p. (1924).

Dixon, M. & Webb, E. C., Enzymes, Acad. Press., New York, 950 p. (1964).

Emery, K. O., The sea off southern California, John Wiley, New York, 366 p. (1960).

Eriksson, E., The yearly circulation of sulfur in nature, Jour. Geophys. Res., v. 68, p. 4001–4008 (1963).

Harrison, A. G. & Thode, H. G., Mechanism of the bacterial reduction of sulphate from isotope fractionation studies, Trans. Faraday Soc., v. 54, p. 84–92 (1958).

Kaplan, I. R., Emery, K. O. & Rittenberg, S. C., The distribution and isotopic abundance of sulphur in recent marine sediments off southern California, Geochim. et Cosmochim. Acta, v. 27, p. 297–331 (1963).

Kemp, A. L. W. & Thode, H. G., The mechanism of the bacterial reduction of sulphate and of sulphite from isotope fractionation studies, Geochim. et Cosmochim. Acta, v. 32, p. 71–93 (1968).

Kuenen, Ph. H., Marine Geology, John Wiley, New York, 568 p. (1950).

Ostroumov. E. A., Volkov, I. I. & Fomina, L. C., Distribution pattern of sulfur compounds in the bottom sediments of the Black Sea, Akad. Nauk. S.S.S.R., Inst. Okeanol. Trudy, v. 50, p. 93–129 (1961).

Ross, D. A., Degens, E. T. & MacIlvaine, J., Black Sea: Recent sedimentary history, Science, v. 170, p. 163–165 (1970).

Skopintsev. B. A., Recent studies of the hydrochemistry of the Black Sea, Okeanologiya, v. 1, p. 243–250 (1961).

Sorokin, Yu. I., Experimental investigation of bacterial sulfate reduction in the Black Sea using S^{35}, Mikrobiologiya, v. 31, p. 402–410 (1962).

Stuiver, M., The sulfur cycle in lake waters during thermal stratification, Geochim. et Cosmochim. Acta, v. 31, p. 2151–2167 (1967).

van Andel, Tj. H., Recent marine sediments of Gulf of California, Am. Assn. Petroleum Geol. Memoir 3, p. 216–310 (1964).

Zobell, C. E. & Rittenberg, S. C., Sulfate reducing bacteria in marine sediments, Jour. Mar. Research, v. 7, p. 602–617 (1948).

Discussion 7b. Iron Sulphide. Phosphate Budget

Rickard

Although it is widely accepted that particulate iron is the major source of reactive (towards H_2S) iron in sediments, some textural studies reveal apparent mobility of iron in sediments. If this is a real phenomenon, what mechanism is involved?

Berner

There is no doubt that the particulate iron can be solubilized during anaerobic diagenesis by iron bacteria, and in the presence of gradients in Fe^{2+} and H_2S, migration as well as the formation of pyrite aggregates actually occurs. For further details consult: Berner, R. A., "Migration of iron and sulfur within anaerobic sediments during early diagenesis", Amer. J. Sci., *267*, 19 (1969).

Fonselius

Is the phosphorus increase in the Bodensee caused by dissolution of P from the sediments, during anaerobic conditions or is it caused by direct discharge of wastes?

When were the values measured?

Stumm

It is caused by discharge of wastes and agricultural drainage. Usually the sediment-water interface is aerobic. Always during Spring turnover.

Rickard

According to the Broecker system, an increase in anaerobiosis on a global scale will result in an increase in the atmospheric oxygen content. This is because the rise in oxygen in the atmosphere is related to the burial of un-oxidised organic carbon in sediments. Furthermore, increased organic productivity caused by increased nutrient supplies through pollution will also ultimately result in a greater preservation of organic carbon, thus enhancing this effect. Have you any comments?

Stumm

Any subsequent increase in O_2 of the atmosphere would in turn enhance the oxygenation of settling organic debris. According to Broecker [J. Geophys. Res., 75, 3553 (1970)], an increase in atmospheric oxygen would cause a decrease in the proportion of water that is anaerobic. This would then increase the proportion of organic carbon that is oxidized before burial and so permit the inorganic oxygen sinks to decrease the free oxygen. An incipient decrease in atmospheric oxygen would have the reverse effect. The O_2 level of the atmosphere seems to be very well buffered, but the response time may be very slow. There is still considerable uncertainty on the various factors that regulate the stability of atmospheric oxygen.

Berner

This past summer I have been checking the possibility that the uptake of dissolved phosphate on the surface of $CaCO_3$ as found experimentally by Leckie (Ph. D thesis, Harvard University, 1969; see also Stumm and Morgan, 1970, p. 559–563) may be an important reaction for controlling the level of phosphate in the oceans. My own experiments indicate that dissolved phosphate in deep sea water is rapidly removed in the laboratory upon passage through a column of natural $CaCO_3$ beach sand. Also, analyses of interstitial water chemistry of natural carbonate sediments indicate an apparent equilibrium with apatite, whereas those of non-carbonate sediments indicate supersaturation. This agrees with Leckie's contention that the surface of calcite acts as a nucleating agent for calcium phosphate precipitation

As calcium carbonate particles derived from dead foraminifera, etc. fall from low-phosphate shallow water into the phosphate-rich deep water of the ocean, surface reaction may occur and, thus, the carbonate particles may remove some phosphate before they become buried in deep sea sediments. Obviously, this contention needs much further checking.

Resolution to the United Nations 1972 Conference on the Human Environment

The scientists of the Nobel Symposium 20 on "The Changing Chemistry of the Oceans" wish to bring the following matters of concern to the UN Conference:

1. Our knowledge of transport and mixing processes, as well as of chemical and biological reactions in the oceans, is insufficient to permit the identification of any area where pollutants may be introduced with the assurance that they will not be carried within one generation, comparatively undiluted, to a region important to man. Controlled dumping in deep water followed by intensive study of the consequences may provide the necessary knowledge. Uncontrolled dumping should be prohibited.

2. Some pollutants, especially chlorinated hydrocarbons (such as PCB:s and DDT) and also lead are distributed globally via the atmosphere. Their concentrations may reach levels sufficient to damage ecosystems irreversibly on a world-wide scale before the damage is recognized. To determine the impact of such pollutants, intensive study is required of their origins and ultimate sinks as well as their routes through the food webs and effects on the ecosystem including man. Their entry to the marine environment should be curtailed to every practical extent, even if this requires restrictions on their production and use. Other globally distributed pollutants posing similar threats should be similarly treated.

3. Studies necessary to gain adequate understanding of the behaviour and importance of some pollutants, notably the PCB:s, are rendered impossible because information on production and distribution is not made public. Two of the requirements for local and global control of marine pollution are

a) that information on the production and disposal of potential pollutants be freely available internationally, and

b) that careful monitoring be maintained of potentially dangerous pollutants and threatened ecosystems.